STRUCTURE OF MATTER SERIES

MARIA GOEPPERT MAYER

Advisory Editor

SMALL-ANGLE

SCATTERING OF X-RAYS

SMALL-ANGLE

SCATTERING OF X-RAYS

ANDRÉ GUINIER

Professor, Université de Paris (France)

GÉRARD FOURNET

Lecturer, École Supérieure de
Physique et Chimie, Paris

Translation by
CHRISTOPHER B. WALKER

Institute for the Study of Metals
University of Chicago

Followed by a bibliography by
KENNETH L. YUDOWITCH

Johns Hopkins University

New York · JOHN WILEY & SONS, Inc.

London · CHAPMAN & HALL, Ltd.

1955

Library of Congress Catalog Card Number: 55-9772

PRINTED IN THE UNITED STATES OF AMERICA

PREFACE

X-ray diffraction was first utilized in establishing the atomic structure of crystals. Later the technique of X-ray diffraction found other applications, however, and branched off from pure crystallography, extending to studies of imperfections in crystals, sizes of crystallites, and even to studies of the atomic structure of amorphous bodies. These fields of application of X-rays were made possible by further developments in the theory of the diffraction of X-rays by matter and also by improvements in experimental methods.

The small-angle scattering of X-rays is one of these fields that has been rather recently opened. Although the first observations were made in 1930 [295] particular attention has been given to this field only since the late 1930's. At the present time a large, ever-increasing number of laboratories are interested in small-angle scattering, as is shown by the number of references compiled in the bibliography of this book.

For these reasons it seemed worth while to us to devote a monograph to this specific branch of X-ray diffraction. In fact, the theories that are used in this field are generally not discussed in textbooks on X-rays. They are quite distinct from the concepts that are customarily associated with X-ray diffraction; almost no use of Bragg's law will be made in this book, except to point out that the habit, so natural to crystallographers, of interpreting every detail in a diffraction pattern in terms of lattice distances should be discarded. The experimental aspect also is different; small-angle scattering in general cannot be studied with the usual apparatus of a crystallography laboratory; special cameras and sometimes special tubes are required.

Since the late 1930's many theoretical works have appeared in this field; starting from different points of view, these have occasionally arrived at different, but non-contradictory, results. In a parallel manner, apparatus based on quite varied principles have been used in experimental methods. We believed that it was now time to collect and evaluate the results that have been obtained from the different approaches. Our object has been to make the new research in this field more rapid and more efficient. Finally, we have also tried to evaluate the different attempts at applications in order to specify those which are the most fruitful.

v

The plan of this book is as follows: in a first, short chapter we present the phenomenon of small-angle scattering and investigate its physical significance.

The second chapter is devoted to a discussion of the progress realized in the theoretical study of small-angle scattering. We have tried to show the problems that have actually been solved and the limitations that now appear to us as difficult to overcome.

In a third chapter we discuss the experimental methods that have been employed, trying not to treat all the details but giving the general principles that should be satisfied in a small-angle scattering system. Evidently these techniques will be similar whether the objective is the study of continuous scattering or the study of crystalline diffraction patterns. Thus it will be seen that problems are mentioned in this section which are not considered from a theoretical point of view in the second chapter.

The fourth chapter is devoted to the problem of the interpretation of the experimental results and includes several examples which demonstrate the validity of the theoretical results.

In a fifth chapter we compare the results of small-angle X-ray scattering with the results of other physical methods for measuring particle sizes, such as interpretations of Debye-Scherrer line widths and measurements with the electron microscope.

The sixth and last chapter is devoted to a discussion of the applications of small-angle X-ray scattering. These are found in a number of diverse fields, such as chemistry, biology, and metallurgy. Some applications are of technical interest, as, for example, the study and testing of catalysts. Others are of interest to theoretical physics, as, for example, the structure of liquid helium below the λ-point.

Although the object of the first chapters of this book is to present all the theoretical and experimental data necessary to the specialist in X-ray diffraction, the last chapter has been written without use of mathematics and without details of X-ray techniques so that it can be read without difficulty by a non-specialist. Our object has been to present the different types of problems that can be studied by small-angle scattering and the results that have actually been obtained up to the present. Thus a chemist, biologist, or metallurgist should be able to decide from this whether or not any given problem can be approached effectively by means of X-rays.

In this monograph we have tried more to give a logical, ordered presentation of this subject than to give a complete compilation of all the published papers. Any gaps can be filled by the reader by referring to the bibliography. Let us point out that several general articles on small-angle scattering have now appeared: the article by Hosemann [84] and another by Porod [137] are particularly noted. As a result we have been able to shorten our discussion on several points, since the reader can find the complete development of these ideas in the works cited.

When reference is made in the text to a formula in the same chapter, the formula is denoted by a single number, as, for example, 36. When the formula has been developed in a different chapter, it is denoted by a double number, such as 2.36 (equation 36 of Chapter 2).

If a bibliographic reference appears as numbers within brackets, [ ], the reference will be found in the general bibliography at the end of the book. References appearing as "Author (year)" are tabulated in a special bibliography at the end of each chapter.

Our sincere thanks are extended to Dr. R. S. Bear, Dr. W. W. Beeman, Dr. J. W. M. DuMond, Dr. A. N. J. Heyn, Dr. R. A. Van Nordstrand, and Dr. C. B. Walker for having made available to us papers which are as yet unpublished and drawings or original photographs which they have authorized us to reproduce here. Permission has been given to reproduce a number of illustrations from technical journals, for which we wish to thank both the authors and the publishers.

We are particularly grateful to Professor P. P. Ewald, who encouraged us to publish this book, and to Professor W. W. Beeman, whose criticism and advice were very helpful in the final editing of our manuscript.

Finally we want to thank Dr. C. B. Walker for the careful translation which has made the original manuscript more accessible to many readers.

A. GUINIER
G. FOURNET

Paris, France
August, 1955

CONTENTS

1. ORIGIN AND CHARACTERISTICS OF SMALL-ANGLE X-RAY SCATTERING

The fundamental relation describing the diffraction of X-rays by crystalline matter, $\lambda = 2d \sin \theta$, shows that the angle of diffraction, θ, varies inversely with the separation of the diffracting lattice planes. In ordinary crystals, particularly those of inorganic matter, the majority of the observed lattice spacings are of the same order of magnitude as the X-ray wavelengths generally employed, so that the angles θ are usually rather large. This advantageous condition has had important consequences, both in the discovery of the phenomenon of X-ray diffraction and in its employment in studies of crystal structures.

The study of small-angle X-ray diffraction was introduced when it became desirable to detect large lattice spacings, of the order of tens or hundreds of interatomic distances. These spacings are found in some particular minerals and in certain complex molecules, such as the high polymers or proteins. In studies of the structures of macromolecular crystals the X-ray diffraction patterns must be extended to include very small angles. For example, with Cu $K\alpha$ radiation and a spacing of 100 A the diffraction angle θ is equal to 0.45°, and, with a period of 1000 A, θ equals 0.045° or 2'. This illustrates the importance of small-angle scattering techniques in such fields as biochemistry, for example.

One might consider using longer-wavelength X-rays to obtain larger diffraction angles for a given lattice spacing. This is not generally feasible, however, since the long-wavelength X-rays are absorbed to a very great extent in matter, which not only complicates the necessary diffraction apparatus and the means of detection of the X-rays but also considerably diminishes the intensity of the diffracted beam. For these practical reasons we must recognize a gap in the spectrum of useful electromagnetic radiation extending from wavelengths of the order of 2 A up to those of the remote ultraviolet.

In studying crystals with large periodicities only the operational technique is different, since the interpretation of the patterns is based on the same principles as the usual structure determinations. The difficulties encountered are greater, however, as a result of the complexity of the unit cell and the imperfection of the crystals. One can intuitively picture "perfect" crystals as being formed only by the grouping of small numbers

1

of atoms bound by strong forces. In molecular and macromolecular crystals the degree of perfection is much less; only rarely is the theory of diffraction by perfect crystals a good approximation in small-angle diffraction phenomena. In this domain the theory of diffraction by imperfect crystals assumes particular importance, as is illustrated by the correlation of small-angle diffraction and the diffraction by imperfect crystals in an X-ray study of high polymers by Hosemann [84]. Since diffraction by imperfect crystals is a theoretical problem not confined to small-angle scattering and one that has been well discussed elsewhere, we shall not examine it further in this monograph.

If a sample has a non-periodic structure or if its lattice has been sufficiently perturbed, the diffraction patterns are not limited to spots or lines but contain more or less extended regions of scattering. Let us examine schematically the origin of this scattering at small angles.

It is well known that the diffraction pattern of a sample can be simply described in terms of a reciprocal, or Fourier, space. If we designate by $\rho(\mathbf{x})$ the electronic density of the diffracting body at a point defined by the vector $\mathbf{x}$, then $A(\mathbf{h})$, the transform of $\rho(\mathbf{x})$ at the point defined by the vector $\mathbf{h}$ in reciprocal space, is given by

$$A(\mathbf{h}) = \int \rho(\mathbf{x}) e^{-i\mathbf{h}\cdot\mathbf{x}} \, d\mathbf{x} \tag{1}$$

The theory of X-ray diffraction is based on the fact that $A(\mathbf{h})$ represents the amplitude of the diffracted radiation when $\mathbf{h}$ is defined as

$$\mathbf{h} = (2\pi/\lambda)(\mathbf{s} - \mathbf{s}_0)$$

where λ is the wavelength of the radiation and $\mathbf{s}_0$ and $\mathbf{s}$ are unit vectors in the direction of the incident and diffracted rays, respectively. The magnitude of $\mathbf{h}$ is then equal to $(4\pi \sin \theta)/\lambda$, where 2θ is the scattering angle (the angle between the incident and scattered rays). Thus scattering at very small angles corresponds to small values of h.

Equation 1 can be interpreted as follows: the scattered intensity observed for conditions corresponding to a certain value of $\mathbf{h}$ is equal to the square of the value of $A(\mathbf{h})$, where $A(\mathbf{h})$ is the component corresponding to $\mathbf{h}$ in the development of $\rho(\mathbf{x})$ in a Fourier series. For small values of $\mathbf{h}$, that is, at very small angles, the terms in $\rho(\mathbf{x})$ that primarily control the magnitude of $A(\mathbf{h})$ are those that show a periodicity of $x = 2\pi/h$, a periodicity large with respect to the X-ray wavelength. These general considerations show again that diffraction at very small angles (less than a few degrees) gives information concerning the structure of matter on a scale that is large compared to the X-ray wavelength.

It has been experimentally observed that certain samples cause an intense, *continuous* scattering below angles of the order of $2°$ without producing the usual type of diffraction effects found on ordinary X-ray patterns. This was first observed by Krishnamurti [295] and Warren [171] for certain varieties of finely divided carbons, carbon blacks, and various other substances, all having in common the characteristic of being present as fine particles of submicroscopic size. Actually it was later recognized that the continuous scattering in the neighborhood of the direct beam is related to the existence of matter in the form of *small particles*, or, more generally, to the existence of *heterogeneities in the matter*, these heterogeneities having *dimensions from several tens to several hundred times the X-ray wavelength*. This offers another example of the general relation previously cited.

It is relatively easy to describe qualitatively the central scattering due to the presence of small particles. This is analogous to the well-known phenomenon of optical diffraction, where a halo is produced by the passage of a light ray in a powder whose grain dimensions are of the order of a hundred times the wavelength of the light.

Let us consider a particle bathed in a beam of X-rays; all the electrons are then sources of scattered waves. When the scattering direction is the same as that of the incident ray, these scattered rays are all in phase, and, as the scattering angle increases, the difference in phase between the various scattered waves also increases. The amplitude of the resultant scattered wave then decreases with increasing angle because of increasing destructive interference; it becomes zero when there are as many waves with phases between 0 and π as there are between π and 2π. This will occur for a scattering angle of the order of $2\theta = \lambda/D$, D being the "average dimension" of the particle, demonstrating how the study of the continuous central scattering offers a method for obtaining particle dimensions.

This method is applicable only for particles whose sizes lie within certain limits. If D is too large the scattering is limited to angles so small as to be inaccessible to experiment, and if D is too small, of the order of several wavelengths, the scattering is widely spread but too weak to be observable.

These rough qualitative considerations can be made more precise. To show exactly on which factors the small-angle scattering depends, let us consider a small particle that has been cut from a section of matter of electronic density $\rho(\mathbf{x})$. Let us define a "form factor" of this particle, $s(\mathbf{x})$ (Ewald (1940)), that has the value 1 when the vector $\mathbf{x}$ lies within the particle and the value 0 when $\mathbf{x}$ lies outside the particle. The amplitude of radiation scattered by this particle, as found from equation 1, is then

$$A_1(\mathbf{h}) = \int \rho(\mathbf{x})\, s(\mathbf{x}) e^{-i\mathbf{h}\cdot\mathbf{x}}\, d\mathbf{x} \tag{2}$$

There is a general theorem related to the operation of "folding" in the theory of Fourier transformations stating that, if $A(\mathbf{h})$ and $S(\mathbf{h})$ are respectively the Fourier transforms of $\rho(\mathbf{x})$ and $s(\mathbf{x})$, then

$$A_1(\mathbf{h}) = \int A(\mathbf{y})S(\mathbf{h} - \mathbf{y})\,d\mathbf{y} \tag{3}$$

where $\mathbf{y}$ is a variable of integration.

Given the dimensions of the region in which $s(\mathbf{x})$ is different from zero, its transform, $S(\mathbf{h})$, is fully determined, and, if the particle has dimensions of several tens to several hundreds of atomic diameters, $S(\mathbf{h})$ will be different from zero only for very small values of $\mathbf{h}$.

Let us consider now the function $A(\mathbf{h})$. If we first assume that the sample is of constant electronic density, $\rho(\mathbf{x}) = k$, the transform $A(\mathbf{h})$ acts as a Dirac delta-function,[1] being zero everywhere except at $\mathbf{h} = 0$, where it is infinite. For the more general case of a homogeneous body whose electronic density shows periodicities only on an atomic or molecular scale, the transform $A(\mathbf{h})$ shows a large number of peaks. However, all these peaks except the one for $\mathbf{h} = 0$ are produced for values of $\mathbf{h}$ well outside the domain in which $S(\mathbf{h})$ has a non-zero value.

Then, since $A(\mathbf{y})$ is essentially a Dirac delta-function about $\mathbf{y} = 0$, it may be predicted that around the origin of the reciprocal space the amplitude $A_1(\mathbf{h})$ is simply proportional to $S(\mathbf{h})$, the function $\rho(\mathbf{x})$ not intervening. *The scattering around the center is thus practically independent of the "short-range order" of the atoms, depending only on the exterior form and dimensions of the particle.*

Small-angle scattering thus appears as a means of studying the dimensions of colloidal particles, and it is in this direction that the technique has been generally exploited. It was quickly realized, however, that the assumptions adopted in the first theoretical approaches (widely separated, identical particles) were not being satisfied in the constitution of real samples. Interpretation of the scattering then demanded that the theory be generalized to take into account the diversity of particles sizes and the effect of the closer packing of the particles. Also, without speaking of particles, the possibility should be considered of obtaining an expression for the intensity scattered near the center in terms of the electronic density at all points of the sample. The theoretical approaches to these and other problems are discussed in the following chapter.

REFERENCE FOR CHAPTER 1

Ewald, P. P.   (1940), *Proc. Phys. Soc. (London)*, 52, 167.

---

[1] The Dirac delta-function $\delta(\mathbf{x})$ is zero for $\mathbf{x} \neq 0$, infinite for $\mathbf{x} = 0$, and $\int \delta(\mathbf{x})\,d\mathbf{x} = 1$.

When a small particle (an atom, for example) is being considered, the point M_k will refer to a volume element, small even on the angstrom scale, surrounding the point M_k. The scattering factor f_k then equals $\rho_k \, dv_k$, where ρ_k is the electronic density of the particle in the neighborhood of the point M_k, and dv_k is the volume element considered.

In general we will find it convenient to describe the structure of a particle in terms of elements which are small enough so that the scattering factors of these elements can be considered as constants, independent of the angle of scattering, over the range in which the structure factor of the particle under consideration is different from zero.

2.1.2. MOVING PARTICLE

In the majority of low-angle scattering investigations, such as examinations of solutions, suspensions, and emulsions, the particles are capable of motion. This motion can always be described as the sum of a translation and a rotation. A translation, defined by a vector $\mathbf{V}$, introduces the multiplicative factor $e^{-i\mathbf{h}\cdot\mathbf{V}}$ in the expression for the scattered amplitude, but this has no effect on the scattered intensity. Only rotations intervene in the calculation of an average intensity.

When the probabilities of different orientations are defined, we can obtain from equations 3 or 6 the expression for the observed average intensity

$$\overline{I(\mathbf{h})} = I_e(\mathbf{h}) \overline{F^2(\mathbf{h})}$$

this relation defining the average of the square of the structure factor. There would be a temptation to describe $\overline{F^2(\mathbf{h})}$ as equal to $\overline{F(\mathbf{h})}^2$, the square of the average of the structure factor. However, in order that the average of a product, ab, be equal to the product of the averages of a and b, it is necessary that the variables be completely independent, that is, that knowledge of the value of a in no way modifies the probabilities of the different values of b. This limitation is not met by the structure factors, since $a \equiv b \equiv F(\mathbf{h})$. The only general case in which $\overline{F^2}$ and $\overline{F}^2$ are equal is that pertaining to spherically symmetric particles, for then a rotation of the particle around its center does not modify the distribution of scattering centers and consequently leaves $F(\mathbf{h})$ unchanged. For this case one finds

$$\overline{F^2} = \overline{F}^2 = F^2$$

In this section, the discussion is restricted almost entirely to considering all particle orientations as equally probable; a treatment of the more general case will be found at the end of the chapter. When this assumption is made, the only mathematical problem is one of calculating the average of the function, $\cos(\mathbf{h} \cdot \mathbf{r})$, as the vector $\mathbf{r}$, of magnitude r, takes all orientations with equal probability. To calculate this average, let us define the angle between the vectors $\mathbf{h}$ and $\mathbf{r}$ as the angle φ, a variable with limits of 0 and π radians. The probability that this angle is contained between the values φ and $\varphi + d\varphi$ is equal to $\frac{1}{2}\sin\varphi\,d\varphi$. The average of the phase function, $\cos(\mathbf{h} \cdot \mathbf{r})$, is then

$$\int_0^\pi \cos(hr\cos\varphi)\,\frac{\sin\varphi}{2}\,d\varphi$$

$$= \int_0^{\pi/2} \cos(hr\cos\varphi)\sin\varphi\,d\varphi$$

$$= -\frac{1}{hr}\int_0^{\pi/2} \cos(hr\cos\varphi)\,d(hr\cos\varphi)$$

$$= -\frac{1}{hr}\int_{hr}^0 \cos u\,du$$

leading to the classic result

$$\overline{\cos(\mathbf{h} \cdot \mathbf{r})} = \frac{\sin hr}{hr} \tag{7}$$

The result depends only on the magnitude of $\mathbf{h}$; the distribution of scattered intensity thus contains an axis of revolution coinciding with the incident beam.

Equation 3 then resolves into the expression for $\overline{F^2(h)}$ [1] expressed by Debye (1915),

$$\overline{F^2(h)} = \sum_k \sum_j f_k f_j \frac{\sin(h\,|\,\mathbf{M}_k\mathbf{M}_j\,|)}{h\,|\,\mathbf{M}_k\mathbf{M}_j\,|} \tag{8}$$

2.1.2.1. Centrosymmetric Particle

When a center of symmetry exists, application of equation 7 to equation 5 results in a simple expression for the average of the structure factor:

$$\overline{F(h)} = \sum_k f_k \frac{\sin(h\,|\,\mathbf{OM}_k\,|)}{h\,|\,\mathbf{OM}_k\,|} \tag{9}$$

Generalization of this equation to include particles with a continuous distribution of scattering points leads to the following expression:

$$\overline{F(h)} = \int_V \rho(M_k)\,\frac{\sin(h\,|\,\mathbf{OM}_k\,|)}{h\,|\,\mathbf{OM}_k\,|}\,dv_k$$

[1] The notation $f(h)$ will be used when the function depends only on the magnitude of $\mathbf{h}$; the notation $f(\mathbf{h})$ will demonstrate dependence of the function on both magnitude and direction of $\mathbf{h}$.

The coefficient of the term $\sin hr/hr$ in this integral, obtained by considering the ensemble of points defined by $\left| \mathbf{OM}_k \right| = r$, is

$$\int_r^{r+dr} \rho(M_k)\, dv_k = \bar{\rho}(r)4\pi r^2\, dr$$

this defining the function $\bar{\rho}(r)$. The generalization of equation 9 then takes the form

$$\overline{F(h)} = \int_0^\infty \bar{\rho}(r) \frac{\sin hr}{hr} 4\pi r^2\, dr \tag{10}$$

We see thus that the average of the structure factor is uniquely determined by the distribution of scattering centers as a function of their distance from the center of the particle.

Equation 3 shows that the parameters possessing physical significance in the expression for the intensity are the distances $\left| \mathbf{M}_k\mathbf{M}_j \right|$ between each of the pairs of scattering centers. Nevertheless, for convenience of calculation one might on occasion prefer an expression for the intensity in which the distances $\left| \mathbf{OM}_k \right|$ and $\left| \mathbf{OM}_j \right|$ are the essential parameters, where O designates the center of symmetry of the particle. Fournet [48] has shown this to be

$$\overline{F^2(h)} =$$

$$\sum_k \sum_j \left\{ f_k f_j \sum_{p=0}^\infty \pi(2p + \tfrac{1}{2}) \frac{J_{2p+1/2}(h\left| \mathbf{OM}_k \right|)\, J_{2p+1/2}(h\left| \mathbf{OM}_j \right|)}{h\sqrt{\left| \mathbf{OM}_k \right|\left| \mathbf{OM}_j \right|}} P_{2p}(\cos \Phi_{kj}) \right\} \tag{11}$$

where P_m represents the Legendre polynomial of order m, and Φ_{kj}, the angle $\measuredangle M_kOM_j$. [The Legendre polynomial of order m, $P_m(x)$, can be described as the coefficient of the term y^m in the expansion of the function $(1 - 2yx + y^2)^{-1/2}$.] In certain cases this equation can be employed more simply than equation 8 (Fournet [48]).

Fournet has employed equation 11 to illustrate the difference between $\overline{F^2(h)}$ and $\overline{F(h)}^2$. If we evaluate the sum of terms for $p = 0$,

$$\sum_k \sum_j f_k f_j \frac{\pi}{2} \frac{J_{1/2}(h\left| \mathbf{OM}_k \right|)J_{1/2}(h\left| \mathbf{OM}_j \right|)}{\sqrt{h\left| \mathbf{OM}_k \right|}\sqrt{h\left| \mathbf{OM}_j \right|}} = \left[\sum_k f_k \sqrt{\frac{\pi}{2}} \frac{J_{1/2}(h\left| \mathbf{OM}_k \right|)}{\sqrt{h\left| \mathbf{OM}_k \right|}} \right]^2$$

then, on transforming the Bessel functions into sine functions with the relation $J_{1/2}(x) = \sqrt{(2/\pi x)} \sin x$, we find that the sum of these terms is equal to

$$\left[\sum_k f_k \frac{\sin h\left| \mathbf{OM}_k \right|}{h\left| \mathbf{OM}_k \right|} \right]^2$$

which is the square of the average of the structure factor. Thus we can write

$$\overline{F^2(h)} = \overline{F(h)}^2$$
$$+ \sum_k \sum_j \left\{ f_k f_j \sum_{p=1}^{\infty} \pi(2p + \tfrac{1}{2}) \frac{J_{2p+1/2}(h \,|\, \mathbf{OM}_k\,|) \, J_{2p+1/2}(h \,|\, \mathbf{OM}_j\,|)}{h\sqrt{|\,\mathbf{OM}_k\,|\,|\,\mathbf{OM}_j\,|}} \, P_{2p} \, (\cos \Phi_{kj}) \right\}$$
$$(12)$$

2.1.2.2. Spherically Symmetric Particle

A particularly important case to be considered is that of the spherically symmetric particle. The electronic density at any point depends only on the distance r of this point from the center of the particle and can thus be denoted by $\rho(r)$.

The structure factor is then obtained from equation 10, replacing $\bar{\rho}(r)$ by $\rho(r)$:

$$F(h) = \int_0^{\infty} \rho(r) \frac{\sin hr}{hr} 4\pi r^2 \, dr \tag{13}$$

For this particular case, rotation of the particle does not modify the amplitude of scattered radiation, leading to the relation

$$\overline{F^2(h)} = \overline{F(h)}^2 = F^2(h) \tag{14}$$

2.1.2.3. Calculation of the Average Intensity

The calculation of the average intensity can be made by several methods.

(a) *Analytical Method*: The intensity scattered by the particle in an arbitrary position is calculated (see equation 3). Then the expression is averaged, taking into account the different orientations, in a manner similar to that employed by Guinier ([65], p. 195) and Fournet ([48], p. 45). This method is particularly simple when applied to a spherically symmetric particle; equations 13 and 14 can then be used directly.

(b) *Geometrical Method*: Kratky and Porod [108]. Equation 8 can be generalized intuitively to allow the consideration of a particle of volume V, defined by an electronic density $\rho(M_k)$; the resulting expression is

$$\overline{F^2(h)} = \int_V \int_V \rho(M_k)\rho(M_j) \frac{\sin (h \,|\, \mathbf{M}_k\mathbf{M}_j\,|)}{h \,|\, \mathbf{M}_k\mathbf{M}_j\,|} \, dv_k \, dv_j \tag{15}$$

Let us consider the coefficient of $\sin hr/hr$ in the integral, assuming for the moment that ρ is a constant. This coefficient is obtained by considering the ensemble of terms where $|\,\mathbf{M}_k\mathbf{M}_j\,| = r$. The number of electrons at distances between r and $r + dr$ from a volume element dv_k of the particle is simply $\rho\{V_k(r + dr) - V_k(r)\}$, in which $V_k(r)$ designates the part of the volume of the particle situated at a distance smaller than or equal to r from dv_k. When we now consider all possible positions of dv_k, we can introduce a function, $p(r)$, defined by the relation

$$\int_V \rho\{V_k(r + dr) - V_k(r)\}\rho\, dv_k = \rho^2 p(r)\, dr \qquad (16)$$

The average of the square of the structure factor can then be expressed as

$$\overline{F^2(h)} = \rho^2 \int_0^\infty p(r) \frac{\sin hr}{hr}\, dr \qquad (17)$$

In order to determine the physical significance of $p(r)$, let us describe the volume element dv_j of equation 15 in a system of spherical coordinates centered on the point M_k, for which $dv_j = r^2\, d\omega\, dr$. Equation 15 then becomes

$$\overline{F^2(h)} = \int_V \left\{\rho(M_k) \int_V \rho(M_j) \frac{\sin hr}{hr} r^2\, d\omega\, dr\right\} dv_k \qquad (18)$$

The point M_j in the integral with respect to $d\omega\, dr$ is any point in the particle situated at a distance r from the point M_k, where

$$\mathbf{OM}_j - \mathbf{OM}_k = \mathbf{r} \quad \text{with} \quad |\mathbf{r}| = r$$

and the integral extends only over the volume V of the particle. This integral can be extended over all space by writing

$$\overline{F^2(h)} = \int_V \left\{\rho(\mathbf{OM}_k) \int_0^\infty \int_0^{4\pi} \rho(\mathbf{OM}_k + \mathbf{r}) \frac{\sin hr}{hr} r^2\, d\omega\, dr\right\} dv_k \qquad (19)$$

on condition that $\rho(\mathbf{OM}_k + \mathbf{r})$ is taken equal to the density of the particle ρ if the point $\mathbf{OM}_k + \mathbf{r}$ is inside the particle, and to zero if the point is outside.

We can now write that the partial integral

$$\int_V \rho(\mathbf{OM}_k)\rho(\mathbf{OM}_k + \mathbf{r})\, dv_k$$

is equal to the product of ρ^2 times the volume $V(\mathbf{r})$ of the solid common to the particle and to the "ghost" of the particle translated by the vector $\mathbf{r}$ (Wilson (1949)) (Fig. 2). $V(\mathbf{r})$ is evidently a function of the direction of the vector $\mathbf{r}$. If we introduce the average value, as defined by the relation

$$\int_0^{4\pi} V(\mathbf{r})\, d\omega = 4\pi\, \overline{V(r)}$$

equation 19 becomes

$$\overline{F^2(h)} = \rho^2 \int_0^\infty \overline{V(r)} \frac{\sin hr}{hr} 4\pi r^2\, dr$$

Let us now introduce a function $\gamma_0(r)$, defined as

$$\gamma_0(r) = \frac{\overline{V(r)}}{V(o)} = \frac{\overline{V(r)}}{V} \tag{20}$$

Our last equation then becomes

$$\overline{F^2(h)} = V\rho^2 \int_0^\infty \gamma_0(r) \, \frac{\sin hr}{hr} \, 4\pi r^2 \, dr \tag{21}$$

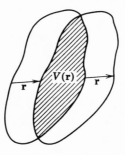

Fig. 2.   A representation of the function $V(\mathbf{r})$.

A comparison of equations 17 and 21 shows that the functions $p(r)$ and $\gamma_0(r)$ are related by the following expression:

$$p(r) = 4\pi r^2 V\gamma_0(r) \tag{22}$$

2.1.2.4. The Characteristic Function of the Particle $\gamma_0(r)$

The characteristic function $\gamma_0(r)$ was introduced by Porod [137]. It has no intuitive connection with the form of the particle.

$\gamma_0(r)$ represents the probability that a point at a distance r in an arbitrary direction from a given point in the particle will itself also be in the particle.

Let us consider an arbitrary line in the particle, terminating on its boundaries to form a segment of length M, and let us further consider an arbitrary point on this segment. The probability that a second point on the line at a distance r from the first is also inside the segment M is: $\gamma_M(r) = 1 - (r/M)$ if $r < M$ and is zero if $r > M$ (Fig. 3). If $g(M)$[1] is

---

[1] A precise definition of $g(M)$ is as follows: Through a point $\mathbf{r}$ in the particle there will pass an infinite set of randomly oriented lines. If $g_{\mathbf{r}}(M)$ is the distribution function for the lengths M of these lines, then $g(M)$ is the average of this function as the point $\mathbf{r}$ takes all positions in the particle, i.e.,

$$g(M) = \frac{1}{V} \int g_{\mathbf{r}}(M) \, dv_{\mathbf{r}}$$

the distribution function for the group of such lines in the particle, then

$$\gamma_0(r) = \int_{M=r}^{\infty} \left(1 - \frac{r}{M}\right) g(M)\, dM \qquad (23)$$

It can be shown from equation 23 that

$$g(M) = M \left(\frac{d^2\gamma_0}{dr^2}\right)_{r=M}$$

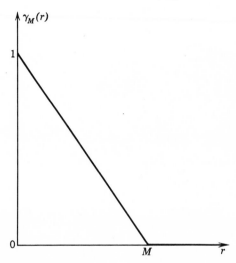

Fig. 3   The function $\gamma_M(r)$ for a single segment of length M.

The function $\gamma_0(r)$ possesses the following general properties:

1. At $r = 0$, $\gamma_0(r)$ has the value unity; as r increases, $\gamma_0(r)$ decreases, always staying positive, and becomes zero beyond the value $r = R_1$ corresponding to the line of maximum length through the particle.

2. An integration from zero to infinity of the two sides of equation 16 gives

$$\rho^2 \int_0^{\infty} p(r)\, dr = \int_V \rho V \rho\, dv_k = \rho^2 V^2$$

which, when combined with equation 22, leads to the relation

$$\int_0^{\infty} 4\pi r^2 \gamma_0(r)\, dr = V$$

3. *The initial slope of $\gamma_0(r)$ is a function of the external surface of the particle, S.* Let us trace around the particle the shell of thickness r (Fig. 4), where r is small with respect to the dimensions of the particle.

We can now calculate $\gamma_0(r)$ by means of equation 16, neglecting the terms smaller than r^3.

$$\int_V \rho[V_k(r + dr) - V_k(r)]\rho \, dv_k = 4\pi\rho^2 Vr^2\gamma_0(r) \, dr$$

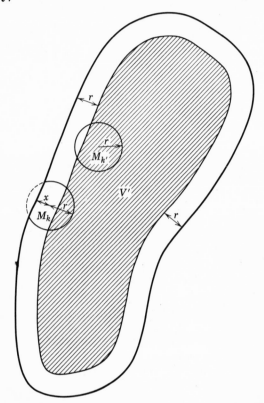

Fig. 4. Calculation of the initial slope of the characteristic function $\gamma_0(r)$.

For a point $M_{k'}$ in the inner volume $V' = V - Sr$

$$V_k(r + dr) - V_k(r) = 4\pi r^2 \, dr$$

and therefore

$$\int_{V'} \rho[V_k(r + dr) - V_k(r)]\rho \, dv_k = 4\pi\rho^2 r^2(V - Sr) \, dr$$

For a point M_k in the shell at a depth x from the surface (Fig. 4),

$$V_k(r + dr) - V_k(r) = 2\pi r(r + x) \, dr$$

and therefore

$$\int_{\text{shell} = Sr} \rho[V_k(r + dr) - V_k(r)]\rho \, dv_k = \int_{x=0}^{x=r} 2\pi\rho^2 r(r + x)S \, dx \, dr = 3\pi r^3 \rho^2 S \, dr$$

Thus as a first approximation

$$4\pi\rho^2 r^2 V \gamma_0(r)\, dr = 4\pi\rho^2 r^2 \left(V - \frac{Sr}{4} \right) dr$$

or

$$\gamma_0(r) = 1 - (S/4V)r + \cdots \qquad (24)$$

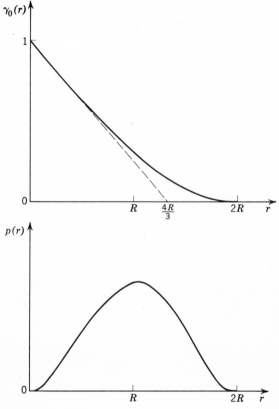

Fig. 5.   The functions $p(r)$ and $\gamma_0(r)$ for the sphere of radius R.

As an example, let us consider a *spherical* particle of radius R. The volume $V(\mathbf{r}) = \overline{V(r)}$ common to two spheres of radius R whose centers are separated by the distance r is given by a simple geometrical calculation as

$$\overline{V(r)} = (\pi/12)(2R - r)^2(4R + r)$$

Consequently,

$$\gamma_0(r) = 1 - \frac{3r}{4R} + \frac{1}{16} \left(\frac{r}{R} \right)^3$$

Equation 24 gives a similar result when V is replaced by $(4/3)\pi R^3$ and S by $4\pi R^2$ (Fig. 5).

Figure 3 shows that, for the line in the particle of length M, $\int \gamma_M(r)\, dr = M/2$. The integral of the characteristic function of the particle is thus

$$\int_0^\infty \gamma_0(r)\, dr = \int_0^\infty \frac{M}{2} g(M)\, dM = \frac{\bar{l}}{2} \tag{25}$$

The integral of the characteristic function is therefore equal to one-half of an average length of all the lines contained in the particles.

Thus for a spherical particle

$$l = 2 \int_0^{2R} \left[1 - \frac{3}{4}\frac{r}{R} + \frac{1}{16}\left(\frac{r}{R}\right)^3 \right] dr = \frac{3}{2} R$$

It can be verified that $(3/2)R$ is the average length of the lines passing through all the points in a sphere in all directions and terminating on its boundaries.

We see therefore that this function shows properties analogous to those of the Fourier transform of the profiles of Debye-Scherrer lines broadened by the effect of the small size of a crystal (Bertaut (1950)).

2.1.2.5. General Properties of $\overline{F^2(h)}$

From these general properties of the function $\gamma_0(r)$ we can deduce the following consequences for the function $\overline{F^2(h)}$:

1. The value of $\overline{F^2(h)}$ at $h = 0$, $F^2(0)$, is

$$F^2(0) = V\rho^2 \int_0^\infty 4\pi r^2 \gamma_0(r)\, dr = V^2\rho^2$$

This is the square of the total number of electrons in the particle. All the scattered waves are in phase and the amplitudes are added.

2. The value of $F^2(h)$ at small values of h is found from equation 21 by making the expansion

$$\frac{\sin hr}{hr} = 1 - \frac{h^2 r^2}{6} + \frac{h^4 r^4}{120} + \cdots$$

Then, by introducing the factor $F^2(0)$, this equation becomes

$$\overline{F^2(h)} = F^2(0) \left\{ 1 - \frac{h^2}{6}\frac{1}{V}\int_0^\infty 4\pi r^4 \gamma_0(r)\, dr \right.$$

$$\left. + \frac{h^4}{120}\frac{1}{V}\int_0^\infty 4\pi r^6 \gamma_0(r)\, dr + \cdots \right\} \tag{21a}$$

Thus, as h increases from zero, $\overline{F^2(h)}$ decreases following a parabolic curve. The curvature of this curve is determined by an integral in which the values of $\gamma_0(r)$ for large r play a predominant part because of the factor r^4. In §2.1.3.1 we shall see a simple and much more important expression for the curvature of $\overline{F^2(h)}$ at small angles.

3. A useful representation of the value of $\overline{F^2(h)}$ for large values of h can also be obtained from the function $\gamma_0(r)$. This comes from the fact that, since $h\overline{F^2(h)}$ and $r\gamma_0(r)$ are related by a Fourier transform, the high-angle part of the curve of $\overline{F^2(h)}$ corresponds to the part of the curve of $\gamma_0(r)$ at small values of r, and an approximate expression for this part of $\gamma_0(r)$ is known.

$\gamma_0(r)$ can be expressed as a polynomial in r, of which the first two terms are known:

$$\gamma_0(r) = 1 - (S/4V)r + \cdots$$

We also know that $\gamma_0(r)$ becomes zero beyond $r = R_1$. Therefore, by making the substitutions $hr = y$ and $hR_1 = u$, equation 21 becomes

$$\overline{F^2(h)} = \frac{4\pi V \rho^2}{h^3} \int_0^u \left(y - \frac{S}{4Vh} y^2 + \frac{\alpha y^3}{h^2} + \cdots \right) \sin y \, dy$$

By integrating by parts the following formulas can be established:

$$\int_0^u y \sin y \, dy = -u \cos u + \sin u$$

$$\int_0^u y^2 \sin y \, dy = -u^2 \cos u + 2u \sin u + 2 \cos u - 2$$

$$\int_0^u y^n \sin y \, dy = -u^n \cos u + n u^{n-1} \sin u - \int_0^u n(n-1) y^{n-2} \sin y \, dy$$

Therefore

$$\overline{F^2(h)} = \frac{2\pi \rho^2 S}{h^4} + \frac{A}{h^6} + \cdots + \frac{f_1(u,h) \cos u}{h^3} + \frac{f_2(u,h) \sin u}{h^3}$$

At large values of h the principal term in $\overline{F^2(h)}$ is $2\pi\rho^2 S/h^4$, to which are added damped oscillations of pseudoperiod $hR_1/2\pi$. The average curve of the continuous decrease of $\overline{F^2(h)}$ is therefore given as

$$\overline{F^2(h)} \approx \frac{2\pi \rho^2 S}{h^4} \tag{26}$$

This depends uniquely on the external surface of the particle.

4. A Fourier inversion of equation 21 gives

$$r\gamma_0(r) = \frac{2}{\pi} \int_0^\infty \frac{h\,\overline{F^2(h)}}{4\pi\rho^2 V} \sin hr\, dh$$

or

$$\gamma_0(r) = \frac{1}{2\pi^2\rho^2 V} \int_0^\infty h^2\overline{F^2(h)}\, \frac{\sin hr}{hr}\, dh \tag{27}$$

Evaluated at $r = 0$, this becomes

$$\int_0^\infty h^2\overline{F^2(h)}\, dh = 2\pi^2\rho^2 V \tag{28}$$

The integral of $h^2\overline{F^2(h)}$ depends only on the *volume of the particle* and not on its form. This is a particular illustration of a general theorem regarding the integral in reciprocal space of the intensity scattered by an arbitrary object, which relates this integral to the total number of scattering electrons in the object.

5. Let us calculate an average value l of the length of all the lines contained in a particle by evaluating the integral $\int_0^\infty \gamma_0(r)\, dr$. By making the substitution $y = hr$, the integral of equation 27 becomes

$$l = 2\int_0^\infty \gamma_0(r)\, dr = \frac{1}{\pi^2\rho^2 V} \int_0^\infty \int_0^\infty h\overline{F^2(h)}\, \frac{\sin hr}{r}\, dh\, dr$$

$$= \frac{1}{\pi^2\rho^2 V} \int_0^\infty \frac{\sin y}{y}\, dy \int_0^\infty h\overline{F^2(h)}\, dh$$

or

$$l = \frac{1}{2\pi\rho^2 V} \int_0^\infty h\overline{F^2(h)}\, dh \tag{29}$$

This integral can be expressed in terms of the total energy E scattered in all the low-angle scattering region. On a film placed at a distance p from the sample, the area that receives the rays scattered through the small angles contained between 2θ and $2\theta + d(2\theta)$ can be written to a first approximation as

$$d\sigma \simeq 2\pi p^2 2\theta\, d(2\theta)$$

or

$$d\sigma \simeq (\lambda^2/2\pi)\, p^2 h\, dh$$

Equations 4 and 6 then give

$$E = I_e(h)\int \overline{F^2(h)}\, d\sigma = \frac{\lambda^2}{2\pi} I_0 \times 7.90 \times 10^{-26} \int \overline{F^2(h)}h\, dh$$

$$= 7.90 \times 10^{-26}\lambda^2 I_0\rho^2 Vl \tag{30}$$

All the results of the preceding discussion are still valid if the electronic density of the particle is not a constant but shows fluctuations around an average value $\bar{\rho}$, if these fluctuations are such that statistically the surroundings of all the atoms in the particle are the same.

If, on the other hand, $\bar{\rho}$ varies from one part to another of the particle (for example, a hollow particle, etc.), equation 16 can be generalized by introducing the function $n_k(r)$, which represents the number of electrons situated at distances smaller than or equal to r from the volume element dv_k enclosing the point M_k. In order to modify our notation as little as possible, we redefine $p(r)$ by the relation

$$\int_V [n_k(r + dr) - n_k(r)]\rho(M_k)\, dv_k = \bar{\rho}^2 p(r)\, dr$$

where $\bar{\rho}$ is the average electronic density. $\overline{F^2(h)}$ can now be obtained by replacing ρ by $\bar{\rho}$ in equation 17, but it is necessary to note carefully that $p(r)$ is no longer uniquely determined by the *geometry* of the particle.

2.1.2.6. A Tabulation of the Average Intensity Distributions for Particles of Different Shapes

We list below the average intensity distributions for particles of different shapes which take all orientations with equal probability. The intensity distribution function tabulated is $i(h)$, rather than $\overline{F^2(h)}$, which is defined by the relation

$$\overline{F^2(h)} = n^2 i(h) = V^2 \rho^2 i(h)$$

where $n = V\rho$ is the total number of electrons in the particle; $i(0)$ is then always equal to unity.

(a) Sphere of radius R (Rayleigh (1914)) (Fig. 6),

$$i(h) = \Phi^2(hR) = \left[3\, \frac{\sin hR - hR \cos hR}{h^3 R^3} \right]^2 = \frac{9\pi}{2} \left[\frac{J_{3/2}(hR)}{(hR)^{3/2}} \right]^2 \quad (31)$$

(b) Ellipsoid of revolution, axes $2a$, $2a$, $2va$ (Guinier [65]) (Fig. 7),

$$i(h) = \int_0^{\pi/2} \Phi^2 (ha\sqrt{\cos^2 \theta + v^2 \sin^2 \theta})\, \cos\, \theta\, d\theta \quad (32)$$

Another equation has been developed for this case by Schull and Roess [155], employing hypergeometric functions.

(c) Cylinders of revolution of diameter $2R$ and height $2H$ (Fournet [48])

$$i(h) = \int_0^{\pi/2} \frac{\sin^2 (hH \cos \theta)}{h^2 H^2 \cos^2 \theta} \times \frac{4J_1^2(hR \sin \theta)}{h^2 R^2 \sin^2 \theta} \sin \theta\, d\theta \quad (33)$$

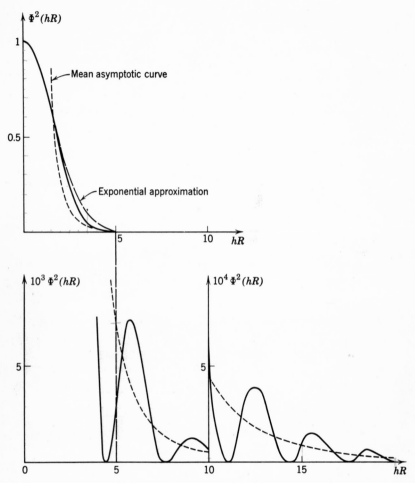

Fig. 6.   Scattered intensity from a sphere of radius R, $\Phi^2(hR)$. The curve is drawn with different scales for the various ranges of hR ($\times$ 1000 for $4 < hR < 10$; $\times$ 10,000 for $hR > 10$).

Exponential approximation: $e^{-\dfrac{h^2R^2}{5}}$ (equation 39);   mean asymptotic curve: $\dfrac{9}{2}\dfrac{1}{(hR)^4}$ (equation 26).

(d) Rod of infinitesimal transverse dimensions and length $2H$ (Neuge-bauer (1943)) (Fig. 8a)

$$i(h) = \frac{Si(2hH)}{hH} - \frac{\sin^2(hH)}{h^2H^2} \tag{34}$$

where

$$Si(x) = \int_0^x \frac{\sin t}{t}\, dt$$

(e) Flat disc of infinitesimal thickness and diameter $2R$ (Kratky and Porod [108]) (Fig. 8b)

$$i(h) = \frac{2}{h^2 R^2}\left[1 - \frac{1}{hR}J_1(2hR)\right] \tag{35}$$

These various functions $i(h)$ behave according to the predictions of the general study: at $h = 0$, $i(h)$ is unity and the tangent to the curve is

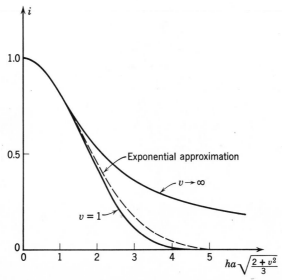

Fig. 7. Scattered intensity from ellipsoids of revolution of axes $2a, 2a, 2va$. The abscissae have been chosen so that the radius of gyration of each ellipsoid corresponds to the same length (§2.1.3.1, p. 26).

Exponential approximation: $e^{-\frac{h^2 a^2}{5}\cdot\frac{2+v^2}{3}}$.

horizontal, and, as h increases, $i(h)$ decreases parabolically, tending finally towards zero along a curve which oscillates somewhat about a curve varying as h^{-4}. For narrow cylinders or thin discs whose small dimension is ϵ, this asymptotic law is valid only if $h \gg (1/\epsilon)$. If in these cases h is large with respect to $1/H$ or $1/R$ but small with respect to $1/\epsilon$, equations 34 and 35 show that the curves decrease respectively as h^{-1} (cylinder) and h^{-2} (disc).

An examination of Figs. 6, 7, and 8 shows that particles of very different forms can have nearly the same scattering curves.

Tables 1–3 will facilitate numerical calculations of equations 31 through 35.

Table 1

$$\Phi(x) = 3 \frac{\sin x - x \cos x}{x^3} \quad \text{and} \quad \Phi^2(x)$$

x	$\Phi(x)$	$\Phi^2(x)$	x	$\Phi(x)$	$\Phi^2(x)$
0.000	1.000	1.000	2.100	0.622	0.388
0.100	0.999	0.998	2.250	0.575	0.330
0.200	0.996	0.992	2.500	0.499	0.248
0.300	0.991	0.982	3.000	0.346	0.119
0.400	0.983	0.968	3.200	0.288	0.083
0.500	0.975	0.951	3.500	0.205	0.042
0.600	0.964	0.930	4.000	0.0875	0.0076
0.700	0.952	0.906	4.493	0.0000	0.0000
0.800	0.937	0.879	5.000	−0.057 0	0.003 25
0.900	0.921	0.849	5.600	−0.085 0	0.007 22
1.000	0.903	0.816	5.760	−0.086 3	0.007 45
1.200	0.863	0.745	5.800	−0.086 0	0.007 40
1.400	0.816	0.668	6.000	−0.084 3	0.007 10
1.600	0.766	0.587	7.300	−0.023 0	0.000 53
1.800	0.702	0.502	7.720	−0.000	0.000 00
2.000	0.654	0.427			

Table 2

$$i(x) = \frac{Si(2x)}{x} - \frac{\sin^2 x}{x^2}$$

x	$i(x)$	x	$i(x)$
0.0	1.000	1.6	0.768
0.2	0.996	1.8	0.719
0.4	0.984	2.0	0.673
0.6	0.961	2.2	0.627
0.8	0.931	2.4	0.583
1.0	0.898	3.0	0.473
1.2	0.858	3.5	0.406
1.4	0.813	4.0	0.357

Table 3

x	$J_1(x)$	x	$J_1(x)$
0.0	0.0000	2.6	0.4708
0.2	0.0995	2.8	0.4097
0.4	0.1960	3.0	0.3391
0.6	0.2867	3.2	0.2613
0.8	0.3688	3.4	0.1792
1.0	0.4401	3.6	0.0955
1.2	0.4983	3.8	0.0128
1.4	0.5419	4.0	−0.0660
1.6	0.5699	4.2	−0.1386
1.8	0.5815	4.4	−0.2028
2.0	0.5767	4.6	−0.2566
2.2	0.5560	4.8	−0.2984
2.4	0.5202	5.0	−0.3276

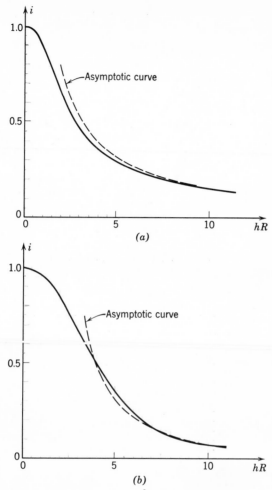

Fig. 8. (a) Scattered intensity from rods of length $2H$. Asymptotic curve: $\pi/(2hH)$ (equation 34). (b) Scattered intensity from flat circular discs of radius R. Asymptotic curve: $2/(h^2R^2)$ (equation 35).

2.1.2.7. Particle with Preferred Orientations

For simplicity we shall consider only particles with a center of symmetry; the structure factor is then given by equation 5. Let us fix the particle in a system of three mutually perpendicular axes, Ox, Oy, Oz. The space in which the particle is found is described by a second set of three mutually perpendicular axes, OX, OY, OZ. The centers of these two systems of axes can be made to coincide without loss of generality, since only relative orientations are of interest. Euler's angles, χ, θ, and φ, will be employed to mark the orientation of the particle system with respect to the spatial system. (In this paragraph θ will designate only the Euler angle, the scattering angle appearing only in terms of h.) We arbitrarily orient the spatial axes so that $\mathbf{h}$ is directed along the axis OZ. The amplitude scattered by a particle of orientation, θ, φ, can be denoted as: $A_e(h)F(\mathbf{h}, \theta, \varphi)$. Then, by designating by $P_1(\mathbf{h}, \theta)$ and $P_2(\mathbf{h}, \varphi)$ the probability density functions of θ and φ (where the notation $P_1(\mathbf{h}, \theta)$ is to recall the particular choice of OZ), the average intensity is found as

$$\overline{F^2(h)} = \int\int F^2(\mathbf{h}, \theta, \varphi) P_1(\mathbf{h}, \theta) P_2(\mathbf{h}, \varphi) \, d\theta \, d\varphi \qquad (36)$$

This approach will be useful whenever exterior physical conditions impose a preferred orientation as, for example, when molecules are oriented by the flow of a solution.

2.1.3. CONCEPT OF A RADIUS OF GYRATION OF A PARTICLE
2.1.3.1. Moving Particle

We shall consider primarily particles for which all orientations are equally probable.

Let us rewrite equation 8, expanding the trigonometric function in a power series:

$$\overline{F^2(h)} = \sum_k \sum_j f_k f_j \left\{ 1 - \frac{h^2}{6} \left| \mathbf{M}_k \mathbf{M}_j \right|^2 + \cdots \right\}$$

$$= \sum_k \sum_j f_k f_j - \frac{h^2}{6} \sum_k \sum_j f_k f_j \left| \mathbf{M}_k \mathbf{M}_j \right|^2 + \cdots \qquad (37)$$

The first term of the expansion is equal to $(\sum_k f_k)^2$, that is, $F^2(0)$. To describe the second term, let us consider a point, O, chosen so that $\sum_k f_k \mathbf{OM}_k = 0$. The point O then defines the electronic center of mass of the particle. Employing this point as an origin, we can write

$$\left| \mathbf{M}_k \mathbf{M}_j \right|^2 = \left| \mathbf{OM}_k \right|^2 + \left| \mathbf{OM}_j \right|^2 - 2 \left| \mathbf{OM}_k \right| \left| \mathbf{OM}_j \right| \cos \Phi_{kj}$$

In the second term of our expansion in equation 37 the contribution of the factor $\left| \mathbf{OM}_k \right|^2$ is

$$-\frac{h^2}{6} \sum_k \sum_j f_k f_j \left| \mathbf{OM}_k \right|^2 = -\frac{h^2}{6} \sum_j f_j \sum_k f_k \left| \mathbf{OM}_k \right|^2$$

The contribution of the factor $|\mathbf{OM}_j|^2$ is the same. The contribution of the angularly dependent term is zero, since

$$2\sum_k \sum_j f_k f_j \,|\mathbf{OM}_k|\,|\mathbf{OM}_j|\cos\Phi_{kj} = 2\sum_j f_j \,|\mathbf{OM}_j|\,\Big\{\sum_k f_k \,|\mathbf{OM}_k|\cos\Phi_{kj}\Big\}$$

and the sum over k can be recognized as being the projection of $\sum f_k \mathbf{OM}_k$ on the vector $\mathbf{OM}_j$. Thus equation 37 reduces to the following:

$$\overline{F^2(h)} = \left\{ (\sum_k f_k)^2 - \frac{2h^2}{6}\sum_j f_j \sum_k f_k\,|\mathbf{OM}_k|^2 + \cdots \right\}$$

or

$$\overline{F^2(h)} = (\sum_k f_k)^2 \left\{ 1 - \frac{h^2}{3}\frac{\sum_k f_k\,|\mathbf{OM}_k|^2}{\sum_k f_k} + \cdots \right\}$$

We can now introduce the parameter R_0, defined by the relation

$$R_0{}^2 = \frac{\sum_k f_k\,|\mathbf{OM}_k|^2}{\sum_k f_k} \tag{38}$$

By analogy with classical mechanics, R_0 can be considered as the electronic radius of gyration of the particle about its electronic center of mass. We can thus hope to have a good approximation by writing (Guinier [65])

$$\overline{F^2(h)} = n^2 e^{-\frac{h^2 R_0{}^2}{3}} \tag{39}$$

where $n = \sum_k f_k$, the total number of electrons in the particle. This relation, the law of Guinier, coincides with the exact expression for terms up to the 4th power of h and, like the exact expression, vanishes with increasing h.

Equation 39 can be derived from the general relation, equation 12, in which $\overline{F^2(h)}$ and $\overline{F(h)}^2$ were expressed in an explicit manner. For simplicity we shall limit the derivation to the case of particles possessing a center of symmetry.

The principal part of the double summation over indices k and j involves terms in h^4 or still higher powers. *Thus any constant term and the term in h^2 in the expression for the average intensity must arise from the square of the average amplitude and consequently must depend only on the distribution of scattering centers as a function of their distance from the center of the particle* (see equation 9). The ratio of the coefficient of the term involving h^2 to the constant term should then be a universal function of this distribution. A calculation

$$\frac{\overline{F(h)}^2}{F^2(0)} = \left[\frac{\sum_k f_k - \frac{h^2}{6} \sum_k f_k r_k^2}{\sum_k f_k} + \cdots \right]^2 = 1 - \frac{h^2}{3} \frac{\sum_k f_k r_k^2}{\sum_k f_k} + \cdots$$

shows that this function is simply

$$\frac{1}{3} \frac{\sum_k f_k r_k^2}{\sum_k f_k} = \frac{1}{3} R_0^2$$

confirming the results of the preceding paragraph.

The curves of the scattering by two particles having the same radius of gyration then coincide at very small angles, and it is only the tails of the curves, due to terms in h^4, h^6, etc., which show the influence of the forms of the particles. When the scattering curves of particles of two different forms are to be compared, it is thus *essential* to choose two particles having the same radius of gyration (see Fig. 7). For example, to a sphere of radius R, one should compare an ellipsoid of revolution of axes

$$2 \sqrt{\frac{3}{2 + v^2}} R \qquad 2 \sqrt{\frac{3}{2 + v^2}} R \qquad 2v \sqrt{\frac{3}{2 + v^2}} R$$

v being the ratio of the unequal axes. Certain authors (Kratky and Porod [108]) have compared reduced curves (curves of the function $i(h)$, chosen so that the abscissae for both are the same for the ordinate $i(h) = 1/2$), but this arbitrary choice does not permit *the separation of the influences of the dimensions and of the forms of the particles*.

In order to eliminate any possible confusion, we want now to emphasize separately two points:

1. *The validity of the concept of a radius of gyration.* We must re-emphasize that the concept of a radius of gyration is sound, whatever the form of the particle (viz., Guinier [65], p. 191, or the discussion of equation 12), since it seems that some authors have recognized this concept only for spherical particles. The magnitude of the slope of the curve of $\log I(h)$ vs. h^2 at the origin is always equal to one-third of the square of the radius of gyration. The influence of the form of the particle manifests itself particularly at larger values of h in the form of deviations of the curve of $\log I(h)$ from the extrapolation of its tangent at the origin.

2. *The validity of the approximate law of Guinier.* To illustrate this, let us consider a family of ellipsoids of revolution of the same radius of

gyration, R_0, and of half axes R,R, and vR; v and R are thus variables. The first terms in the power series describing the intensity are given by

$$\overline{F^2(h)} = F(0)^2 \left[1 - \frac{h^2 R_0{}^2}{3} + \cdots \right]$$

In this family of ellipsoids there are two for which the expression for the scattered intensity coincides with the law of Guinier (equation 39) up to terms of the 6th power of h; these are the flat ellipsoid defined by $v = 0.24$ and the elongated ellipsoid, where $v = 1.88$.

Again, in a family of cylinders of revolution of diameter $2R$ and height $2H$ there is a cylinder for which the same precision of agreement is found; this is the cylinder for which $H/R = \sqrt{30/11} = 1.65$.

These examples show that the particles that obey the approximate law of Guinier closely are those that are nearly isodiametric (see Fig. 6 for the case of a sphere).

On the other hand, rather wide differences will be found for the curves of very elongated ellipsoids, thin discs, and narrow cylinders.

Finally, let us call attention to the fact that experiments have verified that the exponential law, equation 39, is a *very good* approximation for a large number of scattering curves, a surprisingly large number in view of the approximations involved in the derivation.

The precision with which a radius of gyration can be measured in an experiment depends to a certain extent on the form of the particles. The determination of the radius of gyration to the same degree of precision for a series of particles having the same radius of gyration but different forms requires information on the scattering at smaller and smaller angles, the further the particle departs from a spherical form.

Kratky and Porod [108] have given an approximate formula for particles in the form of narrow cylinders or thin discs which is valid for values of h large with respect to the reciprocal of the large particle dimension but small with respect to the reciprocal of the small dimension. In its dependence on the small dimension of the particle this scattering function behaves as though the low-angle region of the curve (the exponential approximation) were involved, whereas in its dependence on the large dimension the scattering behaves as though the tail of the curve (the curves in h^{-1} and h^{-2}, respectively, for cylinders and discs) were involved.

An accurate calculation based on equation 33 gives as the relation for narrow cylinders of diameter $2R$ and length $2H$, containing n electrons each,

$$\overline{F^2(h)} \simeq n^2 \frac{\pi}{2hH} \cdot \frac{4J_1{}^2(hR)}{(hR)^2} \simeq \frac{n^2\pi}{2hH} e^{-\frac{h^2R^2}{4}} \tag{40}$$

and for thin discs of diameter $2R$ and thickness $2H$

$$\overline{F^2 h} \simeq n^2 \frac{2}{h^2 R^2} \cdot \frac{\sin^2(hH)}{(hH)^2} \simeq \frac{2n^2}{h^2 R^2} e^{-\frac{h^2 H^2}{3}} \qquad (41)$$

Let us also recall the equation relating the radius of gyration of a particle and its characteristic function $\gamma_0(r)$. By comparing the expansion of $\overline{F^2(h)}$, equation 21a, p. 16, with equation 39, this is found to be

$$R_0^2 = \frac{1}{2V} \int_0^\infty 4\pi r^4 \gamma_0(r)\, dr = \frac{\displaystyle\int_0^\infty r^4 \gamma_0(r)\, dr}{\displaystyle 2\int_0^\infty r^2 \gamma_0(r)\, dr} \qquad (42)$$

We note that the radius of gyration can then be defined either by equation 39, where, following the method of Guinier, it is determined from a trace of the curve of $\log I$ vs. h^2, or by equation 42, in which case it is convenient to determine the function $\gamma_0(r)$ with the aid of equation 27 and then R_0^2 with equation 42.

2.1.4. SPHERICALLY SYMMETRIC PARTICLE

The calculation of the average intensity is considerably simplified when the particle possesses spherical symmetry. The electronic density function $\rho(r)$ is then sufficient to determine $A(h)$ and, consequently, $F^2(h)$. Conversely, a Fourier transformation of equation 13 gives

$$\rho(r) = \frac{1}{2\pi^2 r} \int_0^\infty h F(h) \sin hr\, dh \qquad (43)$$

and the radius of gyration, from its definition, is determined by the relation

$$R_0^2 = \frac{\displaystyle\int_0^\infty r^4 \rho(r)\, dr}{\displaystyle\int_0^\infty r^2 \rho(r)\, dr}$$

2.1.5. THE DISTRIBUTION OF SCATTERING FROM A FIXED PARTICLE

Figure 9 shows the geometrical relations between the film, the orientation of the particle, and the distribution of scattered intensity on the film. We are interested primarily in the distribution of scattered radiation along the line AB. The corresponding scattering vectors $\mathbf{h}$ are all contained in the plane fixed by $\mathbf{s}_0$ and AB. The limiting direction of $\mathbf{h}$ as the scattering angle 2θ tends to zero is marked by the unit vector $\mathbf{l}_0$ perpendicular to $\mathbf{s}_0$ (since $\measuredangle \mathbf{h s}_0 = (\pi/2) - \theta$; see Fig. 1).

Let us consider how the concept of a radius of gyration appears under these circumstances by studying the series expansion of equation 3. An analogous case has already been considered in §2.1.3, giving immediately the result

$$F^2(\mathbf{h}) = \frac{I(\mathbf{h})}{A_e^{\,2}(h)} = (\sum_k f_k)^2 - \sum_j f_j \sum_k f_k (\mathbf{h} \cdot \mathbf{OM}_k)^2 + \cdots$$

where the point O is defined by the relation

$$\sum_k f_k \mathbf{OM}_k = 0$$

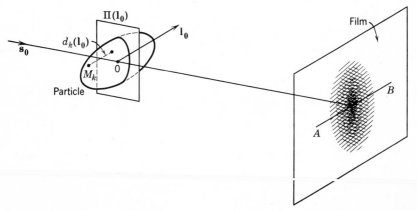

Fig. 9. The relation between the orientation of a particle and the distribution of scattered intensity in the plane of observation.

Then

$$\frac{F^2(\mathbf{h})}{F^2(0)} = 1 - \frac{\sum_k f_k (\mathbf{h} \cdot \mathbf{OM}_k)^2}{\sum_k f_k} + \cdots$$

As a first approximation, the scalar product $\mathbf{h} \cdot \mathbf{OM}_k$ for small values of 2θ is equal to the product of the magnitude h and the scalar product $\mathbf{l}_0 \cdot \mathbf{OM}_k$. This scalar product, $\mathbf{l}_0 \cdot \mathbf{OM}_k$, is equal in magnitude to the distance $d_k(\mathbf{l}_0)$ of the point M_k from the plane $\Pi(\mathbf{l}_0)$ through O perpendicular to $\mathbf{l}_0$. The notation $d_k(\mathbf{l}_0)$ serves to recall the dependence on the orientation of $\mathbf{l}_0$. We can now write the expansion of $F^2(\mathbf{h})$ as

$$\frac{F^2(\mathbf{h})}{F^2(0)} = 1 - h^2 \frac{\sum_k f_k d_k^{\,2}(\mathbf{l}_0)}{\sum_k f_k} + \cdots$$

The coefficient of the term in h^2 can be designated as the square of an average *inertial distance*, $D(l_0)$, of the particle with respect to the particular plane $\Pi(l_0)$. Then, as in the law of Guinier, this expression can be written to a good approximation as

$$F^2(\mathbf{h}) = F^2(0)e^{-h^2D^2(l_0)} \tag{44}$$

Equation 44 explains the distribution of scattered radiation found on the film of Fig. 9. The particle is presenting its largest dimension in the direction parallel to AB. The average inertial distance, the factor of primary importance in determining the scattered intensity, is thus also a maximum for this particular direction. Equation 44 then shows that it is along this line AB that the decrease in intensity with increasing h will be the most rapid.

2.2. SCATTERING PRODUCED BY A GROUP OF IDENTICAL PARTICLES
2.2.1. GENERAL RESULTS FOR FLUIDS[1]
2.2.1.1. Basic Hypotheses

Scattering experiments are rarely conducted with a single particle as the scatterer; thus it is of more practical importance to calculate the intensity scattered by a group of particles. In this section we shall consider the simplest such case, that of a group of identical particles.

We shall also restrict our study by requiring that the structure of the ensemble of particles satisfy two hypotheses. To simplify later references, these hypotheses will be denoted as H_1 and H_2.

Hypothesis H_1. We shall assume that:

1. *All particles, each possessing a center of symmetry, can with equal probability take all possible orientations.*

2. *The knowledge of the relative positions of two particles in no way modifies the probabilities of their different orientations.*

The second part of hypothesis H_1 is always realized for spherically symmetric particles. For the more general case it would seem that, if the particles are not too densely packed and if their shapes are not too anisotropic, this hypothesis should be good at least as a first approximation.

Hypothesis H_2. We shall assume that the group of particles is isotropic and without order at long distances.

In order to clarify hypothesis H_2, let us define $\mathbf{R}_k$ as the vector from an arbitrary origin to the center of the kth particle. The vector joining the centers of the kth and jth particles is then $(\mathbf{R}_k - \mathbf{R}_j)$. Hypothesis H_2 then requires that all vectors $(\mathbf{R}_k - \mathbf{R}_j)$ of the same magnitude have an equal probability of orientation in all directions (isotropic) and that for long distances (viz., 1000 A) the probability of finding vectors $(\mathbf{R}_k - \mathbf{R}_j)$

---

[1] We include in the term "fluids" gases, liquids, solutions, and suspensions. Thus the word fluid refers to all matter satisfying hypotheses H_1 and H_2.

of a given magnitude, r, is a continuous function of r and is nearly constant. This hypothesis is well justified for fluids.

2.2.1.2. Consequences of Hypothesis H_1

Let us consider a group of particles, each possessing a center of symmetry. We shall designate by $\mathbf{r}_{kl}$ the vector extending from the center of the kth particle to a point l of scattering factor f_{kl} in the same particle.

The amplitude of radiation scattered by this group of particles is then given as (cf. equation 2)

$$A(\mathbf{h}) = A_e(h)\sum_k \left\{ \sum_l f_{kl} e^{-i\mathbf{h}\cdot(\mathbf{R}_k+\mathbf{r}_{kl})} \right\}$$

since the position of the scattering point, l, is defined by the vector sum $\mathbf{R}_k + \mathbf{r}_{kl}$.

By virtue of the center of symmetry of each particle, this can be written as

$$A(\mathbf{h}) = A_e(h)\sum_k e^{-i\mathbf{h}\cdot\mathbf{R}_k}\sum_l f_{kl}\cos(\mathbf{h}\cdot\mathbf{r}_{kl}) \tag{45}$$

The sum $\sum_l f_{kl}\cos(\mathbf{h}\cdot\mathbf{r}_{kl})$ corresponds to the structure factor $F_k(\mathbf{h})$ of the kth particle (see equation 5); since the particles are identical, the index k serves only to mark the kth particle.

The mathematical formulations of equation 45 and equation 2 are identical, with the sum over the index l playing the role of the quantity f_k, so the scattered intensity can be found easily by analogy with equation 3:

$$I(\mathbf{h}) = I_e(h)\sum_k\sum_j[\sum_l f_{kl}\cos(\mathbf{h}\cdot\mathbf{r}_{kl})][\sum_m f_{jm}\cos(\mathbf{h}\cdot\mathbf{r}_{jm})]\cos[\mathbf{h}\cdot(\mathbf{R}_k-\mathbf{R}_j)] \tag{46}$$

In equation 46 indices k and j refer to particles, and indices l and m refer to the different scattering points in particles k and j, respectively.

The intensity calculated above is that furnished by one certain configuration of the ensemble of particles. In the course of time this configuration changes, the particles shifting and changing orientation. Thus we can observe only average intensities. We shall discuss here only the general method of calculating the average intensity; for details, see Fournet [48].

First we separate the terms where $k = j$ in equation 46. These terms represent the intensity scattered by one particle multiplied by the average number of particles being examined (see §2.2.1.3). For the calculation of the other terms, use is made of the second part of hypothesis H_1, which enables us to separate the calculation of the averaging of the orientations of the particles from the averaging of the positions of the particles. The final result is:

$$\overline{I(\mathbf{h})} = I_e(h)\{\overline{N\,F^2(\mathbf{h})} + \overline{F(\mathbf{h})}^2 \sum_k \sum_{j \neq k} \cos{[\mathbf{h} \cdot (\mathbf{R}_k - \mathbf{R}_j)]}\} \qquad (47)$$

where $\overline{F^2(\mathbf{h})}$ and $\overline{F(\mathbf{h})}^2$ are the quantities defined earlier (p. 7). The problem that remains is the calculation of the average of the double sum of terms.

2.2.1.3. Consequences of Hypothesis H_2

Let us consider two very small volume elements, Δv_k and Δv_j, located by vectors $\mathbf{R}_k$ and $\mathbf{R}_j$, which are contained in the volume V irradiated by the X-rays. The contribution of this elementary pair, Δv_k, Δv_j, to the desired average is $n_{kj} \cos{[\mathbf{h} \cdot (\mathbf{R}_k - \mathbf{R}_j)]}$, where n_{kj} is the number of pairs of particles found in these volume elements, one particle being in Δv_k and the other in Δv_j. Now, letting the elementary volumes Δv_k and Δv_j approach the volume elements dv_k and dv_j, small even on an atomic scale, we introduce a probability function p_{kj}, in terms of which the probability of finding a particle in dv_k and at the same time a *different* particle in dv_j is: $p_2 = p_{kj}\,dv_k\,dv_j$. It is essential to consider that the particle in dv_j is different from that in dv_k, since we have excluded the case of $k = j$ in the double sum above. The sum of the cosine terms is now found as the integral (see equation 7)

$$\int_V \int_V \frac{\sin{(h\,|\,\mathbf{R}_k - \mathbf{R}_j\,|)}}{h\,|\,\mathbf{R}_k - \mathbf{R}_j\,|}\,p_{kj}\,dv_k\,dv_j$$

The volume element dv_k being infinitesimal, we shall describe a particle as being in dv_k if the center of the particle is found there.

Before calculating p_{kj}, let us carefully define the experimental conditions. We shall designate by V_0 the total volume offered to the particles. This volume contains a well-defined number of particles, N_0. The volume V_0 must be distinguished from the volume V actually irradiated by the X-rays.

1. If V_0 is smaller than or equal to V, then it follows that $N \equiv N_0$, where N is the number of particles in V.

2. If V_0 is larger than V, the case generally met experimentally, then N cannot be known exactly, as previous authors have implicitly assumed. Only statistical information, such as an average value of N, can be known.

We shall assume that V_0 is large as compared with V, as is true of most experiments, and in any event a situation which is easily realizable. Let us now evaluate the probability $p_{kj}\,dv_k\,dv_j$. We know that the probability of occurrence of an ensemble of two events is equal to the probability of the first multiplied by the probability of the second *as modified by the knowledge that the first event exists.* The probability of occurrence of the first event, finding a particle in dv_k, is $(N_0/V_0)\,dv_k$. When this is realized:

1. The remaining $N_0 - 1$ particles are distributed through a volume $V_0 - dv_k$.

2. If the centers of the two volumes dv_k and dv_j, each containing a particle, are separated by a distance r, the centers of the particles are separated by a distance approximately equal to r. It is obvious that the different distances (and uniquely the distances, if the matter being examined is composed of only one phase) cannot all be equally probable; if the particles are spheres of radius R, the distance between particles cannot be less than $2R$. This behavior will be described by a function $P(r)$ such that

$$p_{kj}\,dv_k\,dv_j = \frac{N_0}{V_0}\,dv_k\,\frac{N_0 - 1}{V_0 - dv_k}\,P(|\mathbf{R}_k - \mathbf{R}_j|)\,dv_j \tag{48}$$

The manner in which $P(r)$ has been introduced shows that this function will tend towards unity as r increases, for then the condition discussed above disappears or, rather, does not play a part. We can neglect dv_k with respect to V_0, and usually 1 is negligible compared to N_0 (see §2.4).

By introducing *the average volume offered to each particle,* $v_1 = (V_0/N_0)$, a quantity characteristic of the ensemble of particles, equation 48 reduces to

$$p_{kj}\,dv_k\,dv_j = \frac{dv_k}{v_1}\frac{dv_j}{v_1}\,P(r_{kj}) \tag{49}$$

and the desired average of the double sum becomes

$$\overline{\sum_k \sum_{j \neq k} \cos\left[\mathbf{h} \cdot (\mathbf{R}_k - \mathbf{R}_j)\right]} = \int_V \int_V \frac{\sin hr_{kj}}{hr_{kj}}\,P(r_{kj})\,\frac{dv_k}{v_1}\frac{dv_j}{v_1} \tag{50}$$

2.2.1.4. General Expression for the Scattered Intensity

Since $P(r)$ tends toward unity as r increases, the structure of the ensemble of particles might be better characterized by the function $(1 - P(r))$, this function being different from zero only for small values of r. By making the substitution $P(r) = 1 - (1 - P(r))$ equation 50 takes on the following form:

$$\overline{\sum_k \sum_{j \neq k} \cos\left[\mathbf{h} \cdot (\mathbf{R}_k - \mathbf{R}_j)\right]} = \int_V \int_V \frac{\sin hr_{kj}}{hr_{kj}}\frac{dv_k}{v_1}\frac{dv_j}{v_1}$$

$$- \int_V \int_V \frac{\sin hr_{kj}}{hr_{kj}}\left[1 - P(r_{kj})\right]\frac{dv_k}{v_1}\frac{dv_j}{v_1}$$

Let us examine separately each of these terms.

First term: The contribution of this term to the total scattered intensity is

$$I_1(h) = I_e(h)\overline{F(h)}^2 \int_V \int_V \frac{\sin hr_{kj}}{hr_{kj}} \frac{dv_k}{v_1} \frac{dv_j}{v_1}$$

which (cf. equation 15) can be interpreted as representing the intensity scattered by a "particle" of volume V with a uniform electronic density, $\rho = \overline{F(h)}/v_1$. Given the size of this particle, $I_1(h)$ is effectively *zero for all observable angles*. (Fournet [48] discusses the reasoning of Compton and Allison (1935) on this subject.)

It is important to note the simple, general interpretation of the term $I_1(h)$. A further discussion of this factor is given by James (1948), where the scattering of a spherical volume is considered. To find simply and schematically the limit h_0, beyond which $I_1(h)$ is negligible, it might be considered that for $h = h_0$ the largest phase difference between rays scattered by two points in the particle will be of the order of 2π radians. Then, if the average dimension of the volume irradiated is designated by D_0, h_0 is determined by $h_0 = 2\pi/D_0$.

Second term: Let us consider first the integration with respect to dv_k:

$$\int_V \frac{\sin hr_{kj}}{hr_{kj}} [1 - P(r_{kj})] \frac{dv_k}{v_1}$$

Since the function $[1 - P(r_{kj})]$ approaches zero rapidly as r increases, by neglecting boundary effects this term can be written as

$$\int_0^\infty \frac{\sin hr}{hr} [1 - P(r)] \frac{4\pi r^2}{v_1} dr \tag{51}$$

independent of the index j. The further integration with respect to j then results simply in multiplying equation 51 by a factor $\int \frac{dv_j}{v_1}$, which is equal to $\overline{N}$, the average number of particles in the irradiated volume V. The final relation for the scattered intensity is thus (Fournet [44])

$$\overline{I(h)} = I_1(h) + I_e(h)\overline{N} \left\{ \overline{F^2(h)} - \frac{\overline{F(h)}^2}{v_1} \int_0^\infty \frac{\sin hr}{hr} [1 - P(r)]4\pi r^2 dr \right\} \tag{52}$$

$I_1(h)$ is completely unobservable, and so for $h > h_0$ this becomes

$$\overline{I(h)} = I_e(h)\overline{N} \left\{ \overline{F^2(h)} - \frac{\overline{F(h)}^2}{v_1} \int_0^\infty \frac{\sin hr}{hr} [1 - P(r)]4\pi r^2 dr \right\} \tag{53}$$

If the particles considered are spherically symmetric, we have seen

(§2.1.2) that there is no distinction between the average of the square of the structure factor $\overline{F^2(h)}$ and the square of the average of the structure factor $\overline{F(h)}^2$. For this case equation 53 can be simplified to the following:

$$\overline{I(h)} = I_e(h)\overline{N}F^2(h)\left\{1 - \frac{1}{v_1}\int_0^\infty [1 - P(r)]\frac{\sin hr}{hr}4\pi r^2\,dr\right\} \qquad (54)$$

This expression was derived by Zernicke and Prins [309] and by Debye and Mencke [269]. Equation 53 thus appears as a generalization of this last expression.

The integral figuring in equations 53 and 54 has the dimensions of a volume. We shall define this as the *volume of perturbation*, $v_2(h)$:

$$v_2(h) = \int_0^\infty [1 - P(r)]\frac{\sin hr}{hr}4\pi r^2\,dr$$

We shall see in §2.2.3.1 that this function, which has also been called the "characteristic volume" (Porod [137]), is actually a function of two variables: $v_2 = v_2(h, v_1)$.

To summarize, we have shown that the scattered intensity can be expressed as a sum of two terms:

$$\overline{I(h)} = I_e(h)\overline{F(h)}^2\int_V\int_V\frac{\sin hr_{kj}}{hr_{kj}}\frac{dv_k}{v_1}\frac{dv_j}{v_1}$$
$$+ I_e(h)\overline{N}\left\{\overline{F^2(h)} - \frac{v_2(h)}{v_1}\overline{F(h)^2}\right\}$$

the first of these terms being negligible with respect to the second for $h > h_0$. The value of h_0 is defined by the relation $h_0D_0 = 2\pi$, D_0 being the average dimension of the irradiated volume. In the remainder of this section we shall designate by "intensity $I(h)$" *only the second term* of equation 52, and when a misunderstanding is possible we shall employ the expression "observable intensity" to denote this second term.

2.2.2. WIDELY SEPARATED PARTICLES

The general expression which we have just established shows the influence of interparticle interferences, through the intermediary of $v_2(h)$, on the scattered intensity. Let us now consider in detail the case of rather widely separated particles, for which the expression for the intensity takes on a particularly simple form. We shall later indicate the criterion which defines "widely separated particles," but for the moment we can indicate that a good example of such a system is a gas under low pressure.

2.2.2.1. Expression for the Scattered Intensity

If the particles are widely separated, the average volume v_1 offered to each will be large. Any irregularities of the function $[1 - P(r)]$ demonstrate that certain interparticle distances are favored while others are less probable. These irregularities are the more marked, the more closely the particles are packed, for, in order to contain more matter in a given volume, the degree of organization of this matter must be increased.

We see thus for two reasons that the ratio of $v_2(h)$ to v_1 is very small for widely separated particles. More rigorously, the part of $v_2(h)$ involving the integration from $r = 0$ to r equal to the smallest particle diameter will not vary as the particles become more separated, but, since v_1 increases, the corresponding part of the ratio of $v_2(h)$ to v_1 decreases. In the limit of large separations, we find the classical result

$$\overline{I(h)} = I_e(h)\overline{N}\,\overline{F^2(h)} \tag{55}$$

where we recall that this expression, derived from equation 53, is valid only for $h > h_0$ (h_0 has been defined on p. 34).

The intensity of radiation scattered by an ensemble of widely separated particles is thus identical on a relative scale to the mean intensity scattered by one isolated particle; in obtaining the intensity relative to an ensemble of particles it is necessary only to multiply the intensity scattered by one particle by the average number of particles, $\overline{N}$.

Realizing the practical importance of this simple result, it is opportune to underline its significance and to recognize its limits of validity. Later (§2.2.3.2) we shall demonstrate the connection existing between this expression and the equation of state for ideal gases, $pv_1 = kT$.

Let us compare equation 55 with a well-known problem in optics. It is often indicated in the literature that the intensity of scattering by identical elements distributed at random is formed by the addition of the intensities scattered by each element. This is not always correct, for if $h = 0$, we are led to the result $\overline{I(0)} = \overline{N}\,\overline{F^2(0)}$, whereas the exact result is known to be $\overline{I(0)} = \overline{N^2}\,\overline{F^2(0)}$. The usual reasoning behind the above statement consists of describing the double sum

$$\sum_k \sum_{j \neq k} \cos\left(\mathbf{h} \cdot (\mathbf{R}_k - \mathbf{R}_j)\right)$$

as containing as many positive terms as negative terms, so that consequently the sum is zero. But if $h = 0$ all the cosine terms are equal to unity and this reasoning is no longer true. As a criterion for applicability we can say that this reasoning is correct when the largest phase difference between particles reaches 2π radians; that is, if D_0 is the average dimension of the volume offered to the particles, the reasoning is correct when

$h > (2\pi/D_0) = h_0$. This is simply a restatement of the result that was established in §2.2.1.3.

The classical reasoning is a little too simplified, if not incorrect, and it should be replaced with that due to Lord Rayleigh (1919), who tries first to calculate the probability that the intensity will be between I and $I + dI$ and then afterwards calculates the average intensity. By correcting one error and slightly modifying the reasoning of Lord Rayleigh to render it applicable to the problem of X-ray scattering, equation 55 can be obtained as a first approximation when $h > h_0$. The corrective terms that appear are negligible when $\overline{N}$ is very large (Fournet [48]).

Remarks

For the simple case of widely separated, spherical particles, the scattered intensity (see equation 47) is given by

$$\overline{I(h)} = I_e(h)F^2(h)\{\overline{N} + \overline{\sum_k \sum_{j \neq k} \cos (\mathbf{h} \cdot (\mathbf{R}_k - \mathbf{R}_j))}\}$$

Let us compare the mathematical structure of the square of the structure factor of the particle, $F^2(h)$, with the bracketed term. The intensity scattered by a spherically symmetric particle, whose p scattering centers each have the same scattering factor f, can be described as (cf. equation 3)

$$I_e(h)F^2(\mathbf{h}) = I_e(h)f^2 \sum_l \sum_m \cos (\mathbf{h} \cdot \mathbf{M}_l \mathbf{M}_m)$$
$$= I_e(h)\{pf^2 + f^2 \sum_l \sum_{m \neq l} \cos (\mathbf{h} \cdot (\mathbf{r}_m - \mathbf{r}_l))\} \tag{56}$$

The previous discussion shows that the second term is negligible with respect to the first when h is greater than $h_1 = 2\pi/d$, d being the average dimension of the particle. For angles where h is the order of $h_1/10$, however, each of the terms of equation 56 has approximately the same value, so that the term pf^2 is negligible compared to the double sum.

The total scattered intensity is thus

$$I(h) = I_e(h)f^2 \{p + \sum_l \sum_{m \neq l} \cos (\mathbf{h} \cdot (\mathbf{r}_m - \mathbf{r}_l))\}$$
$$\times \{\overline{N} + \sum_k \sum_{j \neq k} \cos (\mathbf{h} \cdot (\mathbf{R}_k - \mathbf{R}_j))\} \tag{57}$$

The symmetry of this relation is evident; mathematically the description is the same, whether for an ensemble of points in a particle or for an ensemble of particles, but the physical results are very different.

For $0 < h < h_0$, the values of the bracket concerning the ensemble of particles are not interesting to the physicist, since they cannot be reached experimentally. For $h_0 < h < h_1$, the values of the bracket concerning the ensemble of points in a particle are *essential* and permit the determination of the radius of gyration. For an angle of the order of $h_1/10$ and for quasi-homogeneous particles, the second term of the first bracket and the first term of the second bracket are the terms that are important in this expression. The two parts of this equation are shown separately in Fig. 10, in which curve a refers to the first factor and curve b to the second.

2.2.2.2. Remarks on the Babinet Principle of Reciprocity

This principle will be considered at this point not because it is applicable uniquely to ensembles of widely separated particles but rather because our recent concern with just such ensembles permits us to treat it very quickly.

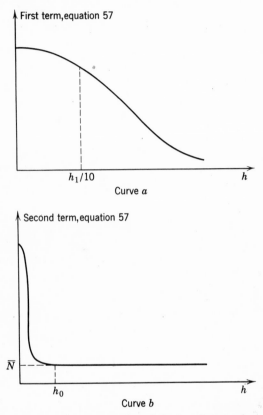

Fig. 10.   A graphical representation of the two factors of equation 57. For clarity h_0 has been greatly exaggerated.

Let us first recall the simplest enunciation of Babinet's theorem: complementary objects produce the same diffraction effects.   The concept of complementary objects will be more precisely defined in the following paragraph, but we can give a simple illustration of a pair of such objects: a screen pierced with circular holes, and an ensemble of circular discs, each disc corresponding in size and position to a particular hole.

The general expression for the amplitude scattered by matter contained in a volume V is

$$A_1(\mathbf{h}) = A_e(h) \int_V \rho_1(\mathbf{r}) e^{-i\mathbf{h}\cdot\mathbf{r}} \, d\mathbf{r}$$

where $\rho_1(\mathbf{r})$ is the electronic density in the volume element $d\mathbf{r}$ whose position is fixed by the vector $\mathbf{r}$. Let us now consider a complementary space, whose electronic density $\rho_2(\mathbf{r})$ is defined as: $\rho_2(\mathbf{r}) = \rho_0 - \rho_1(\mathbf{r})$, where ρ_0 is a constant. The amplitude scattered by this complementary space is then

$$A_2(\mathbf{h}) = A_e(h) \int_V [\rho_0 - \rho_1(\mathbf{r})] e^{-i\mathbf{h}\cdot\mathbf{r}} \, d\mathbf{r}$$

The problem now is to compare

$$I_1(\mathbf{h}) = A_1(\mathbf{h}) \, A_1{}^*(\mathbf{h})$$

and

$$I_2(\mathbf{h}) = A_2(\mathbf{h}) \, A_2{}^*(\mathbf{h})$$

If we write

$$A_0(\mathbf{h}) = A_1(\mathbf{h}) + A_2(\mathbf{h}) = A_e(h) \int_V \rho_0 e^{-i\mathbf{h}\cdot\mathbf{r}} \, d\mathbf{r}$$

then the function,

$$I_0(\mathbf{h}) = A_0(\mathbf{h}) \, A_0{}^*(\mathbf{h})$$

is a maximum for $h = 0$

$$[I_0(0) = I_e(0) V^2 \rho_0{}^2]$$

decreases rapidly with increasing h, and effectively becomes zero beyond an angle defined by $h_0 = 2\pi/D_0$, D_0 being the average dimension of V.

We can now calculate the following:

$$I_2(\mathbf{h}) = [A_0(\mathbf{h}) - A_1(\mathbf{h})][A_0{}^*(\mathbf{h}) - A_1{}^*(\mathbf{h})]$$

$$= I_1(\mathbf{h}) + I_0(\mathbf{h}) - A_1(\mathbf{h})A_0{}^*(\mathbf{h}) - A_0(\mathbf{h})A_1{}^*(\mathbf{h}) \qquad (58)$$

If $h > h_0$, $I_0(\mathbf{h})$ is effectively zero, and consequently $A_0(\mathbf{h})$ and $A_0{}^*(\mathbf{h})$ are also zero. Then $I_1(\mathbf{h}) = I_2(\mathbf{h})$, the usual statement of the reciprocity principle. However, if $h < h_0$, equation 58 shows that this principle is no longer true.

Thus the principle of reciprocity can be applied only to calculate the intensity scattered at angles such that the corresponding values of h are greater than the limit $2\pi/D_0$. The dimension D_0 refers to the average dimension of the volume in which a "complementary" electronic density is defined.

In the experimental systems generally used for the study of low-angle scattering, *the principle of reciprocity can be applied to an ensemble of particles* (that is, an ensemble of cavities in a homogeneous medium can be considered equally well in place of an ensemble of particles), since the intervening dimension is defined by the transverse dimension of the beam, generally of the order of 1 mm. wide, but *it cannot be applied to each single particle* (as, for example, replacing a spherical particle of 100 A diameter containing a concentric spherical cavity of 20 A diameter by a simple sphere of 20 A diameter). This latter method has been employed by some authors, leading to incorrect results; we cite for example the article of Kratky and Porod ([108], p. 45*ff*), in which these authors tried to evaluate the intensity scattered by a "finite packing of lamellae" of submicroscopic dimensions by replacing the lamellae with the interstices contained between them. In a later article, however, Porod is in agreement with the ideas expressed here.

Another application of these ideas is the calculation of the scattering from particles which, instead of being in a vacuum, are *immersed in a homogeneous medium* of electronic density ρ_0 (for example, the solvent of a colloidal suspension). The scattering body can be considered as the superposition of a continuous medium of density ρ_0 and particles of density $\rho - \rho_0$. The scattered amplitude is the sum of the amplitudes scattered by the continuous medium and by the fictitious particles. *The first of these is zero* throughout the region accessible to experiment. The observed scattering is therefore simply that due to the particles of density $\rho - \rho_0$. All the equations which have been established are thus valid on condition that ρ is considered as *the difference between the electronic density of the particle and that of the surrounding medium*. The small-angle scattering becomes zero if the particles have a density equivalent to that of the surrounding medium, even if they have a quite different atomic structure.

2.2.3. INFLUENCE OF THE CLOSER PACKING OF PARTICLES
2.2.3.1. General Considerations

We have just treated the simple case of widely separated particles, in which the total scattered intensity, proportional to the intensity relative to a single particle, generally decreases continuously with increasing scattering angle. It is only for the very particular case of particles with a strongly marked internal structure (for example, CCl_4 molecules) that intensity maxima at non-zero angles can be observed for widely separated particles.

It is well known that numerous liquids whose elementary particles possess simple structures give rise to maxima of intensity at non-zero angles. Zernicke and Prins [309] established their well-known formula (equation 54) in order to explain these results. We should point out that it is difficult to study the effect of the closer packing of particles on the scattering distribution from this equation; when the concentration of matter increases, v_1 decreases, *but there is also an unknown change in the function P(r)*. Writing the equation for the intensity in the form given by Zernicke and Prins could lead to the assumption that the concentration of matter has no influence on the function $P(r)$. To eliminate the possibility of this assumption, we propose to modify slightly the expression of the Zernicke-Prins formula, writing:

$$I(h) = I_e(h)\overline{N} F^2(h) \left\{ 1 - \frac{1}{v_1} \int_0^\infty [1 - P(r, v_1)] \frac{\sin hr}{hr} 4\pi r^2 \, dr \right\} \quad (59)$$

in which the functional dependence of $P(r, v_1)$ appears explicitly.

Numerous authors have studied the influence of the mutual approach of particles on the distribution of scattered radiation, assuming *a priori* a function $P(r)$ more or less well chosen but independent of the concentration of the matter. Among the latest attempts we may cite that of Yudowitch [186]. We believe that it is difficult to determine the validity of the results thus obtained, for in these studies of the influence of concentration on the intensity $I(h)$, one of the most important functions determining this intensity has been assumed *a priori* to be independent of concentration.

The real problem then in any such study is to obtain the function $P(r, v_1)$. This problem is difficult. We feel certain that its solution will require a profound analysis of the thermodynamics of ensembles of particles. We can hope that by such an approach, equations 53 and 54, which may be called "Zernicke-Prins type equations," concerning only the geometry of the ensembles of particles, can be transformed into "thermodynamic equations" by the introduction of certain intrinsic characteristics of the particles.

It is first necessary to find variables that can intervene in a definition of $P(r)$. We have already noted one such variable, v_1. The function $P(r)$ is connected to the *probability* of seeing a certain configuration of two particles realized, so that the calculation of probabilities introduces itself naturally into the problem. If Boltzmann statistics are employed we need to introduce both the temperature and the potential energy $\Phi(r)$ of a pair of particles whose centers are separated by a distance r.

The problem of calculating the function $P(r)$ from v_1, T, and $\Phi(r)$ is the central problem of the latest kinetic theories of fluids (Yvon (1935), Kirkwood (1935), Born and Green [259]). Our own problem is not limited simply to the case of fluids; we are interested to a large extent in solutions of large molecules, suspensions, etc. In each of these cases the functions $P(r)$ and $\Phi(r)$ can always be defined. We shall introduce later the variable, pressure, and the equation of state of the matter being considered. This presents no difficulty in problems concerning gases or liquids. Moreover, it is well known that in solutions the osmotic pressure plays a role analogous to that of pressure in fluids and that the equation of state of *ideal* solutions can be expressed in the form $pv_1 = kT$. If there is difficulty in extending these concepts to the study of emulsions, we can always formally define the pressure by evaluating the change of free energy of the system with respect to the total volume offered.

In the different kinetic theories of fluids cited above, the integral equation determining $P(r)$ is of the form,

$$P(r) = F \left(\frac{P(r)}{v_1}, \frac{\Phi(r)}{kT} \right) \tag{60}$$

where F designates an integration of the functions $P(r)/v_1$ and $\Phi(r)/kT$. In establishing this equation it has been necessary to make a physical approximation known as the "principle of superposition." We shall not give the details of this principle, for these can be found in the article of Kirkwood and Boggs (1942) in which this principle is described and employed for the first time. We may describe equation 60 as having been established in a very general manner from considerations of classical Boltzmann statistics, the only assumption being that of the validity of the principle of superposition.

2.2.3.2. Scattered Intensity and the Equation of State

We have just seen that the kinetic theories of fluids furnish a relation between $P(r)$ and $\Phi(r)$; this shows the manner in which the relation between the function $I(h)$ and $\Phi(r)$ can be established. At this point it seems advantageous to introduce the equation of state, a more familiar quantity than the corresponding mutual potential energy function. This can be written in the following form (Green [273], Yvon (1949)):

$$p = \frac{kT}{v_1} - \frac{1}{6v_1{}^2} \int_0^\infty P(r)\Phi'(r) \; 4\pi r^3 \, dr \tag{61}$$

If the integral is neglected, this reduces simply to the ideal gas law,

$$p = \frac{kT}{v_1} = \frac{N_A kT}{N_A v_1} = \frac{RT}{V}$$

where N_A is Avogadro's number.

Let us first consider the case for which the function $\Phi(r)$ is identically equal to zero. The equation determining $P(r)$ then states that $P(r) \equiv 1$. Two important relations resulting from this particular function $P(r)$ can now be derived:

1. The expression for the scattered intensity becomes (see equation 53)

$$\overline{I(h)} = I_e(h)\overline{N}\,\overline{F^2(h)} \tag{55}$$

the result for widely separated particles.

2. The equation of state, obtained from the general expression of equation 61, becomes

$$pv_1 = kT \tag{62}$$

the ideal gas law.

This result shows that the domains of validity of equation 55 and equation 62 are the same. These two expressions are rigorously true only for point particles, small even on the angstrom scale, as is required when the potential energy is defined as $\Phi(r) \equiv 0$, independent of r. In §2.2.3.4 we shall discuss the conditions under which equation 55 is a good approximation.

Let us remark also that if an attempt is made to find a function $P(r)$ which is independent of v_1 and which is to be defined by equation 60, the only possible solution will be found to be $P(r) \equiv 1$.

Now let us leave the case of widely separated particles and try to treat the general case. By developing $P(r, v_1)$ in a series expansion with v_1 as the variable, we find

$$P(r, v_1) = P_0(r) + v_1 P_1(r) + \cdots$$

where the term $P_0(r)$ is identical to $e^{-\Phi(r)/kT}$.

Thus a first approximation of equation 60 is

$$P(r, v_1) = e^{-\Phi(r)/kT} \tag{63}$$

For this approximation the equation of state becomes

$$pv_1 = kT \left[1 - \frac{(2\pi)^{3/2}}{2} \frac{\beta(0)}{v_1} \right]$$

and the scattered intensity distribution is (cf. equation 54)

$$I(h) = I_e(h) \overline{N} F^2(h) \left[1 + \frac{(2\pi)^{3/2}}{v_1} \beta(h) \right] \tag{64}$$

where the function $\beta(h)$ is defined by the relation

$$h\beta(h) = \frac{2}{\sqrt{2\pi}} \int_0^\infty r\alpha(r) \sin hr \, dr \tag{65}$$

with

$$\alpha(r) = e^{-\Phi(r)/kT} - 1$$

An approximate solution for hard spheres of radius R and volume v_0, with no interactions other than impenetrability, has been considered by Debye [265]. With the probability function defined (cf. equation 63) as

$$P(r) = 0 \qquad 0 < r < 2R$$

$$P(r) = 1 \qquad r > 2R$$

equations 31 and 64 lead to the following expression for the scattered intensity:

$$I(h) = I_e(h) N \Phi^2(hR) \left[1 - \frac{8v_0}{v_1} \Phi(2hR) \right] \tag{66}$$

where the function $\Phi(x)$ is described by equation 31. We shall consider the validity of this expression in §2.2.3.3.

The solution $P(r, v_1) = e^{-\Phi(r)/kT}$ has been proposed as a general solution by Raman (1924), who believed that the solution was exact. His oversight was the following: if an ensemble of only two particles is considered, the probability that these particles are at a distance r from one another is truly $e^{-\Phi(r)/kT}$, but, if an ensemble of a large number of particles is considered, the probability that any two particles are at a distance r cannot be the same, since interactions with the other particles must be taken into account.

A second approximation of equation 60 based on the more complete theories of Born and Green [259] leads to the following result (Fournet [44], [45], [49]):

$$I(h) = I_e(h) \overline{N} \left\{ \overline{F^2(h)} + \overline{F(h)}^2 \frac{\epsilon \beta(h)}{v_1 (2\pi)^{-3/2} - \epsilon \beta(h)} \right\} \tag{67}$$

where ϵ designates a constant approximately equal to unity.

For the simple case of spherically symmetric particles, equation 67 becomes

$$I(h) = I_e(h) \overline{N} F^2(h) \frac{v_1}{v_1 - (2\pi)^{3/2} \epsilon \beta(h)} \tag{68}$$

Let us emphasize that equations 67 and 68 have been derived from certain results of the theory of Born and Green with no additional physical hypotheses or mathematical simplifications.

A simple outline of the derivation of equation 67 is as follows:
The modification added by Rodriguez (1949) to the simple calculation of Green consisted in writing

$$P(r) = e^{-\Phi(r)/kT} e^{f(r)} \tag{69}$$

In obtaining $f(r)$ from equation 60 the value of the function $\alpha(r) = e^{-\Phi(r)/kT} - 1$ is assumed to be different from zero only for small values of r, and in certain cases the product $\alpha(r) f(r)$ is assumed to be replaceable by the terms $\alpha(r) (\epsilon - 1)$, thus defining $(\epsilon - 1)$ as a mean value of $f(r)$ for small values of r. From this, the function $f(r)$ can be described by the Fourier transform

$$rf(r) = \frac{1}{\sqrt{2\pi}} \int_{-\infty}^{\infty} \frac{\epsilon^2 h \beta^2(h)}{v_1 (2\pi)^{-3/2} - \epsilon \beta(h)} \sin hr \, dh \tag{70}$$

neglecting terms in $f^2(r)$, $f^3(r)$, etc.

The calculation of $v_2(h)$ requires a knowledge of the function $[P(r) - 1]$. From equation 69,

$$P(r) - 1 = [\alpha(r) + 1][1 + f(r) + \cdots] - 1$$

or

$$P(r) - 1 \approx \epsilon\alpha(r) + f(r)$$

Thus we can write

$$-\frac{v_2(h)}{v_1} = \frac{1}{h}\frac{(2\pi)^{3/2}}{v_1}\frac{2}{\sqrt{2\pi}}\int_0^\infty r[\epsilon\alpha(r) + f(r)]\sin hr\,dh$$

which, by means of equations 65 and 70, becomes

$$-\frac{v_2(h)}{v_1} = \frac{1}{h}\frac{(2\pi)^{3/2}}{v_1}\left[\epsilon h\beta(h) + h\frac{\epsilon^2\beta^2(h)}{v_1(2\pi)^{-3/2} - \epsilon\beta(h)}\right] \tag{71}$$

Equation 67 is easily found from this last equation.

Let us try to analyze quite generally the different relations which we have established by employing a criterion often used in the statistical theory of ensembles (theory of fluids, the order-disorder transformations in alloys, magnetism): the inclusion in the calculation of particles in units, pairs, triplets, etc. We must point out that a perfect theory should take account of all such possible groups.

Equation 55, correct for widely separated particles, takes account of particles only in units; that is, all interactions between particles have been neglected.

The discussion we have given of the work of Raman with respect to equation 64 shows that this expression takes into account particles considered in units and in pairs; that is, interactions between particles have been limited to a sum of interactions between pairs of particles isolated in space.

In considering the validity of equations 67 and 68 we must first point out that the Kirkwood-Boggs principle of superposition used in establishing equation 60 is presented in the form of a relation, good to a first approximation, between the properties of particles considered in pairs and the properties of particles considered in triplets. Now in the form that Rodriguez has given to the theory of Born and Green, one determines the second approximation to the function $f(r)$, defined by equation 60 and the relation

$$P(r) = e^{-\Phi(r)/kT}e^{f(r)}$$

The first approximation, that of $f(r) \equiv 0$, furnished the solution of Raman, which takes into account only the influence of doublet terms. Thus we can affirm that equations 67 and 68, established from the theory of Born and Green, take account of triplet terms at least to a first approximation, contrary to the opinion of Oster and Riley [128].

To summarize these results, we have listed the expressions of certain equations of state and the corresponding expressions for the scattered intensity.

Summary

EQUATION OF STATE   SCATTERED INTENSITY

$$pV = RT \qquad\qquad I(h) = I_e(h)\overline{N}\,\overline{F^2(h)}$$

$$pV = RT\left[1 - \frac{(2\pi)^{3/2}\beta(0)}{2v_1}\right] \qquad I(h) = I_e(h)\overline{N}\,\overline{F^2(h)}\left[1 + \frac{(2\pi)^{3/2}}{v_1}\beta(h)\right]$$

Born and Green $\qquad\qquad I(h) = I_e(h)\overline{N}\,\overline{F^2(h)}\,\dfrac{1}{1 - \dfrac{(2\pi)^{3/2}}{v_1}\epsilon\beta(h)}$

2.2.3.3. Limiting Value for the Intensity Scattered at Very Small Angles

We have just examined the relation between the equation of state and the scattered intensity, $I(h)$. Let us now restrict the problem to determining which thermodynamic variables are related to $I(0)$. From a previously established relation, equation 53, we find

$$I(0) = I_e(0)\overline{N}\left\{n^2 - n^2\frac{v_2(0)}{v_1}\right\} = I_e(0)\overline{N}n^2\left\{1 - \frac{v_2(0)}{v_1}\right\}$$

n being the number of electrons contained in a particle.

The function $v_2(0)$ can be evaluated as follows: we have seen (§2.2.1.3) that $p_{kj}\,dv_k\,dv_j$ represents the probability that there is at the same time a particle in dv_k and a different particle in dv_j. The double integral of $p_{kj}\,dv_k\,dv_j$ extended over the domain V should then give the average number of pairs of particles existing in the volume V. Designating by N the number of particles in V at a certain instant, we find that

$$\int_V\int_V p_{kj}\,dv_k\,dv_j = \int_V\int_V P(r_{kj})\frac{dv_k}{v_1}\frac{dv_j}{v_1} = \overline{N(N-1)} = \overline{N^2} - \overline{N}$$

since the average of a sum always equals the sum of the averages of each term.

Now by introducing the function $(1 - P(r))$ in terms of these quantities, we have

$$\overline{N^2} - \overline{N} = \int\frac{dv_k}{v_1}\int\frac{dv_j}{v_1} - \int\frac{dv_j}{v_1}\int[1 - P(r_{kj})]\frac{dv_k}{v_1}$$

By making use of the calculations employed in §2.2.1.4, and neglecting only very small terms, we obtain the following expression:

$$\overline{N^2} - \overline{N} = \overline{N}^2 - \overline{N}\int_0^\infty[1 - P(r)]\frac{4\pi r^2}{v_1}\,dr$$

from which we find

$$\frac{1}{v_1}\int_0^\infty[1 - P(r)]\,4\pi r^2\,dr = \frac{v_2(0)}{v_1} = \frac{-\overline{N^2} + \overline{N}^2 + \overline{N}}{\overline{N}} = 1 - \frac{\overline{N^2} - \overline{N}^2}{\overline{N}}$$

With this value of $v_2(0)$, we find that

$$I(0) = I_e(0)n^2(\overline{N^2} - \overline{N}^2) = I_e(0)n^2\overline{(N - \overline{N})^2} \tag{72}$$

This result was first established by the work of Einstein and Smoluchowski; other papers developing this topic which might be cited are those of Zernicke and Prins [309], Bhatia and Krishnan (1948), Yvon (1947), and Fournet and Guinier [53].

Equation 72, which is a result of the hypotheses H_1 and H_2 imposed on the structure of ensembles of particles, shows that the *observable* scattered intensity (see p. 35) at very small angles is a consequence of the existence of fluctuations in the sample. A thermodynamic description of $I(0)$ can be found by recalling a classical result of the kinetic theory of gases,[1]

$$\frac{kT}{V}\beta + \cdots = \overline{\left(\frac{N - \overline{N}}{N}\right)^2} = \frac{\overline{(N - \overline{N})^2}}{\overline{N}^2} + \cdots \tag{73}$$

where β is the isothermal coefficient of compressibility,

$$\beta = -\frac{1}{V}\left(\frac{\partial V}{\partial p}\right)_T$$

V being the total volume offered to the gas. If N is large and the matter is not near its critical point, the terms neglected in equation 73 are small when one writes

$$I(0) = I_e(0)n^2\overline{N}\,\frac{kT}{v_1}\beta \tag{74}$$

thus establishing a simple *relation between $I(0)$ and the isothermal compressibility*.

Values for $I(0)$ have been predicted by several different theories. The expression given by Debye for a model of hard spheres is (cf. equation 66)

$$\overline{I(0)} = I_e(0)n^2N\left(1 - \frac{8v_0}{v_1}\right)$$

where v_0 is the volume of each sphere. (The coefficient, 8, has been omitted in several references in the literature.) The maximum value of v_0/v_1, that for close-packed hexagonal or cubic systems, is 0.74, leading to the prediction of negative intensities for a large domain ($v_0/v_1 > 0.125$). The *linear* model of Kratky and Porod [108], with assumptions similar to those of Debye, leads to a similar factor: $(1 - 2l_0/l_1)$, $[2^3 = 8]$; since the maximum possible value of l_0/l_1 is unity, again negative intensities are possible.

[1] See, for example, R. C. Tolman, *The Principles of Statistical Mechanics*, Oxford, 1946, p. 647.

Equations 67 and 68 give negative results if v_1 is smaller than $(2\pi)^{3/2}$ $\epsilon\beta(0)$. This is not a valid criticism, however, since Fournet [49] has shown that the passage of the Zernicke-Prins type equation to equations 67 and 68 is possible only if there are no roots to the following equation:

$$v_1 - (2\pi)^{3/2}\epsilon\beta(h) = 0$$

When roots to this equation exist, as happens for liquids, equation 67 is no longer correct and must be replaced by another which does not predict negative intensities (for details, see the article of Fournet cited above).

2.2.3.4. Thermodynamic Expression for the Intensity

Let us now consider the general possibilities of employing equation 68,

$$I(h) = I_e(h)\bar{N}F^2(h)\frac{v_1}{v_1 - (2\pi)^{3/2}\epsilon\beta(h)} \tag{68}$$

in a study of spherical particles.[1] Fournet [45], [49] has employed this equation together with the potential energy function $\Phi(r)$ determined by Lennard-Jones (1937) to predict correctly the scattering by gaseous and liquid argon at 150° K.; this is shown in Fig. 11.   When considering a fluid of hard spheres, for which $\beta(h)$ can be calculated, equation 68 becomes

$$I(h) = I_e(h)\bar{N}\Phi^2(hR)\frac{1}{1 + \dfrac{8v_0}{v_1}\epsilon\Phi(2hR)} \tag{75}$$

The corresponding curves are given in Fig. 12 for various values of $(8v_0/v_1)$. Let us recall that, in practice, ϵ can be taken as equal to 1.

We can now establish a precise criterion for defining the term "widely separated particles." Equation 68 can be written in the form

$$I(h) = I_e(h)\bar{N}F^2(h)\frac{1}{1 - \dfrac{(2\pi)^{3/2}\epsilon\beta(h)}{v_1}}$$

which allows us to say that the equation relative to widely separated particles is accurate to within n per cent when the ratio $(2\pi)^{3/2}\epsilon\beta(h)/v_1$ has the value of n per cent.

A certain characteristic behavior of the scattered intensity can be predicted from the mathematical structure of equation 68.   If the value

[1] We shall consider only spherically symmetrical particles in this paragraph in order to simplify the discussion.   For the general case, as expressed by equation 67, the results are analogous.

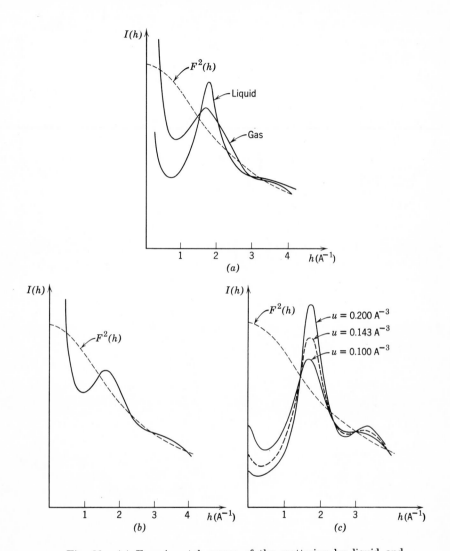

Fig. 11. (a) Experimental curves of the scattering by liquid and gaseous argon at pressures near the condensation pressure at 149.3° K. (Eisenstein and Gingrich [40]). The dotted curve represents the square of the structure factor, $F^2(h)$. (b) Theoretical curve (equation 68) of the scattering from gaseous argon at 149.3° K. and at condensation pressure. (c) Theoretical curves of the scattering from liquid argon of several densities at 149.3° K. $(u = (2\pi)^{3/2}\epsilon(v_1)^{-1}$ [see equation 68]).

of $\beta(h)$ is zero when h equals some value h_1, the reduced intensity, $I(h)/\bar{N}I_e(h)$, evaluated at h_1 is a constant, $F^2(h_1)$, regardless of the concentration of the matter. This fact, predicted from equation 68, is verified quite well by the results found for argon by Eisenstein and Gingrich [40], when their results are considered on the basis of one

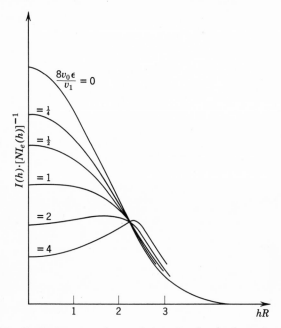

Fig. 12. Scattering curve for non-interacting hard spheres (equation 75).

temperature (see Fig. 7 of the reference cited); the condition of a common temperature for the curves is necessary, since $\beta(h)$ depends on the temperature, as is shown in equation 65.

If the coefficient of $F^2(h)$ in equation 68 is considered, it is seen that the maxima of this function always occur at the same angles (those such that $\beta(h)$ is a maximum), regardless of the concentration of scattering matter; the only effect of a change in concentration is to accentuate the maxima to a greater or lesser degree. This same result is found if the expression derived from only the first approximation is used. (Personal communication from G. W. Brindley.)

A detailed study of equation 68 by Fournet [48] has shown that for the general case, in which $F^2(h)$ decreases in the observable region with increasing h, the intensity maxima are produced at larger and larger angles, the greater the concentration of scattering matter. This is illustrated in Fig. 13, in which we have plotted representative curves of

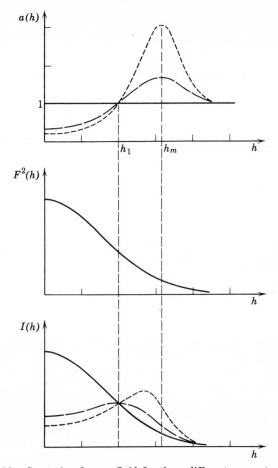

Fig. 13. Scattering from a fluid for three different concentrations of particles. The solid curves correspond to a very low concentration, the dashed curves to an average concentration, and the dotted curves to a high concentration. Note that the maxima of $a(h)$, the interparticle interference function, and $I(h)$, the observed intensity, occur at different scattering angles.

the terms involved as a function of h for three values of v_1; the solid curves refer to the case of v_1 approaching infinity (i.e., widely separated particles), the dashed curves refer to a smaller value of v_1, and the dotted curves to still smaller values of v_1 (i.e., still higher concentrations). The first function, the interparticle interference function

$$a(h) = \frac{v_1}{v_1 - (2\pi)^{3/2}\epsilon\beta(h)}$$

is equivalent to $\dfrac{I(h)}{I_e(h)\ NF^2(h)}$; the second is the function $F^2(h)$; and the
third, the product $F^2(h)a(h)$, is proportional to the intensity. It can be
seen that the product of the continually decreasing function $F^2(h)$ and
the function $a(h)$, with its only slightly accentuated maximum, results in a
function $I(h)$ having a still more diffuse maximum situated at a smaller
value of h than that for the original function, $a(h)$, for each of these cases.
The position of the observed maximum thus depends markedly on the
function $F^2(h)$, that is, on the structure of the particle. The position
of the intensity maximum depends in a very complex way on the
structure of the *arrangement* of the particles *and* on the particular *structure
of each particle.*

2.2.3.5. Fluids and Crystals

In an examination of a crystalline substance by means of an experimental method such as Debye-Scherrer photography, we find that the
function for a perfect crystal which plays the role of $a(h)$, that is, the
function $\dfrac{I(h)}{I_e(h)NF^2(h)}$, is identically equal to zero except for certain
specific values of h, at which points it takes on very large values. The
product of this function with the function $F^2(h)$ then gives a function
$I(h)$ which shows the same structure as $a(h)$, in that it also is identically
zero except for certain specific values of h. The positions of the intensity
maxima (the Debye-Scherrer lines in this example) are identical to those
of the function $a(h)$ and thus can immediately furnish information on the
structural arrangement of the particles (see Fig. 14). This illustrates
one of the essential differences between the classical problems of X-ray
crystallography and the problems that are treated here: the degree of
order in a crystal is in general such that the function $I(h)/F^2(h)$ presents
sharp maxima. As a result the maxima of the function $I(h)$ occur at
the same values of h as the maxima of the function $I(h)/F^2(h)$. *This
result does not apply to fluids*, for they are much less ordered than any
crystal.

We should like now to offer a physical explanation of the fact that the
maximum of the function $I(h)/F^2(h)$ is produced at a constant angle for a
fluid, independent of its concentration. For this very qualitative
explanation let us make the approximation that $P(r) = e^{-\Phi(r)/kT}$. The
factor of physical importance in this problem is the arrangement of particles around any one particle. At very low concentrations the probability
of finding a particle in a volume element dv_j is dv_j/v_1. If it is known that
this element, dv_j, is at a distance r from another particle, the probability

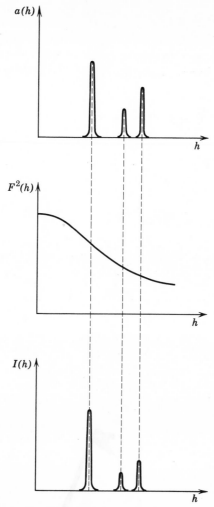

Fig. 14.   Scattering from perfect crystals.   The maxima of $a(h)$ and
$I(h)$ occur at the same scattering angles.

becomes $(dv_j/v_1)e^{-\Phi(r)/kT}$, and the probability density, $d(r)$, from its
definition, is $(1/v_1)\ e^{-\Phi(r)/kT}$.   We have plotted this probability density
in Fig. 15 for two concentrations, $v_1{}'$ and $v_1{}''$.   Whereas the mean
probability density increases when the concentration increases, the
ratio of probability densities for arbitrarily chosen r_1 and r_2 remains a
constant.   Since the position of the maximum of $I(h)/F^2(h)$ is related to
this ratio of probability densities, it can thus be understood that the
position of the maximum will remain invariant.

To summarize, we have shown that there is a great deal of difference between the behavior of the function directly connected to the arrangement of particles, $I(h)/F^2(h)$, and the function $I(h)$ which is observed experimentally. In §4.1.2.2 we shall return to this point to discuss its important consequences in the interpretation of experiments.

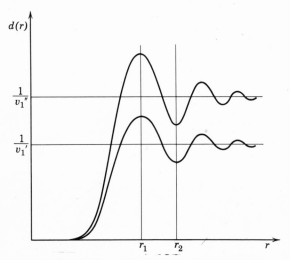

Fig. 15. A schematic representation of the probability density $d(r)$ for two different concentrations of particles.

2.2.3.6. Secondary Maxima

In the course of experiments on the scattering of X-rays by suspensions of latex, Yudowitch [186] and Danielson, Shenfil, and DuMond [25] found several maxima in the scattering curve (Fig. 16). A study of this same suspension by electron microscopy showed that the latex globules were spherical and very regular in size, variations in diameter being less than 10 per cent. These globules were relatively close-packed, so that an explanation based on the theoretical development of §2.2.3.4 can readily explain the principal maximum, the maximum at the smallest angle. The other maxima, which we shall refer to as secondary maxima, appear to be more difficult to interpret.

Yudowitch advanced the hypothesis that these secondary maxima were due to the particular form of the square of the particle structure factor, $F^2(h)$. Let us re-examine the function $F^2(h)$, considering the latex globules as analogous to hard spheres of constant electronic density, this being the same model that we have heretofore designated as "Debye's model."

The intensity scattered by one such sphere is given by the relation

$$F^2(h) = \Phi^2(hR) = \left[3 \, \frac{\sin hR - hR \cos hR}{h^3 R^3} \right]^2 \tag{31}$$

The positions of the maxima and minima of this function are then given by the solutions of the equation

$$2\Phi(u)\Phi'(u) = 2\Phi(u) \, \frac{(u^2 - 3) \sin u + 3u \cos u}{u^4} = 0$$

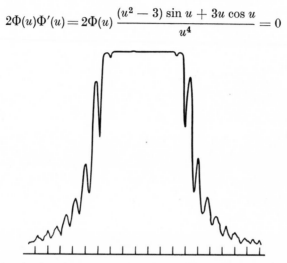

Fig. 16. A microphotometer curve of the diffraction pattern of latex particles showing the secondary diffraction rings. Intervals at the bottom correspond to a scattering angle of 3 minutes of arc (Danielson, Shenfil, and DuMond [25]).

where $u = hR$. The solutions corresponding to the minima are those for which $\Phi(u) = 0$. The positions of the maxima are given as solutions of the equation

$$\tan u_m = \frac{3u_m}{3 - u_m^{\,2}} \tag{76}$$

At these positions we note that

$$\Phi^2(u_m) = \frac{\sin^2 u_m}{u_m^{\,2}} = \frac{9}{u_m^{\,4} + 3u_m^{\,2} + 9} \tag{77}$$

A first approximation to the solutions of equation 76 is found by placing $u_m = k\pi$, where the first maximum is that for $k = 0$, the second for $k = 2$, the third, $k = 3$, etc. A better, second-order approximation (except for $k = 0$) is obtained in writing

$$u_m = k\pi - (3/k\pi) \tag{78}$$

the corresponding intensities being given by

$$I(u_m) = \frac{9}{k^4\pi^4} + \frac{81}{k^6\pi^6} \tag{79}$$

Thus we can establish the following table:

Index of Maximum	1	2	3	4	5	6
k	0	2	3	4	5	6
u_m, equation 78		5.80	9.10	12.33	15.52	18.69
u_m, exact	0.000	5.76				
$10^3 \times I_m$, equation 79		7.37	1.28	0.39	0.15	0.07
$10^3 \times I_m$, exact	1000	7.45				

It should be noted that the second-order approximation gives correct values even for $k = 2$.

Evidently the ratio of $I(u_m)$ at its first maximum, at zero angle, to the value of $I(u_m)$ at its second maximum is very large, actually a value of 1.3×10^2, but, more important, the ratio of the intensities of any two other successive maxima is small; the ratio of the second to the third is only about 5. It is thus possible to observe experimentally several of the maxima that theory predicts for the case of *widely separated* particles.

Next the effect of interparticle interference should be considered. We shall employ equation 75, which has been established for the case of particles with no mutual interaction other than impenetrability; though this represents an approximation, it should be sufficient for the larger angles. Neglecting constant factors (see §2.2.3.4), the scattered intensity is

$$I_2(u) = \frac{\Phi^2(u)}{1 + \dfrac{8v_0}{v_1}\,\epsilon\Phi(2u)}$$

Expanding this function, $I_2(u)$, around the point $u = k\pi + x$, we find that to a second approximation this function is a maximum for

$$u = k\pi - (3/k\pi) + \cdots$$

the same result as that found for the maxima of $\Phi^2(u)$. The values of the intensity maxima are (cf. equation 79):

$$I_2(u_m) = \frac{9}{k^4\pi^4} + \frac{81}{k^6\pi^6} + \frac{27c}{4k^6\pi^6}$$

where c designates the ratio $(8v_0\epsilon/v_1)$, which has a maximum value of about 6.

We see thus that for this model *the positions and magnitudes of the secondary maxima are only slightly modified in passing from a very dilute system to a dense system.* This is not true for the principal maximum; the principal maximum occurs at zero angle for dilute solutions, and as the concentration increases it is displaced towards larger angles, occurring at values of u between 0 and 2.5 for systems of average concentration.

The explanation of the secondary maxima observed by Yudowitch is thus given by a complete calculation of interparticle interferences. These maxima are present in the representative curves of $F^2(h)$ for a single particle, and interparticle interferences, instead of removing these maxima, actually reinforce them slightly, as is shown in Fig. 17.

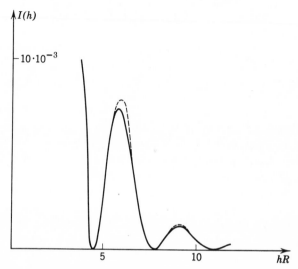

Fig. 17. Scattering from hard spheres. The solid curve represents the intensity scattered by a single sphere of radius R at large value of hR (see Fig. 6). The dotted curve represents the scattered intensity per sphere for a dense group of spheres $((8v_0\epsilon)/v_1 = 5)$.

We must point out that this explanation of the secondary maxima is based on the choice of a model of the particles, but the hard-sphere model seems particularly valid for suspensions of latex globules.

Let us now consider as a second example the secondary maxima that can be observed in the scattering curves of liquid or gaseous argon as determined by Eisenstein and Gingrich (Fig. 11). A comparison of these curves with the square of the structure factor shows immediately that these secondary maxima are due uniquely to interparticle interferences.

2.2.3.7. Remarks on Fourier Transformations

When considering two mutually reciprocal spaces that are connected by a Fourier transformation, as, for example, the real space containing the particles and the reciprocal space of the variable **h**, in which densities are related to scattered intensities, it is known that an unevenness in density in one space corresponds to a periodic variation of density in the other space, with the period in the second space being related to the position of the unevenness in the first.   We know thus that a Debye-Scherrer line, which is a discontinuity in **h** space, is determined by the periodic distribution of certain crystallographic planes in real space, and the position

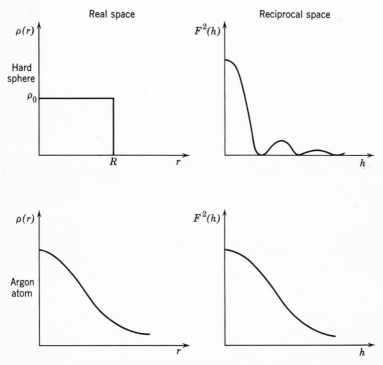

Fig. 18.   Schematic curves of $\rho(r)$ and $F^2(h)$ for a hard sphere and for an argon atom.   The unevenness in $\rho(r)$ for the hard sphere causes a certain periodicity in its $F^2(h)$.

of the line is determined by the period, or distance between consecutive planes, in real space (Bragg's law).   These remarks can now be applied in a discussion of the intensity scattered by a hard homogeneous sphere and by an atom of argon.   Both particles are characterized in the real space by the electronic density $\rho(r)$ at a distance r from the center of a particle and in the **h** space by the function $F(\mathbf{h})$, related to $\rho(r)$ by a Fourier integral (see §2.1).

Since the density $\rho(r)$ is more uneven, in a general sense, for hard spheres than for argon atoms, the graph of $F^2(h)$ for hard spheres will demonstrate a certain periodicity not found in the corresponding curve for argon, as is seen in Fig. 18.

Let us now consider an ensemble of hard spheres and an ensemble of argon atoms. The effects of interparticle interferences, which must be taken into account, will be determined in real space in terms of the potential $\Phi(r)$ associated with the forces acting between two particles

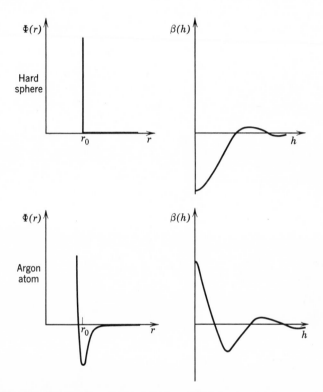

Fig. 19. Schematic curves of $\Phi(r)$ and $\beta(h)$ for hard spheres and for argon atoms. The argon interaction potential is the more uneven, so its function $\beta(h)$ has the more marked periodic character.

separated by a distance r. We have previously shown that the influence of $\Phi(r)$ is felt through the intermediary of a function $\beta(h)$, which is defined as the Fourier transform of $\alpha(r)$, where $\alpha(r) = e^{-\Phi(r)/kT} - 1$. Thus we can say immediately that, since the curve of $\Phi(r)$ with respect to argon is the most uneven, the function $\beta(h)$ of argon will have the more marked periodic character. This is shown in Fig. 19.

The scattered intensity is found by combining the functions $F^2(h)$ and $\beta(h)$ (see §2.2.3.2). The above discussion shows why the secondary maxima from argon are due almost entirely to interparticle effects, whereas form and internal structure are the predominant factors for the case of hard spheres.

2.2.4. PARTICLES UNRESTRICTED BY HYPOTHESES H_1 AND H_2

We have assumed from the beginning of §2.2 that the scattering matter being examined satisfies hypotheses H_1 and H_2. We should like now to remove these restrictions. If the details of the calculations which led to equation 47 are considered, it is seen that the second part of our hypothesis—that which excludes all possible relations between relative positions and probabilities of orientations of particles (i.e., all possible relations between positions and structure factors)—has enabled us to calculate the averages by describing the average of the factor

$$\sum_k \sum_{j \neq k} F_k(\mathbf{h}) F_j(\mathbf{h}) \cos (\mathbf{h} \cdot (\mathbf{R}_k - \mathbf{R}_j))$$

as the product of the averages of $F_k(\mathbf{h})$, $F_j(\mathbf{h})$, and $\cos (\mathbf{h} \cdot (\mathbf{R}_k - \mathbf{R}_j))$. The first part of hypothesis H_1 gave knowledge of the average of $F(\mathbf{h})$, which was convenient for our considerations.

We should like now to try to consider the general problem in order to determine the characteristic magnitudes that are involved in this question.

The general relation, equation 46, shows that only information *relative to pairs of particles* is necessary. Thus it is sufficient to define the statistical correlations existing between two particles. We shall describe these by means of the development offered by Fournet [48]:

$p_1(F, \mathbf{h})$ designates the *a priori* probability density function of the scattering factor F of a particle for a scattering angle corresponding to $\mathbf{h}$. We shall assume this function to be identical for all particles. If we have no information concerning the surroundings of a particle, the probability that its scattering factor for a given value of $\mathbf{h}$ is contained between the values F_0 and $F_0 + dF_0$ is equal to $p_1(F_0, \mathbf{h}) \, dF_0$.

$p_2(F_j, F_k, \mathbf{r}, \mathbf{h})$ designates the probability density function of the scattering factor F_j of a jth particle for a scattering angle corresponding to $\mathbf{h}$ when it is known that the scattering factor for the same angle of a kth particle has a value F_k, where $\mathbf{R}_k - \mathbf{R}_j = \mathbf{r}$. As a consequence of the indistinguishability of particles, p_2 must be the same for the same vector $\mathbf{r}$, regardless of the position of the center of the kth particle.

There is no contradiction in stating that the probability density p_1 is the same for all particles, while defining p_2 as has been done above, if it is realized that the function p_2 concerns ensembles of factors F_k and F_j, whereas p_1 governs the factor F_k or F_j, considered by itself. The relation between p_1 and p_2 can be expressed as

$$\int_0^\infty p_2(F_j, F_k, \mathbf{r}, \mathbf{h}) p_1(F_k, \mathbf{h})\, dF_k \equiv p_1(F_j, \mathbf{h}) \tag{80}$$

Now let us consider the intensity of radiation scattered by an ensemble of identical, arbitrarily shaped particles,

$$I(\mathbf{h}) = I_e(h) \overline{\sum_k \sum_j F_k(\mathbf{h}) F_j(\mathbf{h}) \cos\,(\mathbf{h} \cdot (\mathbf{R}_k - \mathbf{R}_j))} \tag{81}$$

We can group separately the terms for which $k = j$. An analogous problem has been treated in §2.2.1.2, in which the result for the sum of these terms was shown to be

$$I_e(h)\overline{N}\ \overline{F^2(\mathbf{h})} = I_e(h)\overline{N} \int_0^\infty F^2 p_1(F, \mathbf{h})\, dF$$

In the general term of equation 81 for which $k \neq j$ there are found three types of variables:

1. The scattering factor F_k (F_j is related to F_k by means of the functions p_2).
2. The angle $\angle \mathbf{h}(\mathbf{R}_k - \mathbf{R}_j)$.
3. The distance $\left| \mathbf{R}_k - \mathbf{R}_j \right|$.

In order to evaluate the group of terms for which $k \neq j$ we shall perform successive integrations over each of these variables.

Average of the Variable F_k

Let us consider first only the functions F_k as variables. The group of terms of equation 61 for which $k \neq j$ can now be written as

$$\sum_k \sum_{j \neq k} \left\{ \cos\,(\mathbf{h} \cdot (\mathbf{R}_k - \mathbf{R}_j)) \int_0^\infty F_k p_1(F_k, \mathbf{h}) \int_0^\infty F_j p_2(F_j, F_k, \mathbf{r}, \mathbf{h})\, dF_j\, dF_k \right\} \tag{82}$$

We shall assume that correlation between values of the scattering factors does not occur for large distances of separation; the knowledge of F_k gives no information about F_j if $\left| \mathbf{R}_k - \mathbf{R}_j \right|$ is large compared to nearest neighbor distances.

It now follows that $p_2(F_j, F_k, \mathbf{r}, \mathbf{h})$ tends toward the function $p_1(F_j, \mathbf{h})$ for large r. Thus it is useful to express the quantity p_2 as

$$p_2(F_j, F_k, \mathbf{r}, \mathbf{h}) = p_1(F_j, \mathbf{h}) - \{p_1(F_j, \mathbf{h}) - p_2(F_j, F_k, \mathbf{r}, \mathbf{h})\} \tag{83}$$

On replacing p_2 by this expression, equation 82 breaks down into two terms:

First term: This term describes the scattering when the structure factors F_k and F_j follow the same law of probability, independent of one another. We have already solved an analogous problem (§2.2.1.2), which gave as a result

$$\overline{F(\mathbf{h})}^2 \{\sum_k \sum_{j \neq k} \cos (\mathbf{h} \cdot (\mathbf{R}_k - \mathbf{R}_j))\}$$

where

$$\overline{F(\mathbf{h})} = \int_0^\infty F p_1(F, \mathbf{h}) \, dF$$

Second term: This term is of the form

$$-\sum_k \sum_{j \neq k} \{b(\mathbf{r}, \mathbf{h}) \cos (\mathbf{h} \cdot (\mathbf{R}_k - \mathbf{R}_j))\}$$

where

$$b(\mathbf{r}, \mathbf{h}) = \int_0^\infty \int_0^\infty F_k p_1(F_k, \mathbf{h}) \{p_1(F_j, \mathbf{h}) - p_2(F_j, F_k, \mathbf{r}, \mathbf{h})\} F_j \, dF_j \, dF_k \quad (84)$$

The bracketed term in the integrand approaches zero when $|\mathbf{r}|$ becomes large, and consequently the function $b(\mathbf{r}, \mathbf{h})$ behaves in the same manner. Thus in evaluating this second term we can neglect boundary effects and treat the summation over the index j as independent of k:

$$-\sum_k \sum_{r \neq 0} b(\mathbf{r}, \mathbf{h}) \cos (\mathbf{h} \cdot \mathbf{r})$$

where the sum extends over all vectors $\mathbf{r}$ which exist in the sample (except $\mathbf{r} = 0$). The sum over k then results simply in multiplying this result by the average number of particles. The final expression for the scattered intensity is then

$$\overline{I(\mathbf{h})} = I_e(h) \overline{N} \{\overline{F^2(\mathbf{h})} - \sum_{r \neq 0} b(\mathbf{r}, \mathbf{h}) \cos (\mathbf{h} \cdot \mathbf{r})\}$$

$$+ I_e(h) \overline{F(\mathbf{h})}^2 \{\sum_k \sum_{j \neq k} \cos (\mathbf{h} \cdot (\mathbf{R}_k - \mathbf{R}_j))\} \quad (85)$$

or

$$\overline{I(\mathbf{h})} = I_e(h) \overline{N} \{[\overline{F^2(\mathbf{h})} - \overline{F(\mathbf{h})}^2] - \sum_{r \neq 0} b(\mathbf{r}, \mathbf{h}) \cos (\mathbf{h} \cdot \mathbf{r})\}$$

$$+ I_e(h) \overline{F(\mathbf{h})}^2 \sum_k \sum_j \cos (\mathbf{h} \cdot (\mathbf{R}_k - \mathbf{R}_j)) \quad (86)$$

Average with Respect to the Angle $\measuredangle \, \mathbf{h} \, (\mathbf{R}_k - \mathbf{R}_j)$

Keeping the magnitudes of the distances fixed, let us assume that all orientations of the vector $\mathbf{r}$ are equally probable. The function p_2 then depends only on the distance r between centers k and j. The terms in $\cos (\mathbf{h} \cdot \mathbf{r})$ on averaging will then be replaced by terms in $\sin hr/hr$ (a calculation illustrated several times, viz., equation 7). The resulting expression for the intensity is

$$\overline{I(\mathbf{h})} = I_e(h)\overline{N}\Big\{[\overline{F^2(\mathbf{h})} - \overline{F(\mathbf{h})}^2] - \sum_{r \neq 0} b(r, \mathbf{h}) \frac{\sin hr}{hr}\Big\}$$

$$+ I_e(h)\overline{F(\mathbf{h})}^2 \sum_k \sum_j \frac{\sin hr_{kj}}{hr_{kj}} \qquad (87)$$

Average with Respect to Distance r

For this final averaging we proceed as in §2.2.1.3, defining a function $P(r)$ which is related to the probability of finding the centers of two different particles at a distance r. When no external field is applied, all orientations of a vectorial distance $\mathbf{r}$ are equally probable, so that we can begin with equation 87, modified only so that the term $-\overline{N}I_e(h)\overline{F(\mathbf{h})}^2$ is included in the double sum over k and j. Analogous problems have already been treated in §2.2.1.4.

The summations of equation 87 must be replaced by integrations, taking into account the probability of realization of the different distances, r. By replacing $P(r)$ with $1 - [1 - P(r)]$ and considering only angles for which $h > h_0$ (§2.2.1.4), only the term in $[1 - P(r)]$ need be considered in the third term of equation 87. This reasoning cannot be applied to the second term of equation 87, since $b(r, \mathbf{h})$ tends to zero as r becomes large. The final expression is thus (Fournet [48])

$$\overline{I(\mathbf{h})} = I_e(h)\overline{N}\left\{\overline{F^2(\mathbf{h})} - \frac{\overline{F(\mathbf{h})}^2}{v_1} \int_0^\infty [1 - P(r)] \frac{\sin hr}{hr} 4\pi r^2 \, dr\right.$$

$$\left. - \frac{1}{v_1} \int_0^\infty P(r)b(r, \mathbf{h}) \frac{\sin hr}{hr} 4\pi r^2 \, dr\right\} \qquad (88)$$

The first two terms of this expression are identical to those derived on the assumption of complete independence between the orientations and the positions of the particles. The term in $b(r, \mathbf{h})$ thus appears as a corrective term, necessary for the description of the general case.

The complete expression, equation 88, must be used, for example, in calculating the intensity scattered by a dense ensemble of identical ellipsoids of axes $2R$, $2R$, and $2vR$. The scattering factor of an ellipsoid for a given scattering angle, 2θ, depends on the orientation of the ellipsoid. If it is known that the distance between the centers of two ellipsoids is $2R$, the axes of these ellipsoids cannot be oriented in a completely arbitrary manner, and, consequently, their scattering factors must be related. We can see by this example how a relation between scattering factors

F_k and F_j and the distance between their centers can be introduced. It is this dependence which introduces the supplementary term in equation 88.

We have just seen that in the general case, in which the orientations and the positions of particles are related, the expression for the scattered intensity contains *two characteristic functions*, $P(r)$ and $b(r, \mathbf{h})$. *This makes it impossible to determine separately these characteristic functions from the experimental curve of* $\overline{I(h)}$. Equation 88 can serve only to predict intensities for certain models.

To proceed further it would probably be necessary to introduce thermodynamic considerations, defining a potential energy of interparticle forces not as a function $\Phi(r)$ but rather as $\Phi(r, \varphi)$, where at least one angular variable is necessary, and then relating the functions $P(r)$ and $b(r, \mathbf{h})$ to this potential. This problem has not yet been undertaken.

Remarks

In establishing equation 86 we have allowed only the structure factors to undergo variations, so that a simple interpretation can be given to this equation by applying it to a study of crystals and neglecting thermal effects.

The third term of equation 86 represents the intensity scattered by the sample under inspection, if it is supposed that all the scattering centers are identical, with scattering factors $\overline{F(\mathbf{h})}$. The first term varies only slowly with h, while the second term can present intensity maxima that will probably be less sharp than those created by the third term. From this we can see the essential role of the function $b(\mathbf{r}, \mathbf{h})$, a function that is analogous to the Patterson distribution function for crystal structure analyses. If we assume that each of the three intensity terms can be separated, all the information obtainable from experiments will be contained in the function $b(\mathbf{r}, \mathbf{h})$.

In the study of crystals it is often assumed that the structure factors of different atoms all follow the same law, $F(h)$, the magnitudes depending on a coefficient equal to the atomic number Z of the atom considered. If we assume this to be true, all the formulas we have developed can be considerably simplified, for the functions p_1 and p_2 can be treated as being functions uniquely of the Z_k.

The function $b(\mathbf{r}, \mathbf{h})$ becomes

$$b(\mathbf{r}, \mathbf{h}) = b(\mathbf{r}, h) = F^2(h)\sum_k\sum_j Z_k p_1(Z_k)\,[p_1(Z_j) - p_2(Z_j, Z_k, \mathbf{r})]Z_j$$

$$= F^2(h)c(\mathbf{r})$$

The final result is then (Fournet [48])

$$\overline{I(\mathbf{h})} = I_e(h)\overline{N}\,F^2(h)\{[\overline{Z^2} - \overline{Z}^2] - \sum_{r\neq0}c(\mathbf{r})\cos(\mathbf{h}\cdot\mathbf{r})\}$$
$$+ I_e(h)F^2(h)\overline{Z}^2\sum_k\sum_j \cos(\mathbf{h}\cdot(\mathbf{R}_k - \mathbf{R}_j)) \tag{89}$$

The function $c(\mathbf{r})$ can always be calculated from any given model. We have employed this technique in the recalculation of the scattering by a linear model of an alloy with partial short-range order, a model first studied by Guinier and Griffoul (1948). We quickly obtained the same results as those given by these authors.

Equation 86 can be easily used to obtain the intensities scattered by more complicated models. This equation, a particular case of which has been given by

Mac Gillavry and Strijk (1946), can be viewed as a generalization of the expression obtained by von Laue (1941) in considering completely disordered metallic solid solutions, in which all scattering centers were assumed to follow independently the same law. When bound by this assumption, p_2 is equal to p_1 and the function $b(\mathbf{r}, \mathbf{h})$ becomes identically zero. The second term of equation 86 disappears and, on noting that the two types of atoms, A and B, are present in proportions p_A and p_B the Laue equation is obtained:

$$\overline{F^2} - \overline{F}^2 = p_A F_A{}^2 + p_B F_B{}^2 - (p_A F_A + p_B F_B)^2$$
$$= p_A p_B (F_A - F_B)^2$$

2.3. SCATTERING BY GROUPS COMPOSED OF SEVERAL TYPES OF PARTICLES

This problem is quite complicated, and the few equations that can be derived have not yet been employed in experimental studies.

2.3.1. GENERAL THEORY

Simple calculations, in every way analogous to those which have been developed in §2.2.1.4, give the following relation for the scattered intensity (Fournet [48]):

$$I(h) = I_e(h)\overline{N}\left\{ \sum_k p_k \overline{F_k{}^2(h)} \right.$$
$$\left. + \sum_k \sum_j p_k p_j \overline{F_k(h)}\,\overline{F_j(h)}\,\frac{1}{v_1}\int_0^\infty [P_{kj}(r) - 1]\frac{\sin hr}{hr}4\pi r^2\,dr \right\} \qquad (90)$$

where $F_k(h)$ designates the structure factor of the particle of type k; p_k, the probability that one of the $\overline{N}$ particles is of the type k; v_1, the average volume offered to each particle, regardless of its type; and $P_{kj}(r)$, a probability function analogous to the function $P(r)$ defined in §2.2.1.3, which applies to a pair of particles of type k and j. Evidently

$$P_{kj}(r) = P_{jk}(r)$$

This general expression can best be appreciated by comparing it with equation 53, the expression applicable to an ensemble of identical particles. From the first terms we obtain

$$\overline{F^2(h)} = \sum_k p_k \overline{F_k{}^2(h)}$$

while from the second terms

$$\overline{F(h)}^2 = \sum_k \sum_j p_k p_j \overline{F_k(h)}\,\overline{F_j(h)}$$

and

$$\overline{F(h)}^2 P(r) = \sum_k \sum_j p_k p_j \overline{F_k(h)}\,\overline{F_j(h)} P_{kj}(r)$$

By a simple substitution we now find

$$P(r) = \frac{\sum_k \sum_j p_k p_j \overline{F_k(h)}\, \overline{F_j(h)} P_{kj}(r)}{\sum_k \sum_j p_k p_j \overline{F_k(h)}\, \overline{F_j(h)}}$$

which demonstrates that in the general case a function equivalent to $P(r)$ but dependent on the single variable r does not exist.

It is equally impossible to obtain information by means of a Fourier transformation. Equation 90 can be written in the form

$$\frac{I(h)}{I_e(h)\overline{N}} - \sum_k p_k \overline{F_k{}^2(h)} = \sum_k \sum_j p_k p_j \overline{F_k(h)}\, \overline{F_j(h)} \frac{1}{v_1} \int_0^\infty [P_{kj}(r) - 1] \frac{\sin hr}{hr} 4\pi r^2\, dr$$

The right side of the equation depends on the variable h not only in the term $\sin hr/hr$ but also in $\overline{F_k(h)}$ and $\overline{F_j(h)}$, and this prevents the effective application of a Fourier transformation. Results can be obtained by this technique only if the assumption is made that $F_k(h) = a_k f(h)$, that is, that the functions $F_i(h)$ differ only by a constant factor. On making this assumption, we find

$$\frac{I(h)}{I_e(h)\overline{N}} - f^2(h)\sum_k p_k a_k{}^2 = f^2(h)\sum_k \sum_j p_k p_j a_k a_j \frac{1}{v_1} \int_0^\infty [\overline{P(r)} - 1] \frac{\sin hr}{hr} 4\pi r^2\, dr$$

$$(91)$$

with
$$\overline{P(r)} = \frac{\sum_k \sum_j p_k p_j a_k a_j P_{kj}(r)}{\sum_k \sum_j p_k p_j a_k a_j} \tag{92}$$

from which the function $\overline{P(r)}$ can easily be obtained by means of a Fourier transformation.

With the exception of this case, which itself would be hard to interpret, it is difficult to use equation 90 without supplying some model.

2.3.2. WIDELY SEPARATED PARTICLES

When the concentration of scattering matter becomes small equation 90 reduces to the following form:

$$I(h) = I_e(h)\overline{N} \sum_k p_k \overline{F_k{}^2(h)} \tag{93}$$

which describes the total intensity as being given simply by the addition of the intensities scattered by each of the different types of particles, each weighted by its respective probability. On expressing each $\overline{F_k{}^2(h)}$ by the approximate law of Guinier (equation 39), equation 93 becomes

$$I(h) = I_e(h)\overline{N} \sum_k p_k n_k{}^2 \left[1 - \frac{h^2 R_{0k}{}^2}{3} + \cdots \right]$$

$$= I_e(h)\overline{N}[\sum_k p_k n_k{}^2] \left[1 - \frac{h^2}{3} \frac{\sum_k p_k n_k{}^2 R_{0k}{}^2}{\sum_k p_k n_k{}^2} + \cdots \right] \qquad (94)$$

This relation shows that the total curve can still be represented by an exponential function if the Guinier approximation is valid for all of the individual particles, particularly those that are the largest.

These conditions are rarely satisfied in practice. Thus, it is more interesting to consider the tails of the scattering curves. The principal part of the curve of $\overline{F_k{}^2(h)}$ at large values of h for a homogeneous particle of density ρ_k and external surface S_k is given by the function $(2\pi\rho_k{}^2 S_k)/h^4$ (equation 26). The extra terms acting as damped oscillations contain the functions $\cos hR_{1k}$ and $\sin hR_{1k}$, where R_{1k} is the maximum dimension of the kth particle. When the curves for a large number of particles of different dimensions are added together, it is probable that *the sum of the oscillating terms will be zero.* In fact, such oscillations have never been observed on a scattering curve unless the particles of the sample were extremely uniform in size (Fig. 16). The asymptotic behavior of the observed curve is then

$$I(h) = I_e(h)\overline{N}[\sum_k p_k \rho_k{}^2 S_k] \frac{2\pi}{h^4} \qquad (95)$$

This shows that, for a given angle within the domain of validity of equation 26, *the scattered intensity is proportional to the total surface of the group of diffracting particles* if all particles have the same electronic density.

In this discussion we have assumed that the particles were separated sufficiently so that there were no interparticle interferences. In §2.3.3 we shall see that equation 95 is also valid for the case of *packed* powders.

2.3.3. INFLUENCE OF THE CLOSER PACKING OF PARTICLES

Evidently one can try to effect the same sort of generalization of equation 90 as was done with equation 53, the equation of the scattering relative to a single species of particle. The first step is to generalize the theory of Born and Green (Fournet [51], and Rushbrooke and Scoins

(1951)) so as to allow the consideration of this case. The general expression can be obtained in placing

$$P_{kj}(r) = e^{-\frac{\Phi_{kj}(r)}{kT} + f_{kj}(r)}$$

Next the functions $g(h)$ and $\beta(h)$ are defined as

$$hg_{kj}(h) = \frac{1}{\sqrt{2\pi}} \int_{-\infty}^{\infty} rf_{kj}(r) \sin hr \, dr$$

$$h\beta_{kj}(h) = \frac{1}{\sqrt{2\pi}} \int_{-\infty}^{\infty} r(e^{-\Phi_{kj}(r)/kT} - 1) \sin hr \, dr$$

These two functions are connected by the set of relations

$$\frac{v_1}{(2\pi)^{3/2}} g_{kj}(h) = \sum_i p_i \{g_{ki}(h) + \epsilon_{ki}\beta_{ki}(h)\} \epsilon_{ij}\beta_{ij}(h)$$

where the ϵ_{jk} designates a mean value of $(f_{jk}(r) + 1)$ near the origin, $r = 0$.

With the introduction of these functions, equation 90 becomes

$$I(h) = I_e(h)\overline{N} \left\{ \sum_k p_k \overline{F_k^2(h)} + \frac{(2\pi)^{3/2}}{v_1} \sum_k \sum_j p_k p_j \overline{F_k(h)} \, \overline{F_j(h)}[g_{kj}(h) + \epsilon_{kj}\beta_{kj}(h)] \right\}$$

$$(96)$$

The scattered intensity then depends only on the functions $F_k(h)$ and $\beta_{kj}(h)$, since the $g_{kj}(h)$ are expressible in terms of the $\beta_{lm}(h)$. We have given the complete expression for the intensity scattered by ensembles of two types of spherically symmetric particles in another article (Fournet [48]). This complicated equation was applied to *mixtures of homogeneous spheres of the same matter but of radii R and $2R$*; the curves representing the variation of scattered intensity as a function of angle are given in Fig. 20. Two parameters were included in the calculation: k, the ratio of the volume occupied by the particles to the total volume offered them; and x, the ratio of the mass of smaller particles to the total mass of the particles. Short-dashed curves correspond to $k = 0.5$, long-dashed curves to $k = 0.125$, and full-line curves to the case of infinitely separated particles.

For each concentration, x per cent, the curves have been normalized so that the ordinate at $h = 0$ is equal to unity. The essential feature of the curves is that *for constant k, the intensity curves are more sharply varying, the more homogeneous the mixture.*

We believe that this statement is generally true; it is difficult to conceive of a not too compact heterogeneous mixture manifesting a

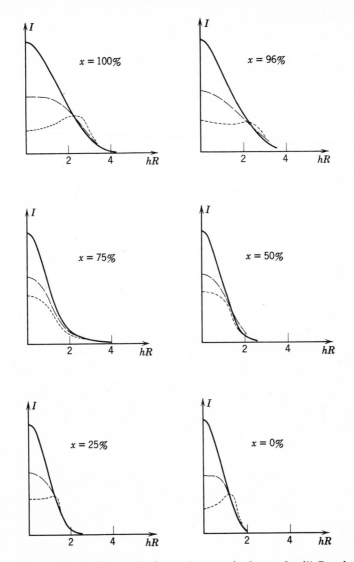

Fig. 20. Scattered intensity from mixtures of spheres of radii R and $2R$. The parameter x denotes the ratio of the mass of the small spheres to the total mass of the mixture, and k represents the ratio of the effective volume of the spheres to the volume occupied by the mixture. ——, $k = 0$; — — —, $k = 0.125$; — — — —, $k = 0.500$.

reasonable degree of order.   In our model, the curve for $k = 0.5$ possesses a maximum only if the mass of smaller particles represents more than 95 per cent or less than 25 per cent of the total mass.

We must remark that this model was based on spherical particles, and that consequently there was a favorable opportunity for observing intensity maxima.   In generalizing the conclusion drawn from a study of this example, it thus would be a temptation to state: *in a mixture of non-identical particles of arbitrary forms and with random distribution (no long-range order) it is improbable that the packing of particles will lead to large changes in the scattering curves and that thus the laws for widely separated particles can furnish the orders of magnitude of the scattering phenomena.*

This idea is in agreement with the calculations of Hosemann [81], [84], who showed that, for arbitrary particles and conveniently chosen functions $P_{kj}(r)$, the packing of the particles caused little change in the distribution of scattered intensity.   We refer the reader to these works for the details of the calculations and results.

Conclusions contrary to these have been given by Kratky and Porod [108], [137], in considering the influence of packing on an ensemble of heterogeneous particles.   However, they considered uniquely a *linear model* composed of a series of parallel plates of different thicknesses situated at variable distances from one another.   In the limiting case the space is completely occupied by the plates, causing the central scattering at observable angles to disappear entirely.   The packing of particles thus creates notable changes in the distribution of scattered intensity.   We believe that this is a result which depends on the *linear character* of the model.

2.4. GENERAL CASE

There are often substances which give rise to strong small-angle scattering that cannot be described as a group of well-defined particles arranged in a more or less close-packed fashion.   This is true, for example, of matter which displays submicroscopic porosity, such as activated carbon. The physical characteristic that can accurately define these substances is the electronic density $\rho(\mathbf{x})$ found at the point defined by the vector $\mathbf{x}$. The intensity scattered by such a substance is then given by the general relation

$$I(\mathbf{h}) = I_e(h) \left[\int_V \rho(\mathbf{x}) e^{-i\mathbf{h} \cdot \mathbf{x}} \, d\mathbf{x} \right]^2 \qquad (97)$$

V being the volume irradiated by the X-rays.   It is well known that it is not possible to determine $\rho(\mathbf{x})$ from the experimental data.   Indeed, low-angle scattering experiments made with different samples taken from a given material give the same experimental curve. Thus it is obvious that the central scattering depends on some statistical property of $\rho(\mathbf{x})$ that defines the state of heterogeneity or porosity of the substance. It is particularly interesting to try to determine the general characteristics that are necessary for the production of an observable scattering at small angles. When considered in this general form, the problem presents special difficulties; we shall first discuss these difficulties and then present the results of the attempts that have been made in this field.

2.4.1. LIMITING VALUE OF THE SCATTERED INTENSITY AT VERY SMALL ANGLES

The property we shall try to calculate is the "experimental" limit of the scattered intensity as the scattering angle tends to zero, that is, the

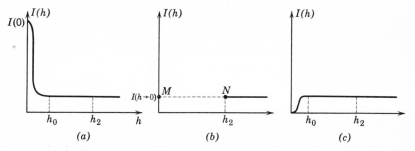

Fig. 21. (a) Schematic representation of a real scattered intensity distribution. (b) The observable intensity and its extrapolated value at $h = 0$. (c) A possible result for a calculated intensity distribution.

intensity that can be obtained by extrapolation of the results of measurements which, as will be seen later, cannot be extended to angles smaller than several minutes of arc, even with the most perfect experimental system.

Let us recall some results of our discussion of an ensemble of particles. The curve of the scattered intensity shows a very important singularity in the neighborhood of $h = 0$, since for extremely small values of h the amplitudes of the waves scattered by all the electrons in the scatterer add together and the scattered intensity approaches the value,

$$I(0) = I_e(0)n^2\overline{N^2} \tag{98}$$

The width of this central peak, defined by the parameter h_0 (see Fig. 21a), depends on the dimensions of the volume V explored by X-rays and is smaller by several orders of magnitude than the minimum observable angle.

A correct calculation of the desired "limiting intensity" should give a formula which reproduces the real curves down to a value of h equal to h_2, the experimental limit, and then, eliminating the central peak, remains practically independent of h (Fig. 21b) in the range between h_2 and 0. This, for example, is the result obtained in the calculations of §2.2.3.3, which pertained to the particular case of an ensemble of particles contained in a volume V_0 large with respect to the volume V of the scatterer explored by the X-rays. The result of this calculation gave

$$I(h \to 0) = I_e(0)n^2(\overline{N^2} - \overline{N}^2) \tag{72}$$

Frequently it can happen that, in trying to eliminate the central peak, a term will be discarded in the course of the calculation which will bring about a marked change in the curve, such as that depicted in Fig. 21c. Such a formula does not give correctly the limiting value of the intensity when h is made equal to zero. It can be quite correct for $h > h_0$, but it will not be useful, since the intensity cannot be easily calculated if h is non-zero.

In the case of an ensemble of particles, the intensity $I(0)$ for $h = 0$ is of the order of $\overline{N}^2$, while the limiting value should be of the order of $\overline{N^2} - \overline{N}^2$, that is, of the order of $\overline{N}$. (This limit is exact for the case of ideally separated particles, viz., equation 55.) Thus we see that in the region of very small angles the limiting intensity, which will be expressed as the difference between the exact expression for the intensity and another term which must be made more definite, is of the order of $1/N$ times the actual intensity. This order of magnitude indicates immediately *the rigor and exactness that must be maintained in all phases of the calculations.*

As an illustration of the effects of a slight inexactness, let us reconsider the reasoning that we have developed in §2.2.1.3 and §2.2.1.4. We have assumed that the volume V_0 is large with respect to the volume V. If we vary V_0 (and thus N_0, the total number of particles), keeping V and v_1 constant, equation 72 predicts a limiting intensity of zero when $V_0 = V$; this is then a good example of the type of curve represented in Fig. 21c.

In order to obtain a relation which will more accurately describe this case, the manner in which the function $P(r)$ was introduced must be reviewed, noting specifically that the probability $p_{kj} \, dv_k \, dv_j$ is defined by the relation

$$p_{kj} \, dv_k \, dv_j = \frac{N_0}{V_0} \, dv_k \, \frac{N_0 - 1}{V_0 - dv_k} \, P(r_{kj}) \, dv_j$$

The infinitesimal volume element, dv_k, is always negligible as compared with V_0, but *this cannot always be said for the comparison of unity with respect to N_0, particularly when V and V_0 are approximately equal* (and, thus, N and N_0). On reconsidering the complete calculation, beginning with the relation

$$p_{kj} \, dv_k \, dv_j = \frac{dv_k}{v_1} \frac{dv_j}{v_1} \frac{N_0 - 1}{N_0} P(r_{kj})$$

we obtain as an expression for the observable intensity (cf. equation 53)

$$\overline{I(h)} = I_e(h)\overline{N} \left\{ \overline{F^2(h)} - \overline{F(h)}^2 \frac{1}{v_1} \frac{N_0 - 1}{N_0} \int_0^\infty [1 - P(r)] \frac{\sin hr}{hr} 4\pi r^2 \, dr \right\} \quad (99)$$

In the limit as $h \to 0$, we then find

$$\frac{v_2(0)}{v_1} = \frac{N_0}{N_0 - 1} - \frac{\overline{N^2} \dfrac{N_0}{N_0 - 1} - \overline{N}^2}{\overline{N}} \quad (100)$$

which gives as an expression for the limiting value of the observable intensity (Fournet [48])

$$I(h \to 0) = I_e(0)n^2 \left[(\overline{N^2} - \overline{N}^2) + \frac{\overline{N}^2}{N_0} \right]$$

$$= I_e(0)n^2 \left[\overline{N^2} - \overline{N}^2 + \overline{N} \frac{V}{V_0} \right] \quad (101)$$

The factor $(\overline{N^2} - \overline{N}^2)$ is of the order of $\overline{N}$, so that, when V/V_0 is small with respect to unity, equation 101 is to a first approximation equivalent to our earlier result, equation 72. The advantage of equation 101 is that a reasonable result is permitted in the case for which $V = V_0$,

$$I_{V=V_0}(h \to 0) = I_e(0)n^2 N$$

We can see by this example how approximations which at first sight are quite logical can completely upset the results of this type of calculation.

We have defined the limiting intensity by an extrapolation of a part of the curve of Fig. 21b, but we have not yet determined whether this quantity has any physical meaning. We know, for example, that the actual curve has a shape which depends on the form of the sample, whereas the limiting intensity should depend only on the statistical properties of the distribution of scattering centers in the sample. It is not obvious that the operation of extrapolation as described should lead to such a result. In any event, we have not yet clearly defined a criterion for the determination of the extrapolated part of the curve (part MN of Fig. 21b). Questions such as these form the obstacles encountered when an attempt is made to resolve the problem of low-angle scattering as calculated from the electronic density function.

As a first approach, let us offer without real proof a qualitative treatment; then we shall present the solution given by Debye and Bueche [322] and that of Porod [137] for a more particular case.

We want to calculate the scattered intensity for a value h_2 near the minimum observable angle (for example, $2\theta = 1'$). Let us divide the irradiated volume V into a series of M equal volumes, $v_1, v_2, \cdots v_m$, where each volume is of the order of $\left(\dfrac{2\pi}{h_2}\right)^3$. (In the example chosen, $v_i \approx 1\mu^3$ for Cu $K\alpha$ radiation; this is still small with respect to the volume V which is of the order of 1 mm^3. in ordinary experiments.) The amplitude of the radiation scattered by the volume element v_i is then $A_i(\mathbf{h})$. We shall assume that there will be negligible interference effects among the waves scattered by the different volume elements when $h > h_2$; this hypothesis is reasonable, for the phase difference between waves will always be much larger than 2π, since the centers of the volumes are separated by distances greater than $2\pi/h_2$. Consequently a very probable value for the total intensity is simply the sum of the elementary intensities, $I = \sum\limits_i |A_i|^2$. In other words, the observed intensity is effectively M times the average intensity scattered by an elemental volume. This result is analogous to that for the problem of a variable number of particles, N, in a volume V (§2.2.3.3), except that the observed intensity is determined by an average over space instead of an average over time as N fluctuates in a constant volume V.

Thus by analogy we are led to the following description of the limiting observed scattered intensity. It is proportional to the mean square fluctuation in the number of electrons in the volume v_i, and will be zero if the number of electrons in the different volumes v_i is fixed. If ρ_i is the electronic density of the volume v_i and $\bar{\rho}$ is the average density as determined by all the volume elements, the observed scattered intensity will be proportional to

$$M \frac{V^2}{M^2} \overline{(\rho_i - \bar{\rho})^2} = V \overline{v_i(\rho_i - \bar{\rho})^2} \tag{102}$$

The volumes $v_i = V/M$ do not really intervene as such, since the mean square fluctuation is inversely proportional to the volume v_i, but their consideration is essential in determining the magnitude of the volume to be used in the calculation of ρ_i.

Equation 102 shows that the *limiting low-angle scattering is a consequence of the heterogeneities in the scattering medium*, but it also allows for the stipulation that this heterogeneity must exist on a scale of several tens to several thousand angstroms if the scattering is to be observable. Let us give several examples of the application of this simple rule. The fact that matter is formed of atoms instead of being continuous is not a cause of low-angle scattering since the corresponding density fluctuations are averaged out in a volume of the order of $1\mu^3$. A lattice with periodic perturbations of density (for example, a period of the order of 50 A) is heterogeneous, but it produces no small-angle scattering since the volume v_i contains a large number of periods, and hence the average density in this volume is approximately constant.

A typical case is offered by the Al–Ag alloy that will be studied further in §6.4.3.1. The silver atoms assemble themselves into spherical clusters while remaining on the sites of the solid solution lattice. Around these clusters is left a spherical shell lacking in silver. The shell diameter is of the order of 50 A, and a large number of these clusters are randomly distributed throughout the solid solution.

This alloy gives a pattern of central scattering containing a diffuse ring whose radius corresponds to a Bragg distance of the order of 25 A, but *the scattered intensity decreases toward the center*, and careful measurements show that it approaches zero. If the small silver clusters exist in the average solid solution without being accompanied by the shell-like regions lacking in silver, only a normal central scattering is observed. Equation 102 furnishes the explanation of these facts. In the first case the cluster contains a number of excess atoms which is just the number of atoms lacking in the shell-like region. The volumes v_i in which the densities ρ_i should be examined are large with respect to the cluster dimensions; thus they contain the same number of silver atoms as they would if the solution were homogeneous. On this scale there are no electronic density fluctuations and the intensity scattered at the center should be zero. If there is no spherical shell around these clusters, these clusters will play the role of particles with an electronic density different from that of the surrounding medium; if the clusters are distributed at random in the solid solution and are not too closely packed, they give rise to a central scattering which is characteristic of their size.

2.4.2. CALCULATION OF THE SCATTERED INTENSITY AS A FUNCTION OF $\rho(x)$

We shall now briefly present the solution of Debye and Bueche [322]. These authors define a function $\eta(\mathbf{x})$ by means of the relation

$$\rho(\mathbf{x}) = \rho_0 + \eta(\mathbf{x})$$

where ρ_0 designates the average density of the substance. We can then write

$$\int \eta(\mathbf{x})\, d\mathbf{x} = 0$$

By means of equation 97 we can immediately write the expression for the scattered intensity as (cf. §2.1.1)

$$I(\mathbf{h}) = I_e(h) \int_V \int_V [\rho_0 + \eta(\mathbf{x}_k)] [\rho_0 + \eta(\mathbf{x}_j)] e^{-i\mathbf{h}\cdot(\mathbf{x}_k - \mathbf{x}_j)} \, d\mathbf{x}_k \, d\mathbf{x}_j$$

Recognizing the difficulties discussed previously, we shall take account of more details in our calculation than was done by the original authors. We will divide the intensity expression into the four terms corresponding respectively to terms in $\rho_0{}^2$, $\rho_0\eta(\mathbf{x}_k)$, $\rho_0\eta(\mathbf{x}_j)$, and $\eta(\mathbf{x}_k)\eta(\mathbf{x}_j)$ and consider each term separately.

First term:

$$I_1(\mathbf{h}) = I_e(h)\rho_0{}^2 \int_V \int_V e^{-i\mathbf{h}\cdot(\mathbf{x}_k - \mathbf{x}_j)} \, d\mathbf{x}_k \, d\mathbf{x}_j$$

We have already studied analogous terms (p. 34) and have seen that they correspond to intensities that are practically zero for all observable angles, since V is the order of 1 mm³.

Second and third terms: Since the second and third terms are complex conjugates, we can write

$$I_2(\mathbf{h}) + I_3(\mathbf{h}) = 2\mathrm{Re}\left\{I_e(h)\rho_0 \int_V \eta(\mathbf{x}_k) \, d\mathbf{x}_k \int_V e^{-i\mathbf{h}\cdot(\mathbf{x}_k - \mathbf{x}_j)} \, d\mathbf{x}_j\right\}$$

or

$$I_2(\mathbf{h}) + I_3(\mathbf{h}) = 2I_e(h) \, \mathrm{Re}\left\{\int_V \eta(\mathbf{x}_k)e^{-i\mathbf{h}\cdot\mathbf{x}_k} \, d\mathbf{x}_k \int_V \rho_0 e^{i\mathbf{h}\cdot\mathbf{x}_j} \, d\mathbf{x}_j\right\}$$

Therefore

$$I_2(\mathbf{h}) + I_3(\mathbf{h}) < 2I_e(h) \left| A_1{}^*(\mathbf{h}) \right| \cdot \left| \int_V \eta(\mathbf{x})e^{-i\mathbf{h}\cdot\mathbf{x}} \, d\mathbf{x} \right|$$

The first factor $\left| A_1{}^*(\mathbf{h}) \right|$ is the modulus of the amplitude from which $I_1(\mathbf{h})$ is derived. As we shall see below, the second factor is just the modulus of $A_4(\mathbf{h})$, the amplitude corresponding to the fourth term. Therefore I_2 and I_3 as well as I_1 are negligible as compared with I_4.

Fourth term:

$$I_4(\mathbf{h}) = I_e(h) \int_V \int_V \eta(\mathbf{x}_k)\eta(\mathbf{x}_j)e^{-i\mathbf{h}\cdot(\mathbf{x}_k - \mathbf{x}_j)} \, d\mathbf{x}_k \, d\mathbf{x}_j$$

Let us place $\mathbf{x}_j = \mathbf{x}_k + \mathbf{r}$. The above equation then transforms to

$$I_4(\mathbf{h}) = I_e(h) \int_V \int_V \eta(\mathbf{x}_k)\eta(\mathbf{x}_k + \mathbf{r})e^{i\mathbf{h}\cdot\mathbf{r}} \, d\mathbf{x}_k \, d\mathbf{r}$$

Let us consider first the integral with respect to $\mathbf{x}_k$,

$$\int_V \eta(\mathbf{x})\eta(\mathbf{x} + \mathbf{r}) \, d\mathbf{x}$$

This integral depends uniquely on $\mathbf{r}$. For $r = 0$, the value of the integral is proportional to $\overline{\eta^2}$, the mean value of the square of the density fluctuations, since

$$\int_V \eta(\mathbf{x})\eta(\mathbf{x}) \, d\mathbf{x} = \int_V \eta^2(\mathbf{x}) \, d\mathbf{x} = \overline{\eta^2} V$$

Conforming to the notation of Debye and Bueche, let us define a function $\gamma(\mathbf{r})$ by the relation

$$\int_V \eta(\mathbf{x})\eta(\mathbf{x} + \mathbf{r}) \, d\mathbf{x} = \overline{\eta^2} V \gamma(\mathbf{r}) \tag{103}$$

The equation for $I_4(\mathbf{h})$ then takes the form

$$I_4(\mathbf{h}) = I_e(h)\overline{\eta^2} V \int_V \gamma(\mathbf{r})e^{i\mathbf{h}\cdot\mathbf{r}} \, d\mathbf{r}$$

This integral can undergo two modifications:

1. For large $\mathbf{r}$ there is no relation between the fluctuations of $\eta(\mathbf{x})$ and $\eta(\mathbf{x} + \mathbf{r})$; the function $\gamma(\mathbf{r})$ thus tends to zero as r increases. The integration over the domain V can then be replaced by an integration over an infinite region.

2. It can often be assumed that, in the region of vectors $\mathbf{r}$ of small magnitude, the only domain in which $\gamma(\mathbf{r})$ is different from zero, the properties of $\gamma(\mathbf{r})$ depend only on the magnitude r.

The final expression for the intensity is then

$$I(h) = I_4(h) = I_e(h)\overline{\eta^2} V \int_0^\infty \gamma(r) \frac{\sin hr}{hr} 4\pi r^2 \, dr \tag{104}$$

This is the expression developed by Debye and Bueche to describe the intensity scattered by the matter under examination.

Let us consider the limiting value of $I(h)$ as $h \to 0$:

$$I(0) = I_e(0) \int_V \int_V \eta(\mathbf{x}_k)\eta(\mathbf{x}_j) \, d\mathbf{x}_k \, d\mathbf{x}_j$$

$$= I_e(0) \int_V \eta(\mathbf{x}_k) \, d\mathbf{x}_k \int_V \eta(\mathbf{x}_j) \, d\mathbf{x}_j \tag{104a}$$

The integral $\int \eta(\mathbf{x}) \, d\mathbf{x}$ is zero in a large volume on the average, but the irregularity of the distribution of matter in the volume V irradiated by X-rays gives it a value which fluctuates around zero. The two integrals of equation 104a are taken over the same volume; the two factors are thus *not* independent, and the average of the product is *not* the product of the average of each factor. Therefore, although the average value of each integral is zero, the average value of $I(0)$ is *not* zero. A calculation shows that the limiting value for the intensity scattered at zero-angle is given by equation 102.

2.4.3. MATTER OF UNIFORM DENSITY AND RANDOM DISTRIBUTION

Porod [137] studied a more particular system, that of a sample made up of a random distribution of matter of constant density. The density $\rho(\mathbf{x})$ in the volume V of the sample can take only two values, ρ and 0. If c is the fraction of the volume occupied by matter, the average density of the sample is ρc. In the parts occupied by matter $\eta = \rho(1 - c)$, and in the empty regions $\eta = -\rho c$. Therefore

$$\overline{\eta^2} = \rho^2 c(1 - c) \tag{105}$$

Porod defines the distribution of matter by a function, $Z(r)$, which represents the probability that a point in the volume at a distance r from a point *occupied* by matter is itself also *occupied*. It is assumed that this probability is a function only of the distance r (an isotropic sample) and that there is no long-range order, so that $Z(r)$ tends toward c as r approaches infinity. We can therefore put

$$Z(r) = c + (1 - c)\gamma(r) \tag{106}$$

where the function $\gamma(r)$, called the *characteristic function* of the sample, has the value unity when r is zero and approaches zero as r becomes very large. This is identical to the function Debye and Bueche introduced by the definition

$$\int \eta(\mathbf{x})\eta(\mathbf{x} + \mathbf{r}) \, d\mathbf{x} = \overline{\eta^2} V \gamma(r) \tag{103}$$

In order to show this, let us first point out that $Z'(r) = (1 - c) + c\gamma(r)$ represents the probability that a point in the volume at a distance r from a point in empty space (unoccupied) is itself also in empty space. This can be verified easily by equating the two relations each of which describes the probability of one point being occupied and the other unoccupied,

$$c(1 - Z(r)) = (1 - c)(1 - Z'(r))$$

Now in order to calculate the integral in equation 103 we must first set up a table of probabilities for the different situations at points $\mathbf{x}$ and $\mathbf{x} + \mathbf{r}$.

Nature of Points $\mathbf{x}$ and $\mathbf{x} + \mathbf{r}$		Value of $\eta(\mathbf{x})\eta(\mathbf{x} + \mathbf{r})$	Probability of Occurrence
Occupied	Occupied	$\rho^2(1 - c)^2$	$cZ(r) = c^2 + c(1 - c)\gamma(r)$
Occupied	Empty	$-\rho^2 c(1 - c)$	$c(1 - Z(r)) = c(1 - c)(1 - \gamma(r))$
Empty	Occupied	$-\rho^2 c(1 - c)$	$(1 - c)(1 - Z'(r)) = c(1 - c)(1 - \gamma(r))$
Empty	Empty	$\rho^2 c^2$	$(1 - c)Z'(r) = (1 - c)^2 + c(1 - c)\gamma(r)$

Now by carrying out the integration

$$\frac{1}{V} \int \eta(\mathbf{x}) \eta(\mathbf{x} + \mathbf{r}) \, d\mathbf{x} = \rho^2 c(1 - c)\gamma(r)$$

where equation 105 has been used, it can be seen that equations 103 and 106 define the same function.

Thus the scattered intensity can be determined immediately from equation 104,

$$I(h) = I_e(h) V \rho^2 c(1 - c) \int_0^\infty \gamma(r) \frac{\sin hr}{hr} 4\pi r^2 \, dr \tag{107}$$

This expression can be linked to the equation relative to a single particle, equation 21. Let us consider a very dilute system of identical particles of arbitrary orientations. The probability $Z(r)$ is then approximately equal to the function we have called the characteristic function of a particle, $\gamma_0(r)$ (see p. 12), since by virtue of the dilution of the system there is only a negligible chance of finding an occupied point outside of the particular particle in which the origin point is chosen. Then since $1 - c \approx 1$ and c is negligible, equation 106 gives $\gamma(r) = \gamma_0(r)$. In addition Vc is the total volume of particles, Nv_0. Therefore equation 107 is equivalent to equations 21 and 55.

Mathematically, $I(h)$ is determined entirely by a knowledge of $\gamma(r)$. However, the calculation of $\gamma(r)$, very complex for an isolated particle, is rarely possible for systems of particles of a given arrangement. Conversely, the characteristic function of the sample can be determined from the experimental measurement of $I(h)$. This function $\gamma(r)$ contains all the information that can be obtained from the small-angle scattering experiments, but unfortunately this function does not give a direct image of the structure and is quite far from defining it. The effects of both the form of the particles and their mutual arrangement are intermixed in the single function $\gamma(r)$. Theories are discussed in §2.2.3 which have as their object the separation of these two effects.

Nevertheless, several parameters having simple and precise interpretations can be obtained from $\gamma(r)$, as was done for the function of a single particle.

$\gamma(r)$ is equal to unity when r is zero and tends asymptotically to zero as r becomes large. It can take on negative values, greater than $-c/(1 - c)$, while the function for an isolated particle is always positive.

1. The slope of the curve at the origin is

$$\left(\frac{d\gamma}{dr}\right)_{r=0} = \frac{1}{1 - c}\left(\frac{dZ}{dr}\right)_{r=0}$$

The slope of $Z(r)$ at $r = 0$ can be calculated for the complex system in the same way as for the isolated particle. If S is the total surface area of the matter contained in the volume V, the real volume of matter being only Vc, then from equation 24

$$\left(\frac{dZ}{dr}\right)_{r=0} = -\frac{1}{4}\frac{S}{Vc}$$

Therefore

$$\left(\frac{d\gamma}{dr}\right)_{r=0} = -\frac{1}{4c(1-c)}\frac{S}{V} = -\frac{1}{4c(1-c)}S_{sp}$$

where S_{sp}, the specific surface, is the surface area per unit volume of the sample. From this, following the reasoning leading to equation 26, the asymptotic behavior of the intensity curve is found as

$$I(h) \approx I_e(h)\frac{2\pi\rho^2 S}{h^4} \tag{108}$$

The absolute value of the scattered intensity in the tail of the curve depends only on the total surface area of the matter in the sample. If the object is made up of n identical particles of volume v and surface s, the total free surface S is always approximately equal to ns, whatever the degree of aggregation of the particles, provided that these are of some arbitrary form and that they will not become distorted. The intensity can be written as

$$I(h) = I_e(h)n\rho^2(2\pi s/h^4)$$

It is equal to n times the average intensity scattered by one particle. This shows that at large angles interparticle interferences are negligible, even for particles of uniform size. It is therefore valid to apply equation 95 to dense systems. This does *not* mean that the intensity curve at *small* angles will not be modified considerably by the action of particles drawing closer together. Let us point out also that the above argument will not be valid for particles in the form of broad platelets parallel to one another, since the packing together of such particles can make the interfaces disappear, decreasing the total surface and thus the scattered intensity by a large amount. We have already mentioned (p. 70) that the effect of interferences for one-dimensional systems is much larger than for a powder of irregular grains.

2. The area of the curve $\int_0^\infty \gamma(r)\,dr$ can be calculated either from the integral $\int_0^\infty hI(h)\,dh$ (see equation 29) or from the total energy E scattered

in the low-angle region for a given incident beam intensity (see equation 30). Equation 107 gives

$$\frac{l_c}{2} = \int_0^\infty \gamma(r)\, dr = \frac{1}{4\pi V \rho^2 c(1-c)} \int_0^\infty \frac{h I(h)}{I_e(h)}\, dh \tag{109}$$

and

$$\frac{l_c}{2} = \int_0^\infty \gamma(r)\, dr = \frac{1}{2V\rho^2 c(1-c)} \frac{1}{\lambda^2 p^2} \frac{E}{I_e(h)} \tag{110}$$

where p is the distance from the sample to the film. l_c is a parameter that has been called the *distance of heterogeneity* by Kratky and Porod. In an isolated particle $\bar{l}$ (equation 25) represents a mean value of the diameters passing through every point of the particle in all directions, but what is the geometrical significance of l_c for an arbitrary system? Let us draw a straight line in an arbitrary direction *from a point in matter*. This line will be divided into segments which are alternately occupied and unoccupied by matter. The ratio of the total length of occupied segments to that of unoccupied segments is equal to the ratio of the occupied and unoccupied volumes, that is, $c/(1-c)$. The *probable occupied length* in a line of length L drawn from the point chosen as origin is found from the definition of $Z(r)$ (equation 106) to be

$$\int_0^L Z(r)\, dr = Lc + (1-c) \int_0^L \gamma(r)\, dr$$

$$\cong Lc + (1-c) \int_0^\infty \gamma(r)\, dr$$

This length is larger than the mean occupied length Lc of an arbitrary section of length L, because by imposing the condition that the section L starts from a point occupied by matter the chances of finding an occupied section are increased. This excess length is simply $(1-c)\,(l_c/2)$.

3. In the general case there is a normalization relation analogous to equation 28,

$$\int_0^\infty h^2 I(h)\, dh = 2\pi^2 I_e(h)\rho^2 Vc(1-c) \tag{111}$$

4. The roles played by c and $(1-c)$ in equation 107 are symmetric. In addition the characteristic function $\gamma(r)$ is the same for an object and for its complementary object (Fig. 66, p. 192). Therefore the same scattered intensity is found for two complementary objects in the angular region in which equation 107 is valid (§2.2.2.2).

82   SMALL-ANGLE SCATTERING OF X-RAYS

REFERENCES FOR CHAPTER 2

Bertaut, E. F.   (1950), *Acta Cryst.*, *3*, 14.
Bhatia, A. B., and Krishnan, K. S.   (1948), *Proc. Roy. Soc. (London)*, *A192*, 181.
Compton, A. H., and Allison, S. K.   (1935), *X-Rays in Theory and Experiment*, Macmillan, New York.
Debye, P.   (1915), *Ann. Physik*, *46*, 809.
Guinier, A., and Griffoul, R.   (1948), *Acta Cryst.*, *1*, 188.
James, R. W.   (1948), *The Optical Principles of the Diffraction of X-Rays*, Bell, London.
Kirkwood, J. G.   (1935), *J. Chem. Phys.*, *3*, 300.
Kirkwood, J. G., and Boggs, E. M.   (1942), *J. Chem. Phys.*, *10*, 394.
von Laue, M.   (1941), *Röntgenstrahlinterferenzen*, Springer, Leipzig, p. 175.
Lennard-Jones, J. E. (1937), *Physica*, *4*, 941.
Mac Gillavry, C. H., and Strijk, B.   (1946), *Physica*, *11*, 369.
Neugebauer, T.   (1943), *Ann. Physik*, *42*, 509.
Raman, C. V.   (1924), *Phil. Mag.*, *47*, 671.
Rayleigh, Lord   (1914), *Proc. Roy. Soc. (London)*, *A90*, 219.
Rayleigh, Lord   (1919), *Phil. Mag.*, *6*, 37, 321.
Rodriguez, A. E.   (1949), *Proc. Roy. Soc. (London)*, *A196*, 73.
Rushbrooke, G. S., and Scoins, H. I.   (1951), *Phil. Mag.*, *42*, 582.
Wilson, A. J. C.   (1949), *X-Ray Optics*, Methuen, London; Wiley, New York.
Yvon, J.   (1935), *Actualités sci. et ind.*, Hermann, Nos. 202, 542, 543.
Yvon, J.   (1947), *J. phys. radium*, VII, *7*, 201.
Yvon, J.   (1949), *Nuovo cimento, Suppl.*, *2*, 187.

3. EXPERIMENTAL EQUIPMENT

3.1. GENERAL CONSIDERATIONS

The object of an X-ray scattering experiment, whether in the small-angle region or in the usual domain of investigation, is the determination of the variation of the intensity scattered by a sample as a function of the scattering direction, this direction in general being defined by two parameters. In the important particular case in which the scattering is circularly symmetric about an axis coincident with the incident beam, only one parameter, the scattering angle, is involved, and the object of the experiment is simply the determination of the relative value of $I(h)$, with $h = (4\pi \sin \theta)/\lambda$.

Experiments can also furnish a second quantity, less frequently employed, which is the absolute value of the scattering coefficient, σ. This is defined by means of the relation, $I = I_0 \sigma \, dm \, d\Omega$, where I is the power scattered by the particle of mass dm in the solid angle $d\Omega$, and I_0 is the intensity of the incident beam striking the sample. The sample is assumed to be small enough to be non-absorbing.

3.1.1. OPERATIONAL PRINCIPLES

The method employed to realize the objectives discussed above is not different in principle from that used in all experiments in X-ray crystallography. Special difficulties are encountered, however, in investigating the scattering at very small angles.

1. *Geometrical Definition of the Incident Beam.* Following the notation of Fig. 22, let MM' be the portion of the sample which is irradiated. Each point of the sample will receive a beam of rays whose divergence depends on the constitution of the incident beam. Rays will converge at the point of observation P which have been scattered by each of the points of the sample through angles varying in an interval $2d\theta$ about a mean value, 2θ. The interval $d\theta$ is practically independent of θ, so that good definition of the scattering angle in relative value is more difficult to obtain, the closer a scattering angle of zero is approached.

Furthermore, there will always be an angular region inaccessible to experiment; this is the region between N and N' of Fig. 22, in which the scattered radiation received at any point is completely overshadowed by the much greater intensity of the direct beam at this point. Thus, to investigate scattering at small angles, it is necessary to *reduce both the cross section and the divergence of the primary beam*, the restriction being greater, the smaller the limiting angle of observation that is desired. As a result, the beams employed are much less intense than those used in ordinary techniques, so that a determination of the best geometrical conditions is essential.

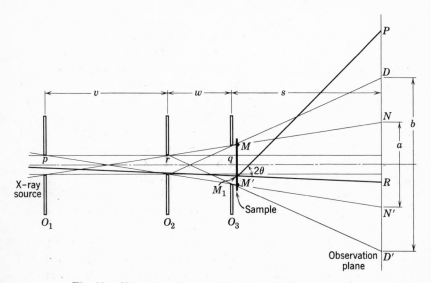

Fig. 22.   Slit system for a small-angle scattering apparatus.

2. *Parasitic Scattering.* The measurement of the intensity received at the point of observation is a correct measure of the intensity scattered by the sample only if there is no parasitic scattering. The term parasitic scattering refers to the radiation received at the point of observation when the sample is withdrawn from the beam. If a Geiger counter or ionization chamber is employed as a detector, the parasitic scattering can easily be subtracted from the observed scattering to give the corrected value, but this procedure is acceptable only if the correction is small. If photographic detection is employed, it is very difficult to make the correction by the above procedure. *The reduction of the parasitic scattering is thus the second important requirement*, and here again the suppression is more difficult, the smaller the angles at which scattering is to be observed.

Thus we can say that the quality of a small-angle scattering apparatus is characterized by the power of the beam for a given fineness of dimensions and by the angle beyond which all parasitic scattering is eliminated.

A third critical property of such an apparatus is the spectral purity of the primary radiation. We shall consider successively equipment without and with monochromatization, showing the different domains of application of each.

3.1.2. INFLUENCE OF THE MONOCHROMATIZATION OF THE PRIMARY RADIATION

Use may be made of either filtered or crystal monochromated radiation, depending on the nature of the sample to be studied.

1. The total radiation from the anode, with the usual filtering to remove the $K\beta$, may be used in a study of low-angle crystalline diffraction effects that are analogous to the usual high-angle phenomena, differing only in that the effective lattice spacings are very large. These patterns contain lines, spots, or rings at well-defined angles, and the corresponding intensities are considerably larger than those at intermediate angles on the patterns. Thus, as with ordinary diffraction patterns, the diffraction effects due to the characteristic radiation emerge from the continuous background of diffraction and scattering caused by the continuous spectrum. Often the primary objective of such a study is to determine the position of the lines or spots, and in these circumstances even a rather strong parasitic scattering may be tolerated.

2. The opposite case is the study of continuous scattering of the type that has been described in the first part of this book. This continuous scattering is often extremely weak and is superposed on the scattering of various other origins, such as the inactive parts of the sample (the solvent, for example, when the scattering of particles in solution is studied). Given the actual state of the theory, it is essential in this type of problem to have a precise evaluation of the function $I(h)$.

It is easy to see that in certain cases the influence of the continuous spectrum may be considerable, since, in addition to the intensity $I(h)$ due to the principal radiation of wavelength λ_0, one will also observe a scattering of the form

$$\int I\left(\frac{\lambda_0}{\lambda}\,h\right) f(\lambda)\,d\lambda$$

where $f(\lambda)$ is the distribution function of the energy in the continuous spectrum. The effect of all the continuous spectrum can thus be large with respect to that of the characteristic radiation. Experiments by several authors have proved that an investigation cannot be made free from all objection without the use of monochromatized radiation.

When Geiger-counter detection is used, the elimination of the continuous spectrum by the double filter method of Ross (Kirkpatrick (1939)) is often sufficient, but this method is not easily applied with photographic techniques. The most practical and the most general method of producing monochromatic radiation involves the use of a *crystal monochromator*. Since the use of a monochromator profoundly modifies the geometry of the equipment, we shall study separately the system with collimation, designed for studies of crystalline diffraction, and the system with monochromatization, especially adapted to the study of the continuous scattering.

3.2. SYSTEMS EQUIPPED WITH COLLIMATORS

The beam (see Fig. 22) is defined by two apertures, O_1 and O_2, separated by a distance v, which are placed before a source of radiation large enough to illuminate the entire opening. As the edges of O_2 are touched by the direct beam, they are sources of scattered and diffracted radiation. Thus it is necessary to protect the plane of observation by introducing a third aperture, O_3, at a distance w from O_2, *whose edges closely approach but do not touch the incident beam.* Apertures O_2 and O_3 then define the region DD' which is not exempt from parasitic scattering. The sample is placed after O_3, as close to it as the supports will permit. The sample and the opening O_3 are thus at approximately the same distance from the plane of observation; this distance is denoted by s.

We want to determine the form and dimensions to give to the various apertures in order to obtain the "best results" for our measurements. We must first specify the known quantities of the problem and the criterion of quality to be required. This cannot be done until the nature of the pattern given by the sample has been specified.

3.2.1. COLLIMATOR FORMED BY TWO SLITS

Let us consider the simple problem of the study of the equatorial line of a crystalline "fiber pattern." Our attention is thus devoted to diffraction effects in only one dimension. The collimator openings can then be infinitely long slits parallel to the "fiber axis" (perpendicular to the plane of Fig. 22), and the diffraction spots will appear as lines. We shall impose the following conditions:

1. Let us define the angular uncertainty of the pattern as the variation in scattering angle of the rays arriving at a point P in the plane of observation. Such rays scattered from an incident ray M_1R are scattered through an angle equal as a first approximation to PR/s, whatever the position of the diffracting point M_1 on the sample. Thus the maximum variation of the scattering angle, $2d\theta$, for the group of rays converging at P (the

angular uncertainty of the pattern), is measured by the quantity, $A = a/s$, where a is the width of the primary beam in the plane of observation, and s is the sample-to-film distance. The largest lattice spacing which can give rise to a line distinct from the direct beam will then be

$$d_{max} = \lambda/A$$

2. The scattering angle inside of which parasitic radiation is found is $B/2 = b/2s$, where b is the width of the part DD' of the film receiving scattered radiation in the absence of a sample. The upper limit of the lattice spacings which will register outside of all parasitic scattering is then $d'_{max} = 2\lambda/B$. Obviously B is larger than A, and usually it is larger than $2A$, so that $d'_{max} < d_{max}$.

3. Either Geiger-Müller counters or photographic plates may be employed as detectors, but the conditions that apply to each are different.

(i) If a Geiger-Müller counter is used, it must be equipped with an entrance slit so that the divergence of the rays scattered by a point on the sample that enter the counter is fixed and clearly less than A ($A/10$, for example). If this condition is satisfied, it is possible, at least theoretically, to correct the observed pattern for the effect of the width of the direct beam (see §3.4).

For a given angular uncertainty, A, the counter slit width is proportional to s. Since, for constant A, s can be arbitrarily chosen without affecting the measured power, it is then advantageous to employ a large value of s so that the counter slit can be more easily constructed. The only restriction is that s must be less than a limiting value, s_c, determined by the mechanical conditions and obstructions.

(ii) The limitations of the photographic method arise from the grain size of the film, which is always rather large for emulsions sensitive to X-rays. X-ray patterns cannot be usefully enlarged by a factor of 10. The resolving power of these films is of the order of a hundredth of a millimeter; thus the exploring slit of the microphotometer should have a width of this order of magnitude, ϵ. Consequently the sample-to-film distance s has a *lower* limit, s_p, such that ϵ/s_p is clearly smaller than A (for example, $A/10$, as suggested in the preceding case).

4. The study of very small angles necessitates the use of beams which are very narrow and, consequently, of low power. It is essential for the success of the experiment that the system be found which allows the most powerful beam, while satisfying the geometrical conditions previously enumerated. Specifically, it is necessary to try to maximize the number of photons received by a counter placed at the center of a diffraction line or to maximize the blackening of this line on a film. The most desirable

form for a sample is that of a small plate intercepting the entire beam, the thickness being chosen in accordance with its absorption coefficient. (It is well known that the optimum thickness is that for which the ratio of the transmitted to incident intensity is the factor, $1/e \approx 1/3$.) Now, for simplicity let us assume that the point of observation is in a region of the pattern in which the variation of intensity with angle is very small, as, for example, in the center of a rather wide diffraction line. Then, for a given slit width, the intensity of the radiation entering the counter will be proportional to the total power of the primary beam incident on the sample per unit collimator slit height, I_1. When photographic detection is employed, the blackening at the same point will be proportional to I_1/s (we are considering one-dimensional diffraction effects, so the factor $1/s$ rather than $1/s^2$ intervenes). *These are the factors that must be maximized respectively in the construction of the collimator* when the detector is a Geiger counter or a photographic film.

Bolduan and Bear [205], in an analogous calculation, chose a criterion which seems to us to be on a less general level; they maximized *not the total power* of the incident beam *but rather the intensity* of the radiation striking the plane of observation at the center of the direct beam. Their conclusions are clearly different from those we shall draw. This shows that, if in a given experimental problem some of our assumptions are not satisfied, it will be necessary to discard our conclusions and to make an analogous calculation with appropriately modified factors.

5. The source of X-rays is assumed to be an X-ray tube with a rectangular focal spot of large length and of width l, so oriented that the long dimensions of the focal spot and the slits are parallel. The emerging rays make an angle, α, with the plane of the target. If the power per unit area delivered to the target by the incident electrons is $\mathscr{P}$, the intensity of the emitted X-rays will be proportional to $\mathscr{P}/\alpha$, if α is larger than a limiting value, α_0, of the order of $1°$ or $2°$ (Bolduan and Bear [205]). We shall fix α at this optimum value, α_0, and we shall place the first slit of the collimator close to the focal spot; the width, p, of the slit O_1 is then determined as the projection of the focal spot, $l\alpha_0$.

Let r be the width of the second slit, O_2, which is placed at a distance v from O_1. The power of the beam defined by the collimator O_1O_2 will then be proportional to

$$\frac{\mathscr{P}}{\alpha_0} p \frac{r}{v} = \frac{\mathscr{P}lr}{v}$$

The third slit, O_3, of width q, is placed at a distance w from O_2. Let us recall that the ratio a/s has been denoted by A and the ratio b/s by B.

The following relations, deduced from simple geometrical considerations, exist between these different quantities (Bolduan and Bear [205]):

$$(p + r)/v < A \tag{1}$$

$$w = 2r/(B - A) \tag{2}$$

$$q = r \left[1 + \frac{2pr}{v(B - A)} \right] \tag{3}$$

$$s = \frac{r}{B - A} \times \frac{2(p + r) + v(B - A)}{Av - (p + r)} \tag{4}$$

3.2.1.1. Calculation of the Optimum Collimator

(a) *Geiger-Müller Counter Detector.* The collimator should be chosen so as to maximize pr/v and thus r/v, since p is fixed. For a given value of v the choice of maximum r by means of equation 1 leads to the relation $r_{max} = Av - p$. This value of r corresponds to an infinite value of s, however, as is seen from equation 4. But, as r and s vary in the same way, if s is made equal to its maximum value, s_c, there will be an optimum value of r, $r_c(v)$, for each value of v. Thus, by letting v vary, a maximum for the ratio $\dfrac{r_c(v)}{v}$ can be found, which determines the value to be selected for v. The rest of the geometry of the system is then determined by means of equations 2, 3, and 4.

(b) *Photographic Detection.* For this system the collimator should be chosen so as to maximize the function $I_1/s = \mathscr{P}lr/vs$. This requires that s be a minimum, that is, that s have the value s_p determined by the grain size. A calculation similar to that outlined for the previous case but with s_c replaced by s_p then leads to the determination of the optimum value of v and the values of the other unknowns of the system.

EXAMPLE. The focal spot of the tube has a width of 1 mm. For an angle of emergence of 1° the source corresponds to a first slit of width $p = 20\ \mu$. The parameter describing the angular uncertainty of the pattern, A, is chosen as $A = 10^{-3}$. This means that for Cu $K\alpha$ radiation ($\lambda = 1.54$ A) the diffraction line for a lattice spacing of 1540 A will just be separated from the trace of the direct beam. In addition we shall require that the parasitic scattering be stopped beyond an angle corresponding to a lattice spacing of 1200 A; this determines B as $B = 2.5 \times 10^{-3}$.

(a) *Counter Detection.* Let the largest possible sample-to-counter distance be $s_c = 500$ mm. The efficiency of the system is given by curve a of Fig. 23 in which the ratio r/v is plotted as a function of the slit separation v. The maximum of the curve determines the following parameters:

$$v = 100 \text{ mm.} \qquad\qquad w = 77 \text{ mm.}$$
$$r_c = 58 \; \mu \qquad\qquad q = 120 \; \mu$$

(b) *Photographic Detection.* Let the minimum sample-to-film distance be: $s_p = 100$ mm. If the film is investigated with a microphotometer

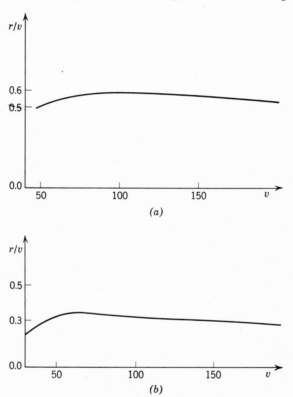

Fig. 23.   Calculated collimator efficiencies.
(a) Counter detection.   (b) Photographic detection.

with a 20μ slit, this slit will then be 5 times as narrow as the trace of the direct beam on the film.   The efficiency of this system is given by curve b of Fig. 23, in which again the ratio r/v is plotted as a function of the slit separation v.

The optimum conditions as determined from this curve are:

$$v = 70 \text{ mm.} \qquad\qquad w = 31 \text{ mm.}$$
$$r_p = 24 \; \mu \qquad\qquad q = 47 \; \mu$$

The maxima in the efficiency plots of both these systems are very flat. The slit separation v could vary between 60 and 190 mm. in the first system or between 50 and 100 mm. in the second without causing a 10 per cent loss. Consequently there is considerable latitude for accommodation of particular supplementary conditions.

The preceding calculations are given as an example, but, as we have already emphasized, they are valid only if all the conditions imposed by the hypotheses are satisfied. If, for example, there is available a demountable tube whose focal spot dimensions can be varied, it is advantageous to diminish the size of the focal spot because the brilliance of the focal spot increases, the smaller its dimensions, at least until the diameter approaches a limiting value between 50 and 100 μ. Such a change of the dimensions of the focal spot has an important influence on the values taken for r and v.

3.2.2. COLLIMATOR WITH CIRCULAR OPENINGS

Let us now consider a sample which gives rise to a scattering in various directions that does not show rotational symmetry, such as, for example, fixed crystals without special orientations. For this study it seems logical to employ cylindrical collimation. We shall preserve the same notation as used in the preceding section, except that p, r, w, a, and b will refer to diameters instead of widths of the apertures and the beam cross sections. The power of the primary beam is then proportional to $\dfrac{\mathscr{P}}{\alpha_0} \dfrac{p^2 r^2}{v^2}$. The quantities to be maximized for Geiger-Müller counter and photographic plate detection are then respectively $\dfrac{\mathscr{P}}{\alpha_0} \dfrac{p^2 r^2}{v^2}$ and $\dfrac{\mathscr{P}}{\alpha_0} \dfrac{p^2 r^2}{v^2 s^2}$. *These are the same conditions as were found for the slit collimators.*

Actually this system is not often employed, because it is more difficult to obtain adjustable holes than adjustable slits. In practice two slits oriented at right angles are generally used, so that the beam is defined by square or rectangular openings. This general problem is too complex, and we shall consider it only for the case in which the sample gives a circularly symmetrical pattern, that is, when the diffracted intensity is a function only of the diffraction angle 2θ.

3.2.3. COLLIMATOR WITH SLITS OF FINITE HEIGHT FOR THE STUDY OF CIRCULARLY SYMMETRICAL DIFFRACTION PATTERNS

Our study will be extended only to the intensity diffracted in the plane perpendicular to the large slit dimension. Experience with ordinary powder patterns has shown that intensity considerations are best served by the employment of beams defined by slits. Let us consider how this concept may be made more specific for a study of small-angle scattering.

Following the notation of Fig. 24, the primary beam, defined by rectangular openings of dimensions p_1, p_2, and r_1, r_2, cuts the plane of observation (Π) in a rectangle of sides a_1 and a_2, these being widths and heights respectively.   Let P be the point of observation in the horizontal plane; the radiation scattered to P from the central ray of the primary beam is scattered through an angle $2\theta = OP/s$.   Similarly, radiation scattered to P from any ray whatsoever of the primary beam which

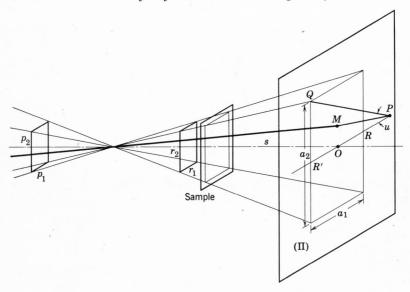

Fig. 24.   Collimator with slits of finite height and width.

intercepts the plane (Π) at the point M is scattered through an angle which, to a first approximation, is $2\theta = MP/s$.   The maximum uncertainty of the scattering angle is then given by

$$A = \frac{PM_{\max} - PM_{\min}}{s} = \frac{PQ - PR}{s}$$

The use of this expression for A to characterize the accuracy of the pattern imposes too severe a condition, since the edges of the beam will intervene much less than the central part (primarily because of a penumbral effect).   A more accurate calculation, however, not only would be more complex but also would lack generality.

It can easily be seen that if $u = \angle OPQ$

$$\tan u = \frac{R'Q}{R'P} = \frac{a_2}{4s\theta + a_1}$$

and

$$A = \frac{PQ}{s} - \frac{PR}{s} = \left(2\theta + \frac{a_1}{2s}\right)\frac{1}{\cos u} - \left(2\theta - \frac{a_1}{2s}\right)$$

If a_1 and a_2 are small with respect to $2s\theta$, then

$$A = \frac{a_1}{s} + \frac{a_2{}^2}{16s^2\theta} \tag{6}$$

For large scattering angles the angular uncertainty A is thus primarily due to the width of the slit, but as small angles are approached the influence of the slit height becomes preponderant. For example, if our system is·to be designed so that the two causes of error, the width and the height of the slit, are to contribute equal parts to A, then if we choose A as 10^{-3}, as in a previous example, the choice must be $a_1/s = a_2{}^2/16s^2\theta$ $= 0.5 \times 10^{-3}$.

For $2\theta = 0.1$ radian, this requires a slit height 40 times the width; on the other hand, for $2\theta = 0.001$ radian, the ratio of height to width is only a factor of 4.

Our primary problem is to determine the best arrangement of two rectangular slits for a collimator to be used for studies of small-angle diffraction. It is impossible to solve this problem for the completely general case. The angular uncertainty of the general pattern is unlike that of the one-dimensional pattern; it cannot be a constant but must increase with decreasing angle. Thus only particular cases can be treated, of which we offer two examples:

(a) Let us consider the system described on p. 89, which employs a counter as a detector, and let us replace the infinite slits by slits of the same widths placed in the same positions but of heights p_2 and r_2, respectively. The sample gives a circularly symmetrical diffraction pattern. An accuracy such that $A = 10^{-2}$ is wanted at an angle $2\theta = 0.01$ radian. Since $a_1/s = 10^{-3}$, equation 6 gives $a_2/s = 0.027$; thus, since $s = 500$ mm., it follows that $a_2 = 13.5$ mm. Now the total power of the beam for a given value of the slit separation v is proportional to the product of the areas of the two openings. The beam power will thus be a maximum when the product p_2r_2 is maximized, since p_1 and r_1 are fixed. There is in addition a geometrical relation between p_2 and r_2 (see Fig. 24)

$$\frac{p_2 + r_2}{v} = \frac{a_2 - r_2}{s}$$

From these relations the optimum parameter values are found to be $p_2 = 1.35$ mm. and $r_2 = 1.14$ mm.

(b) As a second problem let us cite one that has been treated by Yudowitch [241]. If the collimator is formed by two identical apertures separated by a distance v, what form should be given them so that the angular uncertainty of the pattern for *a given beam intensity* should be a minimum at *a given angle*? The first hypothesis implies a fixed area of the collimator openings, $p_1 p_2 = r_1 r_2 = S$. Now the width and height of the beam in the plane of observation at a given distance, s, are proportional, respectively, to p_1 and p_2, and thus they are related by the expression $a_1 a_2 = kS$.

Equation 6 then shows that A is a minimum when

$$a_1/s = 2A/3 \tag{7}$$
$$a_2^2/16s^2\theta = A/3$$

The form of the openings is determined by these relations.

The principal conclusion of this discussion is that the variation of the scattering angle among the various rays reaching the plane of observation at *one* point increases as the average scattering angle decreases. It is therefore necessary to reduce more and more the collimator openings and, consequently, the power of the primary beam, the greater the accuracy desired. This is the major difficulty in experiments concerning small-angle diffraction.

This difficulty can be avoided by either eliminating the cause of the error or by calculating a correction to the experimental results. In the following paragraphs we shall discuss the efforts that have been made in these two directions.

3.3. SYSTEMS USING MONOCHROMATIC RADIATION

A monochromatic primary beam is advantageous, at least theoretically, for every type of investigation, but it is indispensible for the correct interpretation of *continuous scattering*.

3.3.1. SOURCE OF MONOCHROMATIC RADIATION

A first approach is to employ the same system as previously described but to replace the ordinary source by one giving monochromatic radiation. It is well known that the continuous spectrum from a tube is weaker, the smaller the atomic number of the target material and the lower the applied potential. The characteristic radiation of light elements can be excited by very low voltages; a tube with an *aluminum* target operated at 4 kv. emits practically pure Al $K\alpha$ radiation (Hosemann [80], Yudowitch [186]). This technique, however, allows the use of only very long wavelengths (Al $K\alpha$: $\lambda = 8.34$ A); although this offers the advantage of increased dispersion of the pattern, proportional to λ, unfortunately absorption is so great that the very small sample thicknesses that are required can be prepared only with great difficulty.

In another method employing long wavelengths, Henke and DuMond [76''''] isolated the Cu L radiation (13.3 A) by total reflection. The incident radiation struck the surface of a polished glass mirror at an angle such that only X-rays of long wavelengths were totally reflected (Compton and Allison (1935)). The form of the mirrors was ellipsoidal, so that the radiation coming from a point source was focused to a point image.

3.3.2. BALANCED FILTERS

The filtering technique usually employed as a means of decreasing the relative percentage of the $K\beta$ radiation cannot be applied here, since it does not appreciably affect a large part of the continuous spectrum.

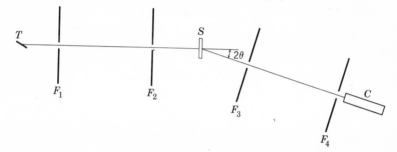

Fig. 25a. A schematic diagram of the Beeman apparatus with slit collimation. T is the X-ray source; F_1 and F_2, the collimator slits; S, the sample; F_3 and F_4, the counter slits; C, the counter.

Ross and later Kirkpatrick (1939) developed a balanced filter technique that uses two patterns, each made with a different filter; the two filters, whose K edges bracket the wavelength to be employed, are of such thicknesses that the difference in the scattered intensity of the two patterns is due almost exclusively to the selected wavelength. For example, if Cu $K\alpha$ radiation is to be used, one filter would be of nickel 6.84 $\times$ 10^{-3} mm. thick, and the other would be of cobalt 7.60 $\times$ 10^{-3} mm. thick. Kratky [112] has used balanced filters in conjunction with photographic detection, but this is a difficult technique, since the differences in intensity of two patterns or of the two halves of one pattern cannot be determined with great accuracy. However, the balanced filter method becomes one of the best techniques when it is used in combination with a Geiger counter.

Figure 25a shows a schematic drawing of the apparatus used in the laboratory of Beeman [376]. The source of X-rays is a rotating anode tube whose high power has been shown to be necessary for studies of weakly scattering substances. The beam is defined by a collimator composed of two slits separated by a distance of 30 to 50 cm. The specimen is placed from 15 to 25 cm. beyond the second slit. A second pair of slits with the same separation as the first pair are placed on an arm which rotates about an axis through the specimen up to an angle of 5° with respect to the incident beam. The third slit, F_3, acts as the aperture O_3 in the general diagram of Fig. 22, serving to stop the parasitic scattering and not defining the geometry of the useful beam. The background intensity may be less than 10^{-7} of that of the direct beam. The double filter is placed immediately in front of the counter. The useful intensity is measured by the difference between the number of counts obtained when first one filter and then the other is employed.

The balanced filter is ineffective if the sample, under the action of the continuous spectrum, emits fluorescence radiation of the same wavelength as that of the principal primary radiation, since the intensity to be measured is found as the difference between very large numbers.

Beeman and his collaborators later used a proportional counter as a detector. When this is employed with the appropriate electronic circuitry, the sensitivity of the apparatus is restricted to wavelengths lying in a narrow band around that of the chosen radiation (Arndt, Coates, and Riley (1953)).

In a new apparatus shown in Fig. 25b, Beeman and his coworkers replaced the collimator slits by pinholes in order to eliminate the difficult corrections for the effects of slit height (§3.4.2). The intensity of the incident beam is reduced considerably by this modification. In order to make possible reliable measurements (for samples that give a circularly symmetric pattern), the counter slit is made in the form of a ring-like aperture centered exactly on the axis of the direct beam. The scattering angle is then varied by displacing the counter and slit along the axis of the direct beam, either towards or away from the sample.

3.3.3. MONOCHROMATIZATION BY CRYSTALLINE DIFFRACTION

Crystalline diffraction offers the most precise method for monochromatization of radiation and the best method for use with photographic measurements. We shall thus consider at length the different techniques that have been proposed.

3.3.3.1. Plane Monochromator

The simplest system is that employing a flat single crystal. The usual crystals can vary in type from the perfect crystal, which gives a sharply defined, low-intensity beam, to the very imperfect crystal, which gives an intense but poorly defined beam whose divergence is equal to the range of orientations of the reflecting crystalline planes.

The characteristics of the different crystals that are most easily obtained have been compared by Lipson, Nelson, and Riley (1945), who recommend for small-angle scattering studies the use of the (100) planes of calcite.

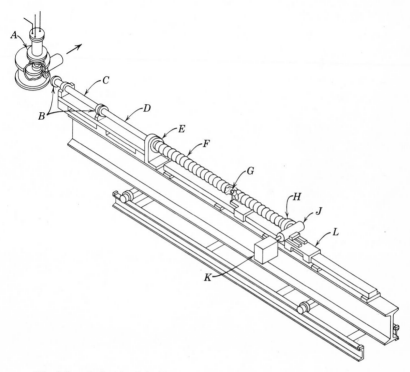

Fig. 25b. A sketch of the Beeman apparatus with pinhole collimation. A is the rotating target tube; B, the collimating pinholes; C, the vacuum connecting tube; D, a vacuum extension tube; E, the guard ring and specimen; F, an extensible plastic tube filled with helium; G, the beam stop for the direct beam; H, the annular slit before the proportional counter J and preamplifier K; L, a sliding base for the annular slit and counter.

These planes, though of weak reflecting power, give an extremely sharp beam in which the $K\alpha_1$ and $K\alpha_2$ reflections can be separated. Quartz (10$\bar{1}$1) planes give a still weaker beam. Pentaerythritol, on the other hand, gives a very intense reflection, but not only is the beam divergence very large, but also the crystal is unstable.

To concentrate the power of the diffracted beam Fankuchen (1937) proposed to cut the surface of the crystal in such a manner as to diminish the cross section of the reflected beam, as is shown in Fig. 26. If the angle between the surface and the reflecting crystalline planes is α and the Bragg angle is θ, the angles made by the primary and diffracted beams with the surface are, respectively, $\theta + \alpha$ and $\theta - \alpha$. This gives the ratio of cross sections as $\dfrac{\sin (\theta - \alpha)}{\sin (\theta + \alpha)}$. Evans, Hirsch, and Kellar (1948) studied in detail the practical possibilities of this process and reached the following conclusions: there is a maximum theoretical intensity gain of 2,

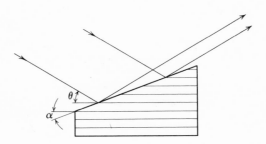

Fig. 26.   The plane monochromator proposed by Fankuchen.

but this factor cannot be attained in practice.   There exists an optimum angle of cut, slightly smaller than θ.   The gain obtained depends to a large extent on the state of the crystal surface; the best results were obtained with calcite crystals which were cut, polished, and then very lightly rubbed with either very fine emery paper or the point of a pencil.

A perfect crystal also collimates the diffracted radiation, functioning in this respect as a slit at an infinite distance viewed through a negligible angle.   Figure 27 shows the arrangement of the diffraction apparatus employing a plane, perfect monochromator.   Radiation from a source of width p is diffracted into a beam of constant width (neglecting the spectral width of the characteristic radiation); thus the width of the direct beam at the plane of observation is p.   The sample is at a distance s from the plane of observation and at a distance w from the monochromating crystal.   It is necessary to place a slit just before the sample to eliminate the strong parasitic scattering arising from that part of the surface of the monochromator touched by the direct, polychromatic beam.   The angular uncertainty of the scattering pattern is given by the quantity $A = p/s$, and the angular region within which there is parasitic scattering is $B/2$, where

$$B = b/s = (2p/w) + (p/s)$$

Thus for given values of A and B these relations determine the values of w and s, the source width p being fixed.

In determining the angular region obscured by parasitic radiation we have assumed that only the useful region on the monochromating crystal receives radiation. This requires that the equipment include a second slit, *F*, of width *p*, placed as close as possible to the monochromating crystal. This slit plays no role in the collimation of the incident beam but acts only to reduce the parasitic scattering. After the monochromator crystal has been adjusted so as to produce the reflected beam,

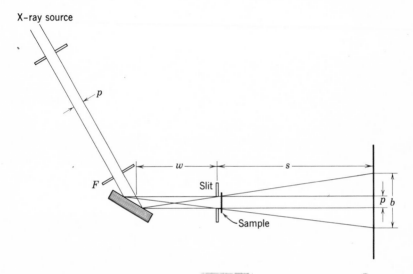

Fig. 27. A small-angle scattering apparatus employing a plane monochromator.

the independently adjustable edges of this slit should be closed to the precise width at which the reflected beam begins to be narrowed: the extent of the region containing parasitic scattering will then be a minimum.

If the monochromator crystal is not perfect, there will be a divergence of the reflected beam equal to the disorientation of the crystalline planes. This disorientation is the minimum value of *A* that can be realized. Another cause of divergence of the reflected beam is the α_1-α_2 doublet nature of the characteristic *K* radiation. For example, the divergence of Cu *K*α radiation reflected from the cleavage planes of calcite is 0.65×10^{-3} radian. This divergence is larger, the greater the diffraction angle of the monochromator. Thus Lipson, Nelson, and Riley (1945) have suggested the use of a crystal of gypsum, which has a very large spacing for its cleavage planes (7.85 A). This would reduce the Cu *K*α divergence to 0.25×10^{-3} radian, making possible theoretically the resolution from the direct beam of reflections due to spacings as great as 6000 A.

The primary disadvantage in the use of plane crystals as mono-chromators is the *low power of the reflected beam,* which seriously limits the possibilities for practical application of this method. Two other methods will now be discussed that offer several important improvements: (1) an increase in intensity of the monochromatic beam: (2) a decrease in the angular uncertainty of the pattern; (3) an elimination of the parasitic scattering beyond quite small angles. These methods depend on the use of the *bent crystal monochromator* and the *double monochromator.*

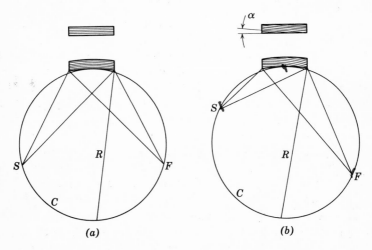

Fig. 28. Johann bent crystal monochromators :
(*a*) symmetrical; (*b*) asymmetrical.

3.3.3.2. Bent Crystal Monochromator

Bent crystals were originally introduced in X-ray spectroscopy, serving as analyzers capable of producing intense spectra; they can serve equally well as monochromators. When they are used as monochromators, a system employing reflection geometry is particularly advantageous. The simplest of these is that described by *Johann* (1931): A thin plate is bent elastically (or plastically) to a radius of curvature R; then, with the arrangement shown in Fig. 28*a*, rays from the source S, diffracted at an angle θ by the bent crystal, are focused approximately at a point F, with the source, the crystal, and the focus lying on a circle C of diameter R. This focusing is exact if the surface of the crystal is coincident with the arc of the circle, the radius of curvature of the lattice planes remaining the same, i.e., R. This is accomplished by the technique of *Johansson* (1933): The plate is first cut cylindrically to a radius R and then curved onto the circle of radius $R/2$; the radius of curvature of the diffracting planes is then R, as before. The Johansson technique is of interest only if beams of large divergence (greater than $1°$) are to be used, which, as we shall see, is not true for small-angle scattering studies.

If the crystal slab is cut so that the reflecting planes make an angle α with the surface of the slab, an *asymmetric monochromator* is obtained (Guinier (1946)) for either the Johann or Johansson systems (Fig. 28b). The ratio of the distances of the source and the focus from the crystal is $\dfrac{\sin(\theta - \alpha)}{\sin(\theta + \alpha)}$. This arrangement has the advantage that the distance of the focus from the crystal can be made large without having to place the source farther away from the crystal.

For small-angle scattering studies, the bent crystal not only serves as a monochromator but it also has *the advantage of producing a beam which is geometrically very well defined*; the diffracted beam converges to a fine line even when the beam divergence, and hence power, is quite large. Thus, if the plane of observation passes through the focus F, normal to the beam, the angular uncertainty of the pattern is not dependent on the beam power, as was true for the system with a simple collimator. The width of the trace of the primary beam is determined primarily by the separation of the $K\alpha$ doublet, the effects arising from the geometry of the system being much smaller. For example, if the monochromator consists of a thin slab of quartz cut at an angle of $\alpha = 3°$ to the reflecting $(10\bar{1}1)$ planes and curved to a radius of 500 mm., the distance from the crystal to the point of focus for Cu $K\alpha$ radiation is 140 mm., and the separation of the α_1-α_2 doublet corresponds to an angle of $2'$; the observed beam width in the plane of observation is then 0.15 mm. If the sample is placed in the beam at a distance $s = 100$ mm. from the plane of observation, the corresponding uncertainty of the pattern will be $A = 1.5 \times 10^{-3}$.

In this as in the other systems, particularly those employed for the study of continuous scattering, the minimizing of the angle beyond which parasitic scattering is eliminated is essential. This is done by placing just in front of the sample a slit whose edges approach the beam as closely as possible, as is shown in Fig. 29. If d is the focal distance, CF, and ω is the divergence of the beam, the angle obscured by the parasitic scattering will be

$$\measuredangle FMD = \frac{B}{2} = \frac{b}{2s} = \frac{d\,\omega}{d - s}$$

It is therefore necessary to restrict the distance s to the smallest value s_p for which the pattern will be legible (cf. p. 87). If, in the example treated above ($d = 140$ mm.), we choose $s_p = 80$ mm., the obscured angle will be $B/2 = 2.2\omega$. We are thus led to the following conclusion: although the convergent property of the beam makes the angular uncertainty of the pattern independent of the beam divergence, *nevertheless this divergence must be strongly limited* in order to diminish the range of angles which are obscured, since experiments have shown that the parasitic intensity is so large that no experiments are possible in this region.

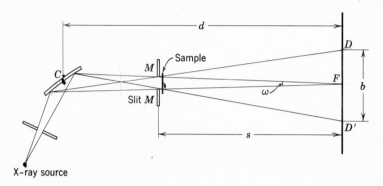

Fig. 29.   A small-angle scattering system employing a bent crystal monochromator.

The system with a bent crystal monochromator then appears to be hampered by the same restriction as the systems with a plane monochromator or a collimator; less and less power can be employed, the smaller the diffraction angle at which a measurement is desired.   There remains one important advantage for this system over the previous systems employing monochromatization, however; as a result of the precise convergence of the direct beam, there is a smaller angular uncertainty in the pattern.

3.3.3.3. Combination of Two Bent Crystal Monochromators

The principal cause of the troublesome parasitic scattering lies in the fact that the surface of the monochromator is irradiated by the very intense direct beam, while use is made of the radiation of a chosen wavelength, which forms only a small fraction of the total power of the beam. This fact led to the idea of employing a double monochromator, in which the focus, F_1, of the first bent crystal served as the source for a second, so oriented as to reflect the entire incident beam into a beam converging to a new focus, F_2 (see Fig. 30).   Fournet [48] has studied the geometry of this system in detail and has shown that the most desirable arrangement is that in which the two crystals are oriented in the antiparallel position, since the parallel position allows a narrow spectral band to be reflected successively by the two crystals at their optimum mutual orientation.

The point of interest of this system is that, even without any protective slits, the parasitic scattering is almost completely eliminated beyond an angle of about *ten minutes* from the direct beam. The sample can then be placed quite close to the second monochromator, so that with very asymmetric monochromators of large radius of curvature, sample-to-film

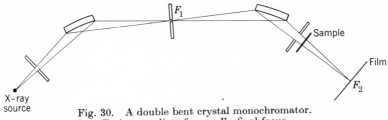

Fig. 30. A double bent crystal monochromator.
F_1, intermediate focus; F_2, final focus.

distances of 300 mm. can be obtained. But, although it has been verified that films which are certainly more easily readable are obtained with such large distances (at the price of increased exposure times), it has proved to be practically impossible to reduce further the angular limit imposed by the remaining parasitic scattering. Fournet has made a detailed theoretical and experimental study of this scattering; it seems to be caused principally by irregularities in the curvature of the lattice planes of the two crystals. These irregularities are the results of defects in the cutting of the crystal and the crystal holders. The mechanical difficulties in making perfect cylinders are well known. Thus from this point of view it would seem advantageous to employ uncut slabs of quartz (the Johann technique). The best method for cutting the holders is that described by DuMond (1947).

In addition to this effect it seems probable that simple elastic curving creates a crystalline imperfection that should cause diffuse scattering. As yet no experimental or theoretical analysis of this effect has been made.

In any event, even for a perfect crystal, there will still be diffuse scattering of thermal origin which will be particularly intense in the neighborhood of the direction of a Bragg reflection. This scattering, however, has never been troublesome in the apparatus we have used.

The following are the details of construction and the characteristics of the double monochromator system we have developed.

First Monochromator. Quartz slab, cut parallel to ($10\bar{1}1$) planes; Johansson technique; elastically bent to 500 mm. radius of curvature. Focusing distance of 115 mm. for Cu $K\alpha$ radiation.

Second Monochromator. Quartz slab, cut at 3° to ($10\bar{1}1$) planes; Johansson technique; elastically bent to 500 mm. radius of curvature. Focusing distance of 140 mm. The sample is generally placed 100 mm. from the film.

Numerous trials have been made with quartz slabs of different curvatures constructed according to the Johann method. We have verified that it is possible, with suitable though delicate adjustments, to eliminate one of the components of the $K\alpha$ doublet in the twice reflected beam.

The parasitic scattering at a point in the observation plane corresponding to a scattering angle of 15′ (the angle for a lattice spacing of 300 A) is 1/100,000th the intensity of the primary beam. If the scattering to be studied is not too weak, it can be registered beyond an angle corresponding to a 400 A spacing, with the necessary correction for scattering from sources other than the sample remaining reasonable.

At first glance it might be thought that the double monochromatization and the large distance from X-ray tube to film would require a prohibitive increase in the exposure time. Actually the loss of power of this system as compared to that with a single monochromator is not too large. This arises from the fact that with a single monochromator it is necessary to use beams of very small divergence in order to limit the parasitic scattering, whereas with the double monochromator the final beam has more than a 1° divergence.

Nevertheless, for ease of adjustment of the second monochromator with a fluorescent screen, it is almost indispensable to have a very powerful source of X-rays. Our system employs a tube with a rotating target. With this tube operating at 45 kv. and 45 ma. *the exposure times are only one-third as long as the exposures necessary with our previous system*, which employed a single monochromator coupled to an ordinary X-ray tube operated at 30 kv. and 7.5 ma. For example, good patterns of a 19 per cent solution of hemoglobin (Fig. 31) were obtained with one hour exposures.

In summary, the system of two bent crystal monochromators is a substantial improvement over the simple system of a single monochromator. It does not require the difficult adjustment of a slit in front of the sample (see Fig. 29), and the patterns are much purer. Its range of application, however, is somewhat limited; parasitic scattering prevents approaching the direct beam to angles smaller than those corresponding to 300 or 400 A for Cu $K\alpha$ radiation (Fig. 31). We do not think that it will be possible to better this limit with such a system. To register larger spacings it is necessary to return to a system of successive slits, and with that arrangement the double crystal monochromator is no longer of interest and a simple crystal monochromator must be used.

3.3.3.4. Monochromator with a Point Focus

Both single and double bent crystal monochromators have the advantage of diminishing the width of the trace of the direct beam and, consequently,

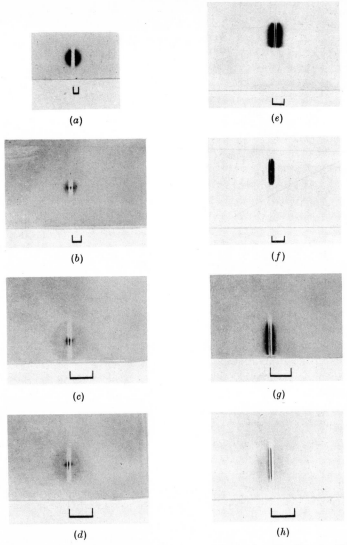

Fig. 31. Some examples of patterns obtained with the double monochromator. The scale indicates 2° in 2θ. Patterns a, b, c, and d were made with incident beams of small height and patterns e, f, g, and h with beams of large height. X-ray tube input: 45 kv. and 40 ma.

(a) Carbon black. Exposure time: $T = 1$ hr.
(b) Solution of human hemoglobin (19%). $T = 1$ hr.
(c) Human red cells. $T = 9$ hr.
(d) Solution of albumin serum (23%). $T = 1$ hr.
(e) Chrysotile. $T = 1$ hr.
(f) Hemocyanine (snail blood). $T = 1$ hr.
(g) Egg yolk. $T = 2$ hr.
(h) Same sample as in d. $T = 3$ hr.

increasing the accuracy of the pattern. The diffracted beam, though of
small width, is large in height, and this causes an angular uncertainty in
the pattern which, as we have seen (p. 93), becomes very important when
approaching very small angles. As in the system with collimators, this
height can be reduced only with the aid of slits, and these also reduce
the usable beam power.

The bent crystal focuses the rays in one dimension. The ideal system
would be one which concentrates the rays to a point instead of a line.
This is the objective of attempts that have been made to develop monochromators with a point focus.

The first technique consists of curving the lattice planes onto a toroidal
surface. In order to describe this, let us consider the cylindrical monochromator giving an image, F, of the point source, S, shown in Fig. 28.
Now let us imagine this system rotated about the axis, SF. The cylinder
generates a toroid, and, if the lattice planes were curved along this
surface, the radiation from S would converge to a point at F.

The toroid, however, is not a developable surface for crystals. A
crystalline slab cannot be shaped onto a toroid without breaking it or
introducing such perturbations in the lattice that all hope for good images
is lost. A solution of this problem consists in deforming a crystal
plastically rather than elastically (Wilsdorf (1948); DuMond [210];
Shacklett [149"]) and in following the plastic deformation with a "poly-
gonization" treatment (Guinier (1952)) by means of a suitable anneal.
This treatment transforms the distorted crystal into a mosaic of small
crystallites whose reflecting planes are very closely tangential to the
toroidal surface. Cauchois, Tiedema, and Burgers (1950) have shown
that excellent images can be obtained with an aluminum crystal cylindrically deformed and polygonized, which offers hope that a good toroidal
crystal can also be made. Hägg and Karlsson [219'] succeeded in
preparing a toroidal crystal of aluminum with which they obtained a
beam 50 times as intense as that from a cylindrically bent quartz crystal.
However, it has not yet been established that this kind of monochromator
is perfect enough to be usable in small-angle scattering experiments.

Another technique, based on the successive employment of two crystals,
is due to DuMond and his collaborators [229]. The two crystals are bent
slabs which have been cut so that the reflecting planes make a small angle
with the surface of the slab. Their arrangement is shown in Fig. 32.
The rays coming from the point source S are diffracted by the first crystal,
A, and converge towards the vertical line focus, F, parallel to the generator
of the surface of A. This converging beam appears to come from a
virtual line source, F', lying in the horizontal plane and situated on the
circle of center M and of radius SM, where M is the midpoint of the arc

SAF. Let *O* be the midpoint of the line *FF'*. If we now pivot the rigid system of source *S* and crystal *A* by a 90° rotation about the axis *FF'* followed by a 180° rotation about a vertical axis through *O*, the crystal *A* is transformed into a crystal at *B*, and the source comes to the point *P*. The beam coming from *P* and diffracted by *B* again is characterized by

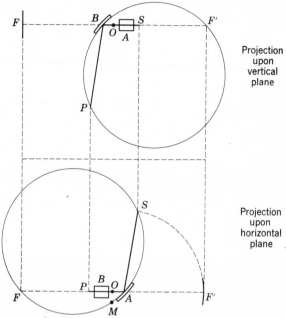

Fig. 32. Horizontal and vertical projections of a point-focusing double monochromator according to DuMond et al. [229].

the same two foci, *F* and *F'*. Thus, by virtue of ordinary optical principles, the beam reflected by the first crystal *A* and then by the second crystal *B* will converge to the point *P*, giving a point image of the point source *S*. Shenfil, Danielson, and DuMond [229] have studied in detail the geometry of this system for the case of an extended source of X-rays. They showed that for a given position of the crystals there was only a small part of the area of the source from which the *K*α radiation could be twice reflected. The experimental results have confirmed the geometrical predictions, and the authors have found a focus of dimensions 0.19 mm. × 1.41 mm. for a focusing distance of the order of 65 cm. The optimum settings for the two crystals can be found only by means of a systematic application of numerous adjustments; without such an approach, no results can be obtained.

An important factor for such a system is the beam intensity remaining after this double diffraction. A primary cause of loss of intensity is the polarization of the beam upon diffraction. If the Bragg angle for the crystals were 45°, there would be complete polarization of the beam after the first diffraction, and the intensity diffracted by the second crystal would be zero. It is thus necessary to use planes affording small Bragg angles. The first tests of this system were made with quartz crystals,

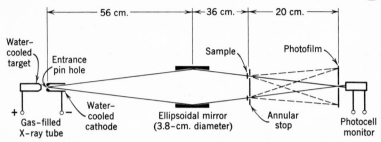

Fig. 33.   Sketch of a high-intensity small-angle diffraction unit for long wavelength X-rays. A large solid angle of X-ray beam is totally reflected and focused to a point by an ellipsoidal mirror of ground and polished Pyrex. Reflection angles are very nearly equal to the critical angle of reflection for the desired line radiation, so that all harder background radiation is essentially cut off. (Henke and DuMond [76′′′′].)

using the (310) planes with a Bragg angle of 40°.   The final beam intensity was so weak that only samples that scattered strongly could be studied. The authors have suggested the use of topaz rather than quartz crystals, predicting an intensity increase of a factor of 4.8.   A consideration of the long path length of the beam brought out the advantage of placing the apparatus in a vacuum or a helium atmosphere; the gain from this modification would be a factor of 3.5.   Also the use of an X-ray source with a smaller angle of emergence from the target surface would permit a further increase in intensity.   When all these factors are considered, the authors believe that a total intensity gain of the order of a factor of 40 over the first system can be obtained.   Such an arrangement, associated with either a powerful X-ray tube or one with a fine focus, would then be capable of producing adequate scattered intensities.

The use of the two monochromators obviously gives this system the same advantages (accuracy of beam definition, absence of parasitic scattering) as those of the system in which the two crystals are arranged with parallel axes of bending.

Another point-focusing system has been developed by Furnas [437], in which transmission by a mica crystal is used after the first reflecting quartz crystal; the principle of the technique is the same as that developed by DuMond.

Let us also mention again the system of Henke and DuMond [76′′′′] which uses total reflection from a mirror having the shape of an ellipsoid of revolution (Fig. 33). A ring-shaped screen placed after the mirror stops the direct radiation and allows only the reflected rays to reach the point P.

Even if we could succeed in producing a beam that converged strictly to a point, there would still remain one source of error, resulting from the examination of the films with a microphotometer. Generally the

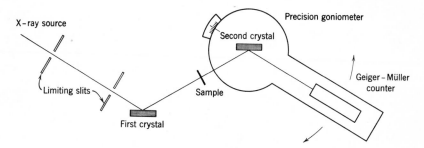

Fig. 34.   A double plane crystal spectrometer for small-angle diffraction measurements.

exploring slit of this apparatus has a height of the order of 1 mm., and this height will introduce an error in the measurements at very small angles.

3.3.3.5. Double Monochromator with Plane Crystals

This system, proposed first by Fankuchen and Jellinek [212] and used by Kaesberg, Beeman, and Ritland [221], is employed for quite different purposes than those of the system with two bent crystals. Interest is centered not on suppressing the parasitic scattering as much as possible but rather on recording the crystalline reflections due to very large lattice spacings.

The apparatus, shown in Fig. 34, may be described as a double crystal spectrometer, with the crystals set in the parallel position.[1] The two crystals are very good specimens of cleaved calcite, and the goniometers are constructed with sufficient precision to permit the determination of orientations to within seconds of arc. The detector, a Geiger-Müller counter, is placed after the second crystal. The first crystal is held fixed, and the intensity is measured as a function of the angle of rotation of the second crystal. In the absence of a sample, a plot of this intensity distribution gives a curve known as a "rocking curve," whose width is a measure of the perfection of the crystal. Neither the spectral width of the radiation nor the width of the slits affects the shape of this curve.

[1] The theory of the double crystal spectrometer can be found treated in detail in *X-Rays in Theory and Experiment*, by Compton and Allison (1935).

The scattering by a sample is determined by performing the same operation with the sample placed between the two crystals. The intensity measured in excess of the normal rocking curve when the second crystal makes an angle, ϵ, with the first then represents the intensity scattered by the sample through this angle. Since the width of the rocking curve of good calcite crystals does not exceed 10″, diffraction lines corresponding to lattice spacings of 20,000 A can be resolved from the direct beam. The angular uncertainty of the pattern, in the sense in which this has previously been defined (p. 87), can thus be 20 times as small as that of other systems. It must be pointed out, however, that this double crystal spectrometer functions schematically as a system of *two slits of infinite height*. There is therefore a very important inaccuracy due to the slit height at very small angles just as in the other systems employing slits, except for samples so oriented as to give a diffraction pattern consisting of parallel lines. Also there is no arrangement for suppressing the parasitic scattering arising principally from the second crystal. This is the source of the very strong small-angle parasitic scattering shown in the curves published by Kaesberg and his collaborators, and others. *This system is not adapted to the study of weak, continuous scattering*, but it is the best for the study of *crystalline diffraction* arising from very large lattice spacings.

Let us mention also a somewhat similar system devised by Banerjee and Maitra [2], in which a single plane crystal is used, the first crystal of Fig. 34 being replaced by a simple slit collimator whose width determines the accuracy that can be attained. For a given setting of the crystal two lines are found in the plane of observation: one corresponds to the characteristic $K\alpha$ radiation scattered by the sample through an angle ϵ and then reflected by the crystal, and the other corresponds to a radiation of unknown wavelength from the continuous spectrum which has traversed the sample without deviation and has then been reflected by the crystal (Laue reflection). The position of this second line determines the orientation of the crystal and thus the angle of scattering, ϵ, of the first line. Since the intensity of a wavelength of the characteristic spectrum is not very great, the intensity of the Laue line will be of the same order of magnitude as that of the characteristic radiation scattered by the sample.

3.3.4. MEASUREMENT OF THE TOTAL SCATTERED INTENSITY

Another use of the double crystal spectrometer has been suggested by Warren [174]. The total energy scattered at small angles by a sample is determined by comparing the energies received by the counter when the sample is placed between the two crystals (position 1) and when it is placed just in front of the counter (position 2). In this second position the scattered rays enter the counter, whereas in the first position they are eliminated by the second crystal. Exploitation of this unique measurement is possible by means of supplementary hypotheses concerning the form of the particles in the sample, by neglecting all interparticle interferences, and by assuming that when the sample is in position 1 the fraction of scattered energy superposed upon the transmitted beam and reflected by the second crystal is small. Warren has shown that, if the sample is assumed to be constituted of spheres of radius r, the difference between the mass absorption coefficients of the sample in positions 1 and 2, μ_{SA}, is proportional to r. The numerical relation was shown to be

$$\mu_{SA} = 0.0108\lambda^2 \rho r$$

where λ and r are expressed in angstroms and ρ is the density of the sample. The measurements cited by Warren for a carbon black give a value of r in good accord with that deduced from an analysis of the low-angle continuous scattering curve.

If the assumption of spherical particles is not made, the measurement of the total scattered energy can still be used by means of equations 2.30 and 2.110.

3.4. METHODS OF CORRECTION OF EXPERIMENTAL SCATTERING CURVES

We have already emphasized that the inaccuracy produced by the dimensions of the direct beam increases as the center of the pattern is approached. This is particularly serious in a study of continuous scattering, where there is need for the entire curve of the intensity and not simply the positions of the maxima, as is the situation in studies of diffraction lines or spots. The errors are due to the *width* and the *height* of the direct beam. We have seen that the bent crystal monochromator with its convergent beam allows a reduction of the error due to the beam *width* without diminishing the beam intensity. It is not actually possible, in the absence of point monochromators, to avoid the error due to the beam *height*. Instead of trying to reduce this error at the price of a very great loss in intensity, methods of correction to determine the real curve from the measured curve have been sought. Such methods exist for the correction of errors due both to the width and to the height of the beam, but, because of the persistence of the slit height error noted above, it is particularly the latter correction that is important.

The cross section of the direct beam in the plane of observation is shown in Fig. 35a. Let the intensity of the direct beam at the point

$P(x, y)$ be denoted by $i(x, y)\, dx\, dy$. In order to simplify the notation for the following calculations, we have adopted as coordinates of P

$$x = (2\pi\overline{OP_x})/s\lambda$$

$$y = (2\pi\overline{OP_y})/s\lambda$$

where s is the sample-to-film distance.

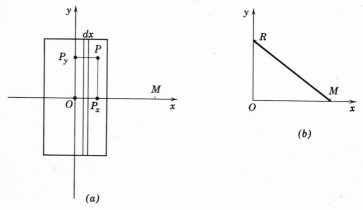

(a)

(b)

Fig. 35.   Calculation of the effect of beam dimensions.

Radiation scattered from this part of the direct beam to the point of observation, M, will be scattered by the sample through an angle equal, as a first approximation, to $2\theta(x, y) = \overline{PM}/s$, so that the parameter h has the value $h(x, y) = (2\pi\overline{PM})/s\lambda$.

We shall assume that the scattered intensity depends only on the scattering angle, this dependence being expressed by the function $I(h)$. The point of observation M is defined by the parameter $h_M = (2\pi\overline{OM})/s\lambda$, and the observed intensity at this point is

$$\mathscr{I}(h) = \int\int i(x, y)I(h(x, y))\, dx\, dy$$

The problem is to deduce $I(h)$ from the measured values $\mathscr{I}(h)$.

3.4.1. CORRECTION FOR THE EFFECT OF BEAM WIDTH

We shall consider a beam of rectangular cross section in which the distribution of intensity along the vertical direction is similar for all values of the horizontal coordinate, that is, $i(x, y)$ can be written

$$i(x, y) = i_1(x)i_2(y)$$

Let $\mathscr{I}_1(h)$ be the scattered intensity that would be obtained at a point a distance $(h\lambda s)/2\pi$ along the x-axis from an infinitely narrow incident beam containing the same power as the real direct beam, the intensity distribution of this incident beam in the vertical direction being proportional to $i_2(y)$. Let $i_{1.0}(x)\,dx$ be the fraction of the total power of the real direct beam striking the plane of observation between the abscissae, x and $x + dx$; that is,

$$i_{1.0}(x) = \frac{i_1(x)}{\int i_1(x)\,dx}$$

The contribution of this elementary direct beam to the observed scattered intensity at M is $i_{1.0}(x)\mathscr{I}_1(h - x)\,dx$. Therefore

$$\mathscr{I}(h) = \int i_{1.0}(x)\mathscr{I}_1(h - x)\,dx \tag{8}$$

An integral equation of this form can be solved by means of Fourier transforms. We shall assume that $\mathscr{I}(h)$, $\mathscr{I}_1(h)$, and $i_{1.0}(x)$ are even functions. Their transforms are then defined by the following equations:

$$\mathscr{I}^*(u) = \int_{-\infty}^{\infty} \mathscr{I}(h) \cos 2\pi hu \, dh$$

$$\mathscr{I}_1^*(u) = \int_{-\infty}^{\infty} \mathscr{I}_1(h) \cos 2\pi hu \, dh$$

$$i^*_{1.0}(u) = \int_{-\infty}^{\infty} i_{1.0}(x) \cos 2\pi xu \, dx$$

One can show that equation 8 can be transformed to the following equation:

$$\mathscr{I}^*(u) = \mathscr{I}_1^*(u) i^*_{1.0}(u) \tag{9}$$

The correction is found by calculating the transforms of the two known functions, $\mathscr{I}(h)$ and $i_{1.0}(x)$, and in forming their quotient. *The transform of this quotient will be the desired function, $\mathscr{I}_1(h)$.*

Let us point out that $\mathscr{I}(h)$ and $i_{1.0}(x)$ are measured by means of a counter or microphotometer and are not known precisely because of the finite width of the exploring slits. But, if the same slit is used to explore the direct beam and the scattered intensity, *equation 9 is still correct*, since an application of the same process shows that the effects due to the "slit transmission" function disappear.

Theoretically one can thus correct exactly for the effect of the width by this process, regardless of the magnitude of this width. Actually we find in practice that the mathematical operations for calculating the transforms give precise results only on condition that the function $i_{1.0}(x)$

is zero outside of an interval which is small with respect to that in which $\mathscr{I}(h)$ undergoes notable variations. If, for example, the width of a continually decreasing central scattering were not much larger than that of the direct beam, the transform of $i_{1.0}(x)$ would have zeroes in the region in which $\mathscr{I}_1(h)$ is to be calculated, which would lead to a very poor determination of $\mathscr{I}_1(h)$. For the same reasons it is necessary that the exploring slit used to determine $i_{1.0}(x)$ be small with respect to the width of the direct beam (less than 10 or 20 per cent).

3.4.2. CORRECTION FOR THE EFFECT OF BEAM HEIGHT

After the correction for the beam width has been made, we must correct for the effect due to a beam which is infinitely narrow but has a certain height along the y-axis. Let M again be the point of observation (Fig. 35b), and let the position of the point R in the direct beam be designated by the coordinate $y = (2\pi\overline{OR})/s\lambda$. The fraction of the total beam power contained in the segment of dimension dy, at the ordinate y, will be denoted by $i_{2.0}(y)\,dy$, where

$$i_{2.0}(y) = \frac{i_2(y)}{\int i_2(y)\,dy}$$

If $I(h)$ is the true scattering distribution (i.e., that obtained with a direct beam of infinitely small radius passing through O), the observed intensity at the point M is

$$\mathscr{I}_1(h) = \int i_{2.0}(y)I(\sqrt{h^2 + y^2})\,dy \tag{10}$$

where

$$h = (2\pi\overline{OM})/s\lambda$$

A very important fact must be pointed out here: when the true scattering distribution is represented by a Gaussian curve, *the observed curve is proportional to the real curve*. This is easily seen, for if $I(h) = Ae^{-k^2h^2}$

$$\mathscr{I}_1(h) = \left[\int i_{2.0}(y)e^{-k^2y^2}\,dy\right]Ae^{-k^2h^2} = \text{constant} \times I(h) \tag{11}$$

If the beam height is large and the intensity of the beam is a constant c, independent of y, equation 11 becomes

$$\mathscr{I}_1(h) = \frac{c\sqrt{\pi}}{k}\,I(h) \tag{11a}$$

This demonstrates that the proportionality factor between the measured and true intensity distributions depends on the coefficient in the exponent. This fact, first pointed out by Hosemann [79], is of considerable interest, since an exponential distribution is often a good approximation of the curves of low-angle scattering.

Shull and Roess [155] have pointed out a possible extension of this remark. If the experimental curve is not sufficiently well represented by an exponential function, one can try to separate it into a series of exponentials. Thus, if the measured intensity can be written as

$$\mathscr{I}_1(h) = \sum_i T_i e^{-k_i{}^2 h^2}$$

the transform of $I(h)$ will be the sum of the transforms of the component exponentials. The expression for the true intensity distribution will then be

$$I(h) = \sum_i T_i{}' e^{-k_i{}^2 h^2}$$

where

$$T_i{}' = \frac{k_i}{\sqrt{\pi}} T_i$$

This method is not generally usable, since not only is the separation of an arbitrary function into a series of exponentials sometimes impossible,[1] but also, even when it is possible, a general method for performing the separation is lacking.

When the equation of the scattering curve for an incident beam of point-like cross section is known, the scattering curve observed for a beam of infinite height can always be calculated by means of equation 10. This was illustrated for an exponential scattering curve in equation 11. Several other such results are found useful:

(i) If the asymptotic shape of the intensity curve is of the form of Kh^{-4} (equations 2.26 and 2.108), the observed curve varies asymptotically as h^{-3}. This is seen from the following:

$$\mathscr{I}_1(h) = K \int_{-\infty}^{\infty} \frac{1}{(h^2 + y^2)^2} \, dy$$

By making the substitution $y = h \tan \alpha$

$$\mathscr{I}_1(h) = \frac{2K}{h^3} \int_0^{\pi/2} \frac{d\alpha}{(1 + \tan^2 \alpha)^2 \cos^2 \alpha}$$

$$= \frac{2K}{h^3} \int_0^{\pi/2} \cos^2 \alpha \, d\alpha = \frac{\pi K}{2h^3} \tag{11b}$$

or

$$h^3 \mathscr{I}_1(h) = \frac{\pi}{2} h^4 I(h)$$

[1] The group of functions $e^{-k_i{}^2 h^2}$ does not form an orthogonal group.

(ii) In equations 2.28 and 2.111 the integral $\int_0^\infty h^2 I(h)\, dh$ appears. In terms of the observed intensity, this should be replaced by the integral $\frac{1}{2}\int_0^\infty h\mathscr{I}_1(h)\, dh$. This can be shown as follows:

$$\int_0^\infty h\mathscr{I}_1(h)\, dh = \int_0^\infty \int_{-\infty}^\infty hI(\sqrt{h^2 + y^2})\, dh\, dy$$

By making the change of variables $y = z \sin\alpha$ and $h = z \cos\alpha$ so that

$$y^2 + h^2 = z^2 \qquad \text{and} \qquad dh\, dy = z\, dz\, d\alpha$$

$$\int_0^\infty h\mathscr{I}_1(h)\, dh = \int_0^\infty \int_{-\pi/2}^{\pi/2} I(z)z^2 \cos\alpha\, dz\, d\alpha$$

$$= 2\int_0^\infty z^2 I(z)\, dz \tag{11c}$$

In the same way it can be seen that

$$\int_0^\infty \mathscr{I}_1(h)\, dh = \pi \int_0^\infty hI(h)\, dh \tag{11d}$$

These results are valid only if the beam can be considered as infinitely high even for the most distant parts of the curve.

(iii) Schmidt, Kaesberg, and Beeman (1954) have calculated numerically the scattering curve observed for spherical particles in a dilute system when the incident beam is of infinite height. (The scattering for an incident beam of point-like cross section is given by equation 2.31.)

3.4.2.1. Slit Correction for Infinite Height

A rigorous method of correction for this case has been described by DuMond [209] and by Guinier and Fournet [216], [217]. It is rigorous only for the particular case in which the beam is of uniform intensity and infinite height. However, if the low-angle scattering decreases continuously from the center, this method can be applied if the beam intensity $i_2(y)$, is constant up to a value of y such that $\mathscr{I}_1(y)$ is negligible. If the pattern consists of one ring of scattering, the beam must have a height at least equal to the diameter of the ring for this method to be applicable. The true intensity distribution is determined by the following equation:

$$I(h) = -\frac{1}{\pi c}\int_0^\infty \frac{\mathscr{I}_1'(\sqrt{h^2 + u^2})\, du}{\sqrt{h^2 + u^2}} \tag{12}$$

where c designates the constant value of $i_{2.0}(y)$,

$$\mathscr{I}_1'(\sqrt{h^2 + u^2}) = \frac{d\mathscr{I}_1(\sqrt{h^2 + u^2})}{d(\sqrt{h^2 + u^2})}$$

and u represents a variable of integration of no physical significance. The derivation of this equation may be outlined as follows:

Equation 10 can be written as

$$\mathscr{I}_1(h) = 2c \int_0^\infty I(\sqrt{h^2 + y^2})\, dy$$

Differentiation with respect to h gives the following:

$$\mathscr{I}_1'(h) = 2c \int_0^\infty I'(\sqrt{h^2 + y^2})\, \frac{h}{\sqrt{h^2 + y^2}}\, dy$$

Dividing by h and then changing the variable h^2 into $h^2 + u^2$ gives

$$\frac{\mathscr{I}_1'(\sqrt{h^2 + u^2})}{\sqrt{h^2 + u^2}} = 2c \int_0^\infty \frac{I'(\sqrt{h^2 + u^2 + y^2})}{\sqrt{h^2 + u^2 + y^2}}\, dy$$

Integrating with respect to u

$$\int_0^\infty \frac{\mathscr{I}_1'(\sqrt{h^2 + u^2})}{\sqrt{h^2 + u^2}}\, du = 2c \int_0^\infty \int_0^\infty \frac{I'(\sqrt{h^2 + u^2 + y^2})}{\sqrt{h^2 + u^2 + y^2}}\, du\, dy$$

A second change of variables, $u = r \cos\theta$, $y = r \sin\theta$, then gives

$$\int_0^\infty \frac{\mathscr{I}_1'(\sqrt{h^2 + u^2})}{\sqrt{h^2 + u^2}}\, du = 2c \int_0^{\pi/2} \int_0^\infty \frac{I'(\sqrt{h^2 + r^2})}{\sqrt{h^2 + r^2}}\, |r|\, dr\, d\theta$$

$$= c\pi \left[I(\sqrt{h^2 + r^2}) \right]_{r=0}^{r \to \infty} = -c\pi I(h)$$

on condition that $I(h)$ approaches zero as h approaches infinity, which is true for scattering experiments at very small angles.

The use of equation 12 requires the determination of the derivative of the experimentally determined function $\mathscr{I}_1(h)$. Then, for each value of h, a curve of $\dfrac{\mathscr{I}_1'(\sqrt{h^2 + u^2})}{\sqrt{h^2 + u^2}}$ is traced and a graphical integration is performed. The process is tedious, but it can be precise, as has been verified by Guinier and Fournet [217].

When the function $\mathscr{I}_1(h)$ differs only slightly from a Gaussian function, the calculation may be shortened considerably by writing

$$\mathscr{I}_1(h) = Te^{-k^2h^2} + f(h) \tag{13}$$

where T, k, and $f(h)$ are determined by means of an auxiliary graph of

$\log \mathscr{I}_1(h)$ as a function of h^2.   Application of equation 12 to equation 13 then gives

$$I(h) = \frac{Tk}{c\sqrt{\pi}} e^{-k^2h^2} - \frac{1}{\pi c} \int_0^\infty \frac{f'\left(\sqrt{h^2 + u^2}\right)}{\sqrt{h^2 + u^2}} \, du$$

This approach leads to a much greater accuracy in the determination of the function $I(h)$.

3.4.2.2. Case of a Beam of Arbitrary Height

If $i_2(y)$ depends on y and, in particular, if the beam is of finite height (for example, $i_2(y)$ is a constant between $-y_0$ and y_0 and is zero outside of this interval), the property discussed above of curves of the form $e^{-k^2h^2}$ is still valid.   For this type of curve the measured distribution can be used directly, whatever the intensity distribution of the direct beam, if only the shape of the curve is important.   If absolute measurements of intensity must be made, equation 11 must be employed to determine the proportionality factor.

The general problem of the arbitrary curve that cannot be resolved into a sum of exponentials remains to be considered.   The solution we shall outline here was pointed out by Kratky, Porod, and Kahovec [111].

The equation to be solved is

$$\mathscr{I}_1(h) = \int i_{2.0}(y) \, I\left(\sqrt{h^2 + y^2}\right) dy \qquad (10)$$

in which $i_{2.0}(y)$ is some arbitrary function of y.   Porod has shown that the solution for this general equation, a relation analogous to equation 12 but containing another function, $g(u)$, is

$$I(h) = -\frac{1}{\pi c} \int_0^\infty \frac{\mathscr{I}_1'\left(\sqrt{h^2 + u^2}\right)}{\sqrt{h^2 + u^2}} g(u) \, du \qquad (12a)$$

The function $g(u)$ is determined by the following condition: on making the change of variables $u = r \cos \theta$ and $y = r \sin \theta$, the integral $\int_0^{\pi/2} i_{2.0}(r \sin \theta) g(r \cos \theta) \, d\theta$ should be a constant, i.e., independent of r. If $i_{2.0}$ is a constant, $g(u)$ is a constant, and equation 12a reduces correctly to equation 12.

The authors did not indicate a method, even numerical, for determining $g(u)$ in the general case.

When the beam is of uniform intensity and limited to the interval between $-y_0$ and y_0, these authors indicated a solution which, though not rigorous, should certainly be a good approximation.   An exact solution of the function $g(u)$ was determined for values of u less than $y_0\sqrt{2}$. For large values of u they found that the function tended towards the value $g(u) = u/y_0$, oscillating about this quantity. For their application they adopted the following values:

$$g(u) = 1 \qquad u < y_0$$
$$g(u) = 2 \qquad y_0 \leq u \leq y_0\sqrt{2}$$
$$g(u) = \frac{u}{y_0} \qquad u > y_0\sqrt{2}$$

In practice, the method of application of this correction is the following: the function

$$F(u) = \frac{\mathscr{I}_1'\left(\sqrt{h^2 + u^2}\right)}{\sqrt{h^2 + u^2}}$$

is constructed as in the previous case for an infinite slit. The integration is more complicated because of the presence of the function $g(u)$. First the integration of the function $F(u)$ is performed over values of u ranging from 0 to y_0. To this is added twice the value of the integration over values of u ranging from y_0 to $y_0\sqrt{2}$. The final contribution is that given by the integral of the product $(u/y_0)F(u)$ over values of u ranging from $y_0\sqrt{2}$ to infinity. Kratky and Porod have shown that this last contribution is given by the ordinate of the experimental curve at an abscissa of $\sqrt{h^2 + 2y_0^2}$. Tests by the authors of this method have shown that the accuracy obtained is of the same order as that found in the correction for beams of infinite height by means of equation 12.

It is not yet possible to say that definite, complete solutions exist for the problem of correction for the height of the incident beam. Thus in practice one should either employ very high beams of uniform intensity and make an important, but calculable, correction, or else diminish the height of the beam as much as possible to diminish the error. We believe that this last solution is to be recommended, provided that the study is not extended to very small angles.

Actually, if the correction is small, an approximate method pointed out both by Fournet and Guinier [216] and by Franklin [214] can be used. The beam is assumed to be of uniform intensity, c, and limited to values of y between $-y_0$ and y_0. The function $I(h)$ is expanded in terms of $\mathscr{I}_1(h)$ and its derivatives, the first terms being

$$2cy_0I(h) = \mathscr{I}_1(h) - \frac{1}{6}\left(\frac{y_0}{h}\right)^2 h\frac{d\mathscr{I}_1(h)}{dh} - \frac{1}{360}\left(\frac{y_0}{h}\right)^4\left[h\frac{d\mathscr{I}_1(h)}{dh} - h^2\frac{d^2\mathscr{I}_1(h)}{dh^2}\right]$$

This method still requires the determination of the slopes of the experimental curve, but these enter only in the corrective terms.

The above relation can be written, to a slightly poorer approximation, as

$$2cy_0 I(h) = \mathcal{I}_1 \left(\sqrt{h^2 - \frac{y_0^2}{3h^2}} \right)$$

3.5. CONSTRUCTION OF LOW-ANGLE SCATTERING SYSTEMS

Systems employing collimators or monochromators have been built following the principles given in the preceding sections, and detailed descriptions of the different pieces of equipment used can be found in the references given in the general bibliography. Our discussion here will be limited to indicating the difficulties generally encountered and the solutions that have been proposed.

3.5.1. SLIT CONSTRUCTION

In systems employing either collimators or monochromators, slits play an essential role in defining the beam and in eliminating the parasitic scattering. These must be very carefully made, and, in the majority of cases, their edges should be independently adjustable to a precision of approximately 0.01 mm. Finally, they should be designed so as to produce the least possible parasitic scattering when they are touched by the direct beam.

Kratky et al. [111] have pointed out the existence of a particular small-angle scattering effect arising from the slits which may be described as follows: when the volume of matter bathed by the X-rays is rather small, as the result of a high absorption coefficient or of the form of the slit edge, a small-angle scattering is created, with the irradiated volume playing the role of the scattering particle.

In order to limit the extent of this scattering, the volume effectively bathed by the direct beam must be increased. This can be done by causing the slit to have sharply angled edges made of a substance of low atomic weight. However, if the slit edges are very thin and not very absorbing, the beam is not sharply defined. The best method is to define the beam precisely with slits formed of steel cylinders with diameters of 2 to 3 mm., for example, and to place a third slit after the first two whose function is to intercept the parasitic scattering. The usable region in the plane of observation is then the part protected by the third slit. This third slit in particular should be very carefully made so that its edges can be independently positioned about 0.01 mm. away from the main beam.

The only important slit in a system that employs a monochromator is the one that stops the parasitic scattering but does not touch the main beam. The nature of the edges of this slit is not important, but their construction should be very precise.

The adjustment of the slits *cannot be made visually* by means of a fluorescent screen, since in general the luminosity of the pattern is insufficient to allow the necessary accuracy to be obtained. The beam form may be recorded photographically, successive exposures determining whether the edges of the slit to be adjusted are touching the beam. If a Geiger-Müller counter is to be used, the power of the direct beam may be measured and each of the edges advanced in turn until the measured power begins to diminish.

3.5.2. STOPPING THE DIRECT BEAM

It is essential to prevent the direct beam from striking the photographic film. It is necessary also that the device used to stop the direct beam does not itself produce scattering. A final requirement of the beam stop is that it should not mask the film in its useful region, that is, outside the zone fogged by parasitic scattering. The construction of a beam stop that will satisfy these conditions is made difficult by the fineness of the direct beam. The most common device is a flat band of metal placed several millimeters from the film. The width of the band is made slightly larger than the beam width, yet slightly smaller than the width of the fogged zone (the quantities a and b, respectively, of §3.2.1), as is shown in Fig. 36a.

It is advantageous to use a rather thin band, so that in the course of the normal exposure the trace of the direct beam will appear on the film with a blackening comparable to that of the scattered radiation. By this means a positioning mark is always available. *If the direct beam is monochromatized* there is a much more important point of interest to the trace of the direct beam, which is that its intensity is proportional to the intensity of the incident beam. This fact allows the measurements of the scattered intensity to be made in absolute units (see §3.5.3).

With a Geiger counter detector, the slit before the counter plays the role of the beam stop. It should therefore be thick enough to stop the radiation completely and constructed in such a way as to prevent any rays scattered by the slit from entering the counter (Fig. 36b).

3.5.3. ABSOLUTE MEASUREMENTS

The difficulty in absolute measurements arises from the great difference in magnitude between the intensity of the direct beam and that of the scattered radiation. Such measurements obviously are worth while only when the direct beam is strictly monochromatic.

If the primary intensity is reduced by an absorber, one essential precaution should be observed. In general a monochromator crystal reflects not only the useful wavelength but also the harmonies of wavelengths $\lambda/2$, $\lambda/3$, etc. If the absorbing band has a much smaller coefficient of absorption for the wavelength $\lambda/2$ than for λ, the trace of the direct beam contains the radiation $\lambda/2$ in a considerable proportion and thus

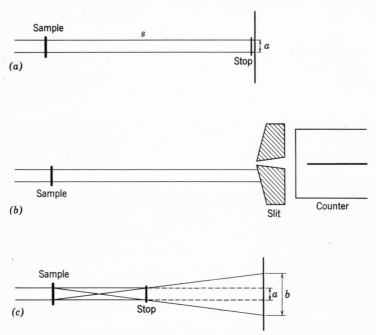

Fig. 36. Beam stops; (a) usual device with photographic detection; (b) arrangement for counter measurements; (c) arrangement proposed by Kratky.

does not give correct information on the intensity of the primary radiation of wavelength λ. This source of error can be avoided by choosing for the absorbing band a substance having a coefficient of absorption for $\lambda/2$ at least as large as that for λ as a result of its K absorption discontinuity. The proportion of $\lambda/2$ in the trace is then equal to or less than its proportion in the direct beam. For example, *copper* or *nickel* serve well for Cu $K\alpha$ radiation and *silver* serves for Mo $K\alpha$. The beam stops in our present system are made from copper sheets of 0.20- to 0.25-mm. thickness. This reduces the Cu $K\alpha$ direct beam in a ratio of 1.2×10^{-4} to 1.2×10^{-5}. The error due to the $\lambda/3$ radiation is not suppressed, but in general this is unimportant since the proportion of $\lambda/3$ in the primary beam is very small.

An inaccuracy in the process of normalization to absolute units that requires the measurement of the total power of the direct beam arises from the fact that the coefficient of absorption is never known to a high enough accuracy to permit a sufficiently sure determination of the weakening of the direct beam.

Kratky and coworkers [111] have developed a very ingenious method for reducing the intensity of the direct beam to a quantity measurable by photographic techniques. They use an X-ray tube powered by unrectified high voltage. The image of the direct beam is received on a photographic plate which is moved in the plane of observation at such a speed that the traces due to successive emissions are resolved. Then by microphotometering one such trace the incident energy can be evaluated for an exposure time of 1/50 second (for 50-cycle current); this is 1/180,000 of the normal exposure time of 1 hour generally necessary for a scattering pattern. In order that the measurement furnish the correct factor, the X-ray tube power must be kept constant. It is not necessary that the displacement of the plate be at constant velocity, so this motion can be provided simply by hand.

Geiger counters cannot measure intensity ratios in excess of 1000 because of counter saturation at high intensities. Therefore, if a counter is to be used for absolute measurements, we must either reduce the intensity of the direct beam by absorption or else measure the scattering from a sample whose scattering power is known (an ideal gas [53] or some light material whose high-angle scattering is essentially free from interatomic interferences).

Ionization chambers were generally discarded when Geiger counters were developed because electrometer measurements were much more difficult than the counting of impulses. These chambers, however, have a big advantage in that precise and direct absolute measurements can be made, for if a sufficiently high collection voltage (800 volts) is used there is no recombination of ions in the chamber, and the charge collected by the central electrode per unit time is proportional to the X-ray flux, even for very intense beams. Laval (1939) and his coworkers (Olmer (1948); Curien (1952)) measured the ionization current by compensating the collected charges with charges induced on the chamber itself (capacity γ) for low beam intensities and with charges induced across a condenser of capacity C for high intensities (Fig. 37). The sensitivity of the chamber is reduced by the ratio of the capacities γ/C in the latter case, and this ratio can be measured very accurately.

3.5.4. VACUUM APPARATUS

It is essential to eliminate air scattering in small-angle scattering experiments, since this scattering can very often be stronger than the intensity scattered by the sample. The best method for eliminating it is to include all the apparatus between the tube and the detector either in an evacuated chamber [48] or, if this is not possible, in an enclosure filled with hydrogen or helium (Fig. 25b) [376], which scatters only weakly. If such a large vacuum chamber cannot be used, a system must be employed in which the air is eliminated in that part of the beam path between the sample and the film or counter.

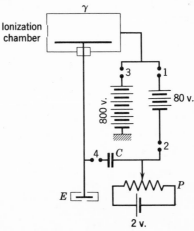

Fig. 37. Ionization chamber circuit for absolute measurements of the scattered intensity. For low intensities switches 1 and 2 are closed and 3 and 4 are open. For high intensities switches 1 and 2 are open and 3 and 4 are closed. The electrometer E is maintained at its zero by adjusting the potentiometer P. If an adjustment of n divisions is required in time t, the ionization current is given by $(n/t)\gamma$ or $(n/t)C$ for the low- and high-intensity settings, respectively (Curien (1952)).

Kratky [111] proposed the following system to simplify the apparatus. The beam stop is moved to a distance s' from the film, as is shown in Fig. 36c, thus suppressing the path of the direct beam in air in the regions closest to the plane of observation. These regions are the most harmful, since the scattered intensity measured at a point varies inversely as the square of the distance from the scatterer.

To find the order of magnitude of the improvement, let us consider a slit collimator for which the fogged region has a width b twice that of the direct beam, a. Here the beam stop can be placed at a point approximately one-third of the distance from the film to the sample without screening a part of the useful region. With the beam stop against the film, the scattering from the air traversed by the direct beam between the sample and the film that is received at a point a distance l from the direct beam trace will be proportional to the integral

$$\int_0^s \frac{dx}{x^2 + l^2}$$

With the arrangement proposed by Kratky, the scattering will be proportional to

$$\int_{s/3}^{s} \frac{dx}{x^2 + l^2}$$

The gain by this arrangement, proportional to s/l, is approximately a factor of 20 at an angle $2\theta = 1°$. The method is thus simple and efficient for very small angles.

REFERENCES FOR CHAPTER 3

Arndt, U. W., Coates, W. A., and Riley, D. P.   (1953), *Proc. Phys. Soc. (London)*, *66*, 1009.

Cauchois, Y., Tiedema, T. J., and Burgers, W. G.   (1950), *Acta Cryst.*, *3*, 372.

Compton, A. H., and Allison, S. K.   (1935), *X-Rays in Theory and Experiment*, Macmillan, New York.

Curien, H.   (1952), *Bull. soc. franç. minéral. et crist.*, *75*, 197.

DuMond, J. W. M.   (1947), *Rev. Sci. Instr.*, *18*, 617.

Evans, R. C., Hirsch, P. B., and Kellar, J. N.   (1948), *Acta Cryst.*, *1*, 124.

Fankuchen, I.   (1937), *Nature*, *139*, 193.

Guinier, A.   (1946), *Compt. rend.*, *223*, 161.

Guinier, A.   (1952) (Ed., W. Shockley), *Imperfections in Nearly Perfect Crystals*, Wiley, New York, p. 402.

Johann, H. H.   (1931), *Z. Physik*, *69*, 185.

Johansson, T.   (1933), *Z. Physik*, *83*, 507.

Kirkpatrick, P.   (1939), *Rev. Sci. Instr.*, *10*, 186.

Laval, J.   (1939), *Bull. soc. franç. minéral. et crist.*, *62*, 137.

Lipson, H., Nelson, J. B., and Riley, D. P.   (1945), *J. Sci. Instr.*, *22*, 184.

Olmer, P.   (1948), *Bull. soc. franç. minéral. et crist.*, *71*, 144.

Schmidt, P., Kaesberg, P., and Beeman, W. W.   (1954) *Biochim. et Biophys. Acta*, *14*, 1.

Wilsdorf, H.   (1948), *Naturwiss.*, *35*, 313.

4. METHODS OF INTERPRETATION OF EXPERIMENTAL RESULTS

In Chapter 2 the small-angle scattering effects were calculated for scattering bodies of given structure. Then in Chapter 3 we reviewed the experimental methods and equipment that are actually employed. Now we can approach the real problem, which is the determination of the structure of the scatterer from the patterns of the small-angle scattering by means of the theories developed in Chapter 2. We shall examine successively the different cases that were considered in that chapter: widely separated identical particles, closer-packed identical particles, groups of particles of different sizes, etc. Then, from what is known of any scattering body, we can determine in advance of an investigation the particular case out of those enumerated into which it must fall. We shall also give the criteria of validity of the hypotheses which are adopted.

4.1. IDENTICAL PARTICLES

Let us begin with the simple case of widely separated particles.

4.1.1. WIDELY SEPARATED, IDENTICAL PARTICLES
4.1.1.1. Equal Probability of All Orientations

We have seen (equation 2.55) that the scattered intensity is given by $\overline{F^2(h)}$, apart from a multiplicative constant. Consequently, we can write

$$\log \overline{I(h)} = \log \overline{F^2(h)} + \text{constant} \tag{1}$$

The approximate law of Guinier (equation 2.39)

$$\overline{F^2(h)} = \overline{F^2(0)}e^{-\frac{h^2 R_0^2}{3}} \tag{2}$$

can be written as

$$\log_{10} \overline{F^2(h)} = -\frac{h^2 R_0^2}{3} \log_{10} e + \text{constant} \tag{3}$$

Therefore

$$\log_{10} \overline{I(h)} = -\frac{h^2 R_0^2}{3} \log_{10} e + \text{constant} \tag{4}$$

The method of analysis is thus simple; the curve of $\log \overline{I(h)}$ vs. h^2 (hereafter denoted by $\log \overline{I(h^2)}$) is plotted, and from its slope the radius of gyration is determined. In the experimental systems generally used the parameter which is most easily obtained directly is the tangent of the scattering angle 2θ ($\tan 2\theta = x/s$, where x represents the distance from the trace of the direct beam to the point on the film being considered, and s is the sample-to-film distance). In the small-angle region we are considering, an angle, its sine, and its tangent can be interchanged without error. Therefore

$$h = 4\pi \frac{\sin \theta}{\lambda} \cong \frac{2\pi}{\lambda} \tan 2\theta$$

and

$$\log_{10} \overline{I(h)} = -(\tan 2\theta)^2 \frac{4\pi^2}{3\lambda^2} R_0^2 \log_{10} e + \text{constant} \tag{5}$$

The slope, $-p$, of the representative curve of $\log I(h)$ as a function of $(\tan 2\theta)^2$ is thus equal to $-(4\pi^2/3\lambda^2)R_0^2 \log_{10} e$. Therefore

$$R_0 = \frac{1}{2\pi} \sqrt{\frac{3}{\log_{10} e}} \, \lambda \sqrt{p} \tag{6}$$

For example, with Cu $K\alpha$ radiation ($\lambda = 1.540$ A)

$$R_0 = 0.645\sqrt{p} \quad \text{(Angstroms)} \tag{7}$$

If, instead of using the approximate law of Guinier, we use the exact formula for the structure factor,

$$\overline{F^2(h)} = \overline{F^2(0)} \left[1 - \frac{h^2 R_0^2}{3} + \alpha h^4 + \cdots \right] \tag{8}$$

we find

$$\log_{10} \overline{I(h)} = - \frac{h^2 R_0^2}{3} \log_{10} e + \beta h^4 + \cdots + \text{constant} \tag{9}$$

From this we can see that, rigorously speaking, *the slope p that should be used in equation 6 is not the average slope of the curve of $\log I(h^2)$ but rather the value of the slope at the origin*, that is, the slope of the curve at $h = 0$.

We know (cf. Chapter 3) that measurements of the scattered intensity cannot be accurately made below an angle θ' which is very small but not zero (this corresponds to the value h' for the parameter h). Therefore an experiment cannot give directly the slope that is required. However, the slope at the origin is the limiting value of the slopes for different values of h^2 as h^2 tends to zero, so that, if measurements are made of the slope $-p(h^2)$ of the curve $\log I(h^2)$ at several points, the limiting value, $-p(0)$, can be determined by means of an auxiliary graph. This extrapolation is very precise if the experimental curve shows only a small curvature over a relatively large part of the small-angle region.

For a particle of given form and radius of gyration R_0 there is a limiting value, $h''R_0$, of the product hR_0 beyond which it is evident that the approximate law of Guinier is no longer valid.   This is illustrated by the graphs of $\log I(h^2R_0{}^2)$ for a sphere (Fig. 38) and for a homogeneous, one-dimensional rod (Fig. 39), in which the dotted lines represent the extrapolations of the slope at the origin.   For the spherical particle the

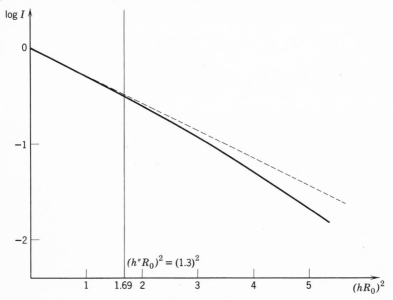

Fig. 38.   Log I vs. $(hR_0)^2$ for spherical particles.

Guinier formula is a very good approximation at small angles, remaining valid up to the limit, $h''R_0 = 1.3$.   For the rod the Guinier formula is not as good an approximation.   It is precisely for particles of this rod-like shape that the difference between the approximate law and the exact expression is greatest; here $h''R_0$ is only of the order of 0.7.   If we assume that the slope of the curve at h' will correctly determine the radius of gyration if $h' \leq h''/2$, we can conclude that an experimental system characterized by a lower angular limit, h', will be capable of correctly measuring the radius of gyration of spherical particles up to an upper limiting radius of $0.65/h'$ A, whereas for rod-like particles the limiting radius will be only $0.35/h'$ A.   Actually it is possible to extend this limit somewhat.   Instead of simply tracing the curve of $\log I(h^2)$, we can plot the curve of the slope, $-p(h^2)$, and extrapolate to the origin, $h^2 = 0$. This method of extrapolation is illustrated in Fig. 40 for the unfavorable case of a homogeneous one-dimensional rod in a system such that $h'R_0 = 1.04$.   The value of $-p(0)$ obtained by extrapolation, 0.0492, is very

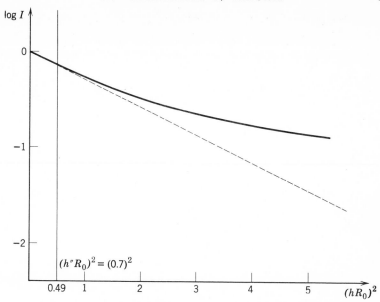

Fig. 39.   Log I vs. $(hR_0)^2$ for homogeneous one-dimensional rods.

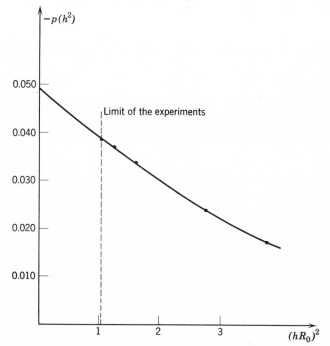

Fig. 40.   Graph of the slope $-p(h^2)$ of log $I(h^2)$ as a function of $(hR_0)^2$.
The slope $-p(0)$ is found by extrapolation.

nearly the correct value, 0.0483, even though the value of $h'R_0$ is considerably *larger* than $h''R_0 = 0.7$.

Within the limits just defined, it is always easy to determine the radius of gyration of the particles being examined. *The radius of gyration is the only precise parameter which can be determined by small-angle scattering experiments without invoking supplementary hypotheses.* It is evident that this one parameter does not entirely define the particle. The curves of $\log I(h^2)$ for particles having the same radius of gyration but different forms will have the same slope at the origin and will coincide so long as $h < h''$, but beyond this point they will diverge. The use of the entire curve in the determination of the form of the particle is very difficult in practice, since rather large changes in the form of the particles produce only small effects on the shape of the tail of the scattering curves. Theoretically, we could trace *a priori* a family of curves of $\log I$ as a function of $\log h$ for different forms of the particles by means of the equations established in §2.1, and then, neglecting simple translations, determine which of the different curves most closely corresponds to the experimental curve as plotted in the same coordinates.

Let us, however, cite a rather remarkable exception. The experimental curve for *very homogeneous* spherical particles can be made to coincide with the theoretical curve $\Phi^2(hR)$ (see equation 2.31) over a very large region; in fact, the successive maxima predicted by theory have been experimentally demonstrated ([186], [25], [76'''']) (Fig. 41). This last result proved that the form of the particles was spherical and allowed the determination of the radius of the particle. This radius agreed well with that calculated from only the very low-angle part of the curve by means of equation 6.

In the general case, once the radius of gyration is determined, further details about the form of the particle can be obtained either by employing auxiliary information or else by making certain hypotheses. For example, if the volume and the general form of the particle are known, its dimensions can be calculated.

As a particular example, let us consider the study of horse hemoglobin given by Fournet [48]. The particles, which can be assumed to be molecules, were found to have a radius of gyration equal to 23 A. The molecular weight of this substance is 66,700, and the density of its solution in water is 1.33 (Perutz (1946)). This auxiliary information determined the volume of each molecule as 83,400 A^3.

If we assume that the molecule has the form of a right cylinder of radius R and height $2H$, two relations between R and H can be determined: the volume of the molecule is $V = 2\pi R^2 H = 83,400$ A^3, and the square of the radius of gyration is $R^{\,2} = (R^2/2) + (H^2/3) = (23)^2$.

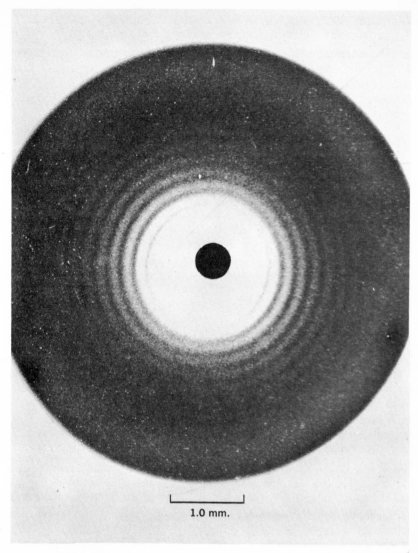

1.0 mm.

Fig. 41. Scattering pattern of uniform spherical particles (Dow Latex) obtained with a point-focusing monochromator (Fig. 32). The first visible ring is the fifth maximum (Fig. 6); on the original film, the rings are visible up to the seventeenth maximum. Sample-to-film distance: 66 cm. Cu $K\alpha$ radiation. Exposure time: 129 hours. (Danielson, Shenfil, and DuMond [25].)

These relations can be expressed as two curves in the R-H plane (Fig. 42) whose intersections define the dimensions of the only possible cylinders which can fit all our information. Figure 42 shows that there are two possibilities: (a) $2R = 42$ A, $2H = 120$ A; (b) $2R = 60$ A, $2H = 30$ A. This last size is very close to that proposed by Perutz [407], which was

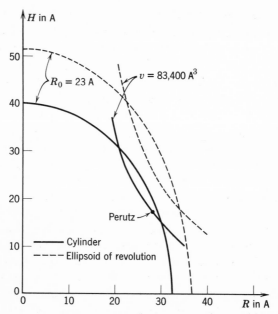

Fig. 42. A graphical approach in the study of the form of particles. The full line curves correspond to cylinders of radius R and height $2H$ and the dotted curves to ellipsoids of axes $2R$, $2R$, $2H$. This figure shows the information that can be determined from a knowledge of the radius of gyration and the volume of a particle.

$2R = 57$ A, $2H = 34$ A. Actually these dimensions will not be sharply defined but will rather be described as zones of possibilities with widths dependent upon the errors in the molecular weight and the radius of gyration.

Similarly, if we assume that the molecule has the form of an ellipsoid of revolution, two relations can be defined between the half axes, R and H. The curves of these relations will again lead to two zones of possibilities centered on the intersections of the curves (see Fig. 42). This graphical method of solution is of interest because by its use we can see directly the consequences of a modification of the data on the form and dimensions of the particle.

We have just seen that it is advantageous to know the volume of the particle in order to obtain more detailed information from its radius of gyration.   It is possible to determine this volume if the intensity measurements are made in absolute units.   We know that the zero-angle scattered intensity, $I(0)$, obtained by an extrapolation of the curve of $\log I(h^2)$, is given as

$$I(0) = I_e(0)\overline{N}n^2 \tag{10}$$

This expression signifies that $I(0)$, expressed in electron units, is equal to the product of the average number of particles $\overline{N}$ and the square of the number of electrons in each particle, n^2.   The total number of electrons in the scattering body, $\overline{N}n$, can be determined from a knowledge of the mass of the sample that is active in scattering and the chemical composition of the scatterer.   Therefore the measurement of $I(0)$ in electron units enables us to determine the number of electrons in each particle, n $= \overline{N}n^2/\overline{N}n$, and from this we can deduce not only the mass of each particle but also its volume, if its density is known.   The application of this method requires several precautions:

(a) We have assumed that there is negligible absorption of the X-rays in the sample, and, if this condition is not satisfied, the necessary correction must be made.

(b) In the case of solutions of large particles, the number of electrons per particle, n, to be considered is, to a first approximation, the difference between the number of electrons effectively contained in a particle and the number of electrons contained in the same volume of the solvent.

Results obtained with the methods described in this section (§4.1.1.1) will be correct only if the hypotheses we have imposed are satisfied. The relative interparticle distances can in general be checked easily if the density of the sample and the density of matter in the particle are known. It is more difficult to be sure of the uniformity of the particles.   A definite criterion cannot be found in the X-ray data alone.   Nevertheless it can be said that, if the curve of $\log I(h^2)$ maintains its linearity over a large part of the small-angle region, it is probable that there is not a very great variation in the sizes of the particles.   More precisely, such a linearity means that the sample does not contain a notable proportion of particles having a radius of gyration *larger* than that determined from the linear part of the curve, for the presence of such particles produces a curvature in the curve at very small angles; on the other hand, very *small* particles can be present.   A bending of the curve of $\log I(h^2)$ with increasing angle cannot be interpreted unambiguously, for this may be due either to the particular shape of supposedly identical particles or to the presence of smaller particles mixed in with those larger ones which primarily determine the initial linear part of the curve (see, for example, p. 151).

4.1.1.2. Identical Particles with a Definite Orientation

Any particle of this system can be derived from any other one by means of a translation. The characteristic of the resulting pattern is that *there is no longer circular symmetry* around the incident beam. In the general case it is therefore necessary to use a beam of very small height, since the methods of correction for beam height effects described in §3.4.2 are valid only if the intensity of scattered radiation depends solely on the scattering angle, 2θ.

Let us assume, then, that the beam cross section is as nearly like a point as possible. The curves of scattered intensity as a function of angle are determined for different azimuths about s_0 (Fig. 3, p. 13). From §2.1.5 (equation 2.44), the approximate exponential function describing the intensity scattered for an orientation defined by the vector l_0 is

$$I(\mathbf{h}) = n^2 \overline{N} e^{-h^2 D^2 (l_0)} \tag{11}$$

Measurements for each orientation of l_0 then lead to the determination of an average inertial distance of the particle with respect to the plane $\Pi(l_0)$ that is perpendicular to l_0 and passes through the center of gravity of the particle. Let us point out that this equation differs from the approximate law of Guinier in that there is no coefficient, $1/3$, in the exponent.

The determination of inertial distances for different orientations gives a rather precise idea of the form of the particle. *This is the principal advantage of the study of oriented particles* as compared to the study of particles without definite orientation.

It is obviously advantageous to direct the incident beam along one of the principal axes of the particle. Let us take as an example an ellipsoid of revolution of axes a, a, and va. We shall direct the incident X-ray beam normal to the unequal axis. The small-angle scattering spot will then have the form of an ellipse. The variation of intensity with angle is (equation 2.44) $e^{-a^2 v^2 h^2/5}$ in the direction parallel to the unequal axis, and $e^{-a^2 h^2/5}$ in the perpendicular direction. Thus two experimental measurements have determined the parameters a and v which define the ellipsoid.

It can be said quite generally, by means of equation 2.44, that the small-angle scattering spot will be elongated in the direction of the minimum dimension of the particle. An ellipsoid or an elongated rod gives a spot elongated in the direction perpendicular to the long axis. A plate-like particle gives a spot elongated in the direction perpendicular to the plane of the platelet. Thus the general aspect alone of the pattern furnishes qualitative information about the general form and orientations of the particles.

If the particles are so elongated that one of their dimensions exceeds the upper limit that can be measured by the equipment, the scattering spot appears as a narrow streak whose width is a function only of the dimensions of the incident beam, and no quantitative information about this long particle dimension can be obtained from the pattern. In this case, in studying the distribution of intensity along the streak an incident beam of large height may equally well be used.

4.1.2. DENSE GROUPS OF IDENTICAL PARTICLES
4.1.2.1. Analysis of the Scattering Curve

It has been recognized since the first studies of small-angle scattering that quite often the particles cannot be considered as being widely separated. This is true when the graph of the intensity has such a form that it is evident that the exponential law is no longer a valid approximation. If the interparticle interferences cannot be neglected, the applicability of the results of the methods we have previously described must certainly be doubted.

This is the reason why it is very important to study the influence of the drawing together of particles on the scattering. In §2.2 we discussed the solutions that had been given for this difficult problem, but no solution, even approximate, has been advanced which has not required several restrictive hypotheses. These hypotheses were that the particles are identical and either that they are spherically symmetric or that their orientations are in no way dependent on the separation of their centers.

Equation 2.68, the fundamental relation for the scattering by spherically symmetrical particles (see §2.2.3.2), gives the observed intensity $I(h)$ as

$$I(h) = I_e(h)\bar{N}F^2(h)\,\frac{v_1}{v_1 - (2\pi)^{3/2}\,\epsilon\beta(h)} \qquad (2.68)$$

where v_1, the volume offered to each particle, is equal to V_0/N_0. The constant ϵ can be taken as unity (see p. 44). The interparticle interferences which modify the curve of $F^2(h)$ are taken into account in the function $\beta(h)$. The first task in the interpretation of the experimental curves is to obtain the function $F^2(h)$ from the measured function $I(h)$, which takes us back to the problem we have just discussed. If the concentration of the particles is not too high, the function $\beta(h)$ only slightly modifies the curve of $F^2(h)$. We can again trace the usual curve of $\log I(h^2)$ and verify that it still has a linear portion at small angles. By applying equation 6 to this linear part we can determine an apparent radius of gyration, R_{0A}; this is not the true radius of gyration, R_0, which would be found from the curve of $\log F^2(h)$ as a function of h^2. A simple mathematical manipulation of equation 2.68 leads to the following relation (Fournet [48]):

$$R_{0A}{}^2 = R_0{}^2 - \frac{3}{2}\frac{\beta''(0)}{v_1(2\pi)^{-3/2} - \beta(0)} \qquad (12)$$

R_{0A} obviously approaches R_0 as the average volume v_1 increases, that is, as the concentration decreases. Furthermore, other experimental results (the decrease of the intensity $I(0)$ with increasing concentration),

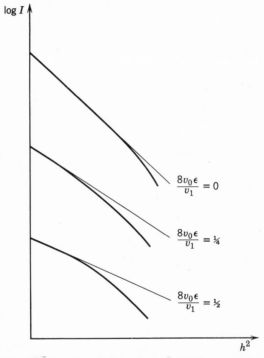

Fig. 43. Log I vs. h^2 for spherical particles packed together in increasing concentrations.

together with certain theoretical considerations (the theory of lyophobic colloids given by Verwey and Overbeck (1945)), have shown that, if equations 2.67 and 2.68, deduced from the theory of Born and Green, are to be used, it is necessary to adopt a function, $\beta(h)$, which is negative for small values of h. Now, when $|\beta(h)|$ is a maximum at $h = 0$, $\beta''(0)$ is of the opposite sign to that of $\beta(0)$, so that in our case $\beta''(0)$ must be positive. Therefore R_{0A} is less than R_0 and becomes even smaller, the greater the concentration of particles.

As an illustration of this, let us consider the model studied earlier

(§2.2.3.4, equation 2.75), which is composed of a group of hard spheres showing no interactions other than impenetrability. We have reproduced in Fig. 43 the curves of log $I(h^2)$ for three values of the ratio $(8v_0\epsilon/v_1)$: 0.00, 0.25, and 0.50. These curves verify not only that the slope at the origin varies with concentration in the manner we have indicated but also that the curves depart more and more from linearity as the concentration increases.

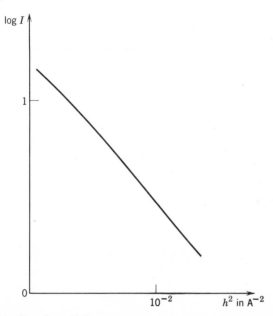

Fig. 44. Log I vs. h^2 for a 9.8 per cent solution of horse hemoglobin.

This is just the aspect Fournet has pointed out on some real experimental curves. The curve of log $I(h^2)$ (Fig. 44) is a straight line for very small concentrations (5 and 10 per cent), whereas for higher concentrations the curves, after an initial straight-line portion at small values of h, drop below the extrapolated straight line.

Summarizing the foregoing discussion, the method to employ to be sure of avoiding all error is the following: After having determined a radius of gyration from particles in a solution, repeat the experiment with a more dilute solution and compare the two results. If, within the limits of experimental error, the results are the same, the measurement is correct. If they are different, then by making several measurements on samples of decreasing concentration, the radius of gyration can be determined by an extrapolation to zero concentration.

If the concentration is high, the curve of $F^2(h)$ is so deformed that it is no longer useful to try to employ the log $I(h^2)$ representation. Let us now show how it is possible to obtain the curve corresponding to an infinitely dilute solution, $F^2(h)$, by means of the curves of $I(h)$ for several different concentrations, even though these concentrations are all rather high. In addition, the function $\beta(h)$ will also be determined.

Let x be the weight percentage of particles in the solution; $d(x)$, the density of the solution at x per cent concentration; and m, the mass of one particle. The volume per particle, $v_1(x)$, is then

$$v_1(x) = \frac{1}{\dfrac{x}{100}\dfrac{d(x)}{m}} = \frac{100\,m}{xd(x)} \tag{13}$$

Equation 2.68 shows that there will be certain points, defined by $\beta(h) = 0$, which will be common to all curves of the function

$$\frac{I(h, v_1)}{NI_e(h)} = f(x, h) \tag{14}$$

It is difficult in general to determine accurately the absolute value of $I(h)$, so that the functions $f(x, h)$ will probably be known only to within some multiplicative constant. In such a circumstance we can select a priori some point to be the common point and then try to verify whether the normalized curves reproduce the different characteristics of the function

$$f(x, h) = F^2(h) \frac{v_1(x)}{v_1(x) - (2\pi)^{3/2}\beta(h)} \tag{15}$$

Let us give as an example the scattering curves for human hemoglobin (Fournet [48]) (Fig. 45) which have been normalized to a common point at a scattering angle of 2.4×10^{-2} radian. The behavior of the functions is in good agreement with the predictions that can be made from equation 2.68: as the concentration increases, the intensity curves become more uneven; at a certain concentration (in this case, 32 per cent) a maximum appears, and this maximum becomes more accentuated and shifts to larger angles as the concentration further increases.

Let us emphasize that, if the experiments are not capable of accurately evaluating the ratio of the intensities scattered by solutions of different concentrations, it is still possible in general to determine whether the experimental facts can be interpreted by means of equation 2.68. A common point, chosen a priori, is imposed on the several curves. An examination of these normalized curves then shows whether or not the curve corresponding to a concentration of x per cent is always contained between the curves for $x + dx$ per cent and $x - dx$ per cent as is predicted by the theory. By successive approximations we can see whether it is possible to find a common point, defined by an angle h_1, for which these conditions will be satisfied by all the experimental curves.

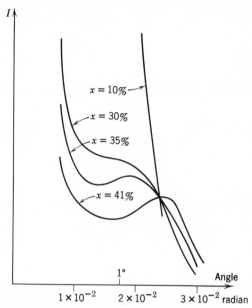

Fig. 45. Experimental scattering curves of solutions of human hemoglobin of different concentrations.

When this common point can be determined, each normalized curve represents a curve of the function $f(x, h)$, apart from an arbitrary constant the same for each curve; this function is

$$f(x, h) = \frac{F^2(h)}{1 - (2\pi)^{3/2} \epsilon\beta(h)[v_1(x)]^{-1}} \tag{15a}$$

Then by use of equation 13, which describes the dependence of the mean volume, $v_1(x)$, on the concentration, x, we find

$$\frac{1}{f(x, h)} = \frac{1 - (2\pi)^{3/2} \epsilon\beta(h)x\, d(x)10^{-2}m^{-1}}{F^2(h)} = \frac{1 - kx\, d(x)\beta(h)}{F^2(h)} \tag{16}$$

For each value of h, the curve of $f^{-1}(x, h)$ as a function of x starts from a value of $1/F^2(h)$ at $x = 0$ and increases in an approximately linear manner. The slope of this curve as a function of x is

$$-k\beta(h)F^{-2}(h)\{d(x) + xd'(x)\} \tag{17}$$

and, since $d(x)$ is in general a function which increases with x, the slope then increases in absolute value as x increases.

If the curves of this function are taken from the curves of Fig. 45, in which $h_1 \cong 2.4 \times 10^{-2}$ radian, the behavior we have predicted will be found.

If the common point of the curves represented in Fig. 45 had been taken as an angle smaller than 2.4×10^{-2} radian (2.2×10^{-2} radian, for example), the general appearance of the curves of $f(x, h)$ would still be satisfying, though less so, but the same cannot be said for the curves of $f^{-1}(x, h)$. For a value of h equal to 1.5×10^{-2}, the extrapolation of the curve of $f^{-1}(x, h)$ gives a negative value for this function at the origin, $x = 0$, which is physically impossible. This example shows that the general appearance of the family of curves of $f(x, h)$ as a function of h is less sensitive than that of the curves of $f^{-1}(x, h)$ as a function of x in determining whether the common point has been well chosen.

The representation of $f^{-1}(x, h)$ as a function of x is of further interest, in that *the function $F^2(h)$ is determined by the reciprocal of the ordinate at $x = 0$.* We must admit that experimentally the plots of these curves will not be very meaningful unless the experimental results are known to a high degree of precision. This requires that a very careful study be made of a large number of solutions. Naturally, accurate measurements, such as are possible with Geiger-Müller counter detectors, are indispensable.

The function $\beta(h)$ can also be determined from the same curves by use of equation 16. Now $\beta(h)$ is related to $\Phi(r)$ by the equation

$$h\beta(h) = \frac{1}{\sqrt{2\pi}} \int_{-\infty}^{\infty} r \left\{ e^{-\frac{\Phi(r)}{kT}} - 1 \right\} \sin hr \, dr$$

Therefore theoretically we can obtain the potential energy, $\Phi(r)$, of the interaction between particles. *Small-angle scattering experiments are thus capable of giving not only the size of the particles but also the law of their interaction.* This method, which is complex, to be sure, but legitimate, as is shown by the calculations of Chapter 2, has not yet been exploited as thoroughly as it should have been.

So far we have considered only spherically symmetrical particles. It is not impossible to treat the case of particles of arbitrary shape if we assume that their relative orientations are independent of their spatial distribution. The formulas are very complex, and the indispensable hypothesis is quite hard to justify in numerous cases. In addition, there are only a very few applications of such a treatment. Therefore it will not be developed here.

4.1.2.2. Interpretation of a Maximum in a Scattering Curve

Disregarding these complex but accurate methods, many authors have been content to use a more simple interpretation of the results of experiments made on dense systems of particles, taking account only of the position of the maximum or bump on the scattering curve. This procedure should be closely examined, since evidently it is not established on a rigorous basis. It is only a rough approximation from which erroneous conclusions can be drawn if the procedure is given more worth than it actually deserves.

In order to simplify the notation in this section we shall consider only spherically symmetrical particles, but it is easy to extend the discussion to all cases for which there is complete independence between the orientations of the arbitrarily shaped particles and the distances between their centers. For spherically symmetrical particles $\overline{F^2(h)}$ and $\overline{F(h)}^2$ are identical, and the scattered intensity can be written in the form

$$I(h) = I_e(h)\overline{N}F^2(h)a(h) \tag{18}$$

The product $\overline{N}a(h)$ is equal to the intensity in electron units which would be scattered by $\overline{N}$ electrons, each positioned at the center of one of the $\overline{N}$ irradiated particles. The function $a(h)$ depends markedly on the concentration of the particles, so we shall denote the function by $a(h, c)$ or $a(h, v_1)$. For example, the function $a(h, v_1)$ for the system described by equation 2.68 is

$$a(h, v_1) = \frac{v_1}{v_1 - (2\pi)^{3/2} \, \epsilon\beta(h)} \tag{19}$$

The angular positions of the maxima of the function $a(h)$ will be denoted by $h_1, h_2, \cdots h_i$ (or $\theta_1, \theta_2, \cdots \theta_i$), and those for the function $I(h)$ by $h_M, h_N, \cdots$ (or $\theta_M, \theta_N, \cdots$).

We shall now give the different possible interpretations.

4.1.2.2.1. Interpretation in Terms of an Average Distance

The presence of a maximum or even a singularity such as a bump in the scattering curve has often been interpreted as showing the existence of an "average distance frequently realized between neighboring particles."

First let us observe that it is *impossible* to define the concept of neighboring particles in a substance which has *no long-range order*, except in the very particular case of a linear model. This concept of an "average distance," which seems simple and natural and which has so often been employed, is in reality never defined in a precise manner.

Let us now look at the arguments which have been advanced by those who employ this idea (for example, Mattoon, Stearns, and Harkins [366]). The formula that is most often cited is that due to Ehrenfest (1915):

$$2\bar{d} \sin \theta_M = 1.23\lambda \tag{20}$$

Actually this formula describes the scattering angle $2\theta_M$, for the maximum in the intensity scattered by a group of widely separated particles, when each particle, having the form of a dumbbell composed of two *points* separated by a distance $\bar{d}$, takes all possible orientations with equal probability.[1] *The Ehrenfest relation therefore cannot be used to interpret*

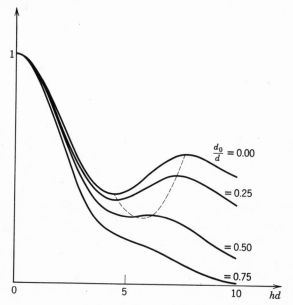

Fig. 46.   A graph of $\dfrac{1}{2}\left(1 + \dfrac{\sin hd}{hd}\right)\Phi^2\left(\dfrac{hd_0}{2}\right)$ for various ratios of d_0/d.

The maximum and minimum of the curve, shown joined by the dotted line, disappear for $d_0/d > 0.52$.

the structure of any fluid. In order to give every possible opportunity to those who would employ this challenged formula, let us make the assumption—which cannot be even a rough first approximation—that the intensity scattered by a fluid composed of spheres of diameter d_0 is proportional to the intensity scattered by a pair of these spheres separated by the distance $\bar{d}$, and then calculate this intensity. This is found to be

$$I(h) = \text{constant}\left(1 + \frac{\sin h\bar{d}}{h\bar{d}}\right)\Phi^2\left(\frac{hd_0}{2}\right) \tag{21}$$

In Fig. 46 we have given the normalized curves of this function for

[1] The intensity scattered by such a system is proportional to $\left(1 + \dfrac{\sin h\bar{d}}{h\bar{d}}\right)$ (Fig. 46), the position of the first maximum being given by equation 20.

different values of the ratio $d_0/\bar{d}$, $\bar{d}$ being kept constant. The curve for $d_0 = 0$ corresponds to the case described by the Ehrenfest relation. As the ratio $d_0/\bar{d}$ increases, there is a limiting value beyond which the intensity $I(h)$ becomes a function that decreases continuously with increasing angle. Now experiments have shown that the observation of a maximum is more probable, the higher the concentration of matter, which for our model means a greater ratio of $d_0/\bar{d}$. But it is precisely for these conditions that equation 21 that supposedly relates the position of a *maximum* to an average distance will not allow a maximum to appear. This internal contradiction thus gives a second reason for abandoning this usage of the Ehrenfest equation.

It is still possible to introduce an average distance into the interpretation of the presence of a maximum by considering a model in which the centers of the particles are arranged on a more or less distorted face-centered cubic lattice. In such a face-centered cubic *paracrystal*, as it has been called by Hosemann, each molecule is surrounded by 12 neighbors which are clearly closer than all other molecules, but the distance from the origin molecule to these 12 neighbors varies from one to the next, fluctuating about a mean distance $\bar{d}$. In this model it is possible to define a mean distance of approach which naturally will be larger than the diameter of a molecule. The cell edge of a cubic paracrystal is equal to $\bar{d}\sqrt{2}$. The scattering angle $2\theta_1$ for the first maximum of the function $a(h)$, that due to (111) planes, is then determined by Bragg's law to be

$$\lambda = 2d_{111} \sin \theta_1 = \frac{2\bar{d}\sqrt{2}}{\sqrt{3}} \sin \theta_1$$

or

$$2\bar{d} \sin \theta_1 = \sqrt{\frac{3}{2}}\, \lambda = 1.22\lambda \qquad (22a)$$

Hosemann has shown that the function $a(h)$ shows maxima not only at the angle θ_1 but also at angles θ_2, θ_3, etc., corresponding to planes in the average lattice of higher indices. The angles for these maxima are similarly defined:

$$2\bar{d} \sin \theta_2 = \sqrt{2}\lambda = 1.41\lambda \qquad (22b)$$

$$2\bar{d} \sin \theta_3 = 2\lambda \quad = 2.00\lambda \qquad (22c)$$

etc. However, these maxima are broader and weaker, the higher the corresponding index and the more distorted the lattice, so that it is possible that only the first two or three can be observed.

This model imposes a certain relation between $\sin \theta_1$ and the volume concentration, c (the ratio of the volume of the particles to the total volume of the system). The maximum value of this volume concentration for spherical particles is 0.74. We can thus write that

$$c/0.74 = (d_0/\bar{d})^3 \qquad (23)$$

where d_0 is the diameter of the sphere. This relation can be transformed to the following:

$$d_0 = \bar{d}c^{1/3}(0.74)^{-1/3}$$

Equation 22a then can take the form

$$\frac{1.22\lambda}{2 \sin \theta_1} c^{1/3}(0.74)^{-1/3} = \frac{1.35\lambda}{2 \sin \theta_1} c^{1/3} = d_0 = \text{constant} \qquad (24)$$

We see thus that the $\sin \theta_i$ are proportional to $c^{1/3}$.

This paracrystalline model leads to the prediction of *several marked maxima* in the function $a(h)$. The value of $\sin \theta_i$ for each maximum varies in proportion to the one-third power of the volume concentration.

Patterns that agree with *all* these results have been only rarely observed (a good application of this model is that of Bernal and Fankuchen [402]), but nevertheless a method of interpretation based on this model has often been employed where the experiment did not show definitely that the paracrystalline model was a good approximation. For example, this method was applied by Riley and Oster [371] to the results for solutions of human hemoglobin obtained by Riley and Herbert [486]. These scattering curves showed only one slightly marked maximum (two maxima were observed at the highest concentration only). Since the maxima of $I(h)$ were very broad, a similar breadth must exist for the maxima of the function $a(h)$. We have already explained in §2.2.3.4 that in a circumstance like this one the intervention of the factor $F^2(h)$ will make the positions θ_M of the maxima of $I(h)$ *very different* from the positions θ_i of the maxima of $a(h)$ (cf. Fig. 13). Therefore conclusions that are valid for the latter maxima, as drawn from equations 22 and 24, cannot be applied to the intensity maxima. The $c^{1/3}$ dependence has almost never been validly observed (Philippoff [369]). Riley and Oster have observed that the position of the first maximum obeys a relation of the form

$$\sin \theta_M = k_M c^{1/3} \qquad (25)$$

If one is to satisfy both equation 25 and the relation

$$\sin \theta_1 = k_1 c^{1/3} \qquad (26)$$

very special conditions must be imposed on the functions $F^2(h)$ and $a(h)$, so we can say that in general equation 26 cannot be satisfied if the experimental results obey equation 25. An entirely different interpretation of equation 26 will be given in §4.1.2.2.4.

Finally, let us point out that the proposed model requires that, when the concentration changes, the same type of short-range order continues to exist while the interparticle distance varies. This would probably require that the interaction potential change with dilution, a mechanism which does not seem very probable.

We have just discussed the attempts at interpretation of real solutions, isotropic in three dimensions, in terms of an average distance. We could give an analogous discussion for cylindrically symmetrical systems. The values of $\sin \theta_i$ would then vary as $c^{1/2}$ if a quasi-crystalline model were adopted. This is the experimental relation that was observed by Bernal and Fankuchen [402].

4.1.2.2.2. Interpretation in Terms of an Average Volume

In order to escape the criticisms based on the impossibility of defining an average distance, we can try to interpret the presence of a maximum in the scattering curve in terms of the existence of a certain average volume v_1 defined as the ratio of the total volume offered to the particles, V_0, to the number of particles, N_0. Equations 2.67 and 2.68 show that this is not possible; $\beta(h)$ plays just as essential a role as does v_1, for it is the ratio of $\beta(h)$ to v_1 which appears. For example, let us consider two identical enclosures of volume V_0, one containing N_0 argon atoms and the other containing N_0 non-interacting hard spheres, whose volumes can be chosen equal to those of the argon atoms. These two groups of particles characterized by the same average volume v_1 give very different scattering patterns, as is shown by a comparison of their functions $\beta(h)$ given in Fig. 19. By generalizing this remark we can say:

1. Although the average volume per particle may be the same in several groups of particles, nevertheless the statistical arrangement of the particles may be quite different in the different groups, since this depends on the function $\Phi(r)$.

2. The scattering of X-rays, through the intermediary of the function $P(r)$, is very sensitive to these differences.

An example of this can be found by a comparison of the behavior of a solution of tobacco virus, which demonstrates the presence of order for very small values of the ratio v_0/v_1 (Bernal and Fankuchen [402]), with the behavior of an ordinary solution of a protein (hemoglobin, for example). Thus the interpretations that depend on the intervention of the volume v_1 cannot be justified.

4.1.2.2.3. Interpretation by Means of an Interparticle Interference Function

Oster and Riley [128] have proposed to get information from the scattering curves of solutions of proteins by means of a function, $a(h)$, obtained from the experimental study of liquid mercury. Equations 2.67 and 2.68 show that $a(h)$ depends only on the ratio $\beta(h)/v_1$, where the function $\beta(h)$ is determined by means of a Fourier transformation of a term involving $\Phi(r)$ (see equation 2.65). Each type of particle has its own potential $\Phi(r)$ and, consequently, an individual function $\beta(h)$. Thus a method of interpretation employing a given $a(h)$-type function cannot be generally correct. This method could be used nevertheless as a first approximation when the particles being examined are somewhat analogous to the particles from which the $a(h)$ function is determined. However, it is not at all obvious that the data from mercury are valid for proteins. A further criticism of this particular comparison follows from the use of *liquid* mercury, since it is known that certain properties of solutions of large molecules (for example, osmotic pressure) can be likened to the properties of *gases* but not to those of liquids.

4.1.2.2.4. Predictions of the Correct Theory

We would like now to summarize the facts that can be predicted about the angular position of a possible intensity maximum from the two types of equations we have discussed in §2.2.3.

The "geometrical" equation for spherically symmetrical particles,

$$I(h) = I_e(h)\overline{N}\,F^2(h)\left\{1 - \frac{1}{v_1}\int_0^\infty [1 - P(r)]\frac{\sin hr}{hr}\,4\pi r^2\,dr\right\}$$

shows that the position of a possible maximum of $I(h)$ depends primarily on two factors:

1. *The function* $P(r)$. The value of the integral for a certain value, h_0, of the parameter h depends on all the values of the function $P(r)$ and not simply on the value $P(r_0)$ corresponding to a certain distance, r_0. Thus there cannot be a law relating a value r_1, corresponding to the first maximum of the function $P(r)$, to the value h_1 at which the integral presents its minimum value. The function $P(r)$ must be known over its entire range in order to calculate h_1.

2. *The structure factor* $F(h)$ and thus the internal structure of the particle. This factor, though often neglected, can be important. In most cases $F^2(h)$ decreases with increasing angle, so that the maximum intensity occurs at a value of h smaller than h_1. Moreover, all other characteristics being equal, the maxima will appear at smaller angles and

to a lesser degree (even disappearing), the less compact the distribution of scattering centers in the interior of a particle.

We see therefore that *in the general case it is difficult to define the relation between the existence of an intensity maximum and the structure of the group of particles being examined, so that it is especially necessary to abandon the idea that the intensity of radiation scattered through a certain angle contains specific information about a certain interparticle distance* (as, for example, the probability of the existence of this distance).

The "thermodynamical" relation for spherically symmetrical particles (Fournet [48])

$$I(h) = I_e(h)\overline{N}F^2(h) \; \frac{1}{1 - \dfrac{(2\pi)^{3/2}\epsilon\beta(h)}{v_1}}$$

shows that the maximum of $a(h, v_1)$ is always produced at the same angle h_1, regardless of the concentration of particles in the sample. The influence of the concentration is felt uniquely in the steepness of the variations of $a(h)$ as a function of h (Fig. 13). The intensity, $I(h)$, determined by the product of $a(h)$ and $F^2(h)$, begins to show a maximum when the concentration reaches a rather high value. This maximum is situated at an angle smaller than h_1. As the concentration increases, the curve of $a(h)$ becomes sharper, and the position of the maximum moves towards h_1. *The maximum in $I(h)$ shifts towards larger angles as the concentration increases.* This behavior is illustrated by the curves of Fig. 13. These were constructed with a function $\overline{F^2(h)}$ which followed the law of Guinier and a function $\beta(h)$ chosen so that the observed maximum obeyed the law found by Riley and Oster (equation 25). The behavior of this $\beta(h)$ is not at all improbable.

Equation 2.67 is an approximate expression, but nevertheless we can still state rigorously that the displacement of $I(h)$ is explained in large part by the mechanism we have indicated in §2.2.3.4 and is not due to a variation in the angular position of the maximum of $a(h)$. Equation 2.67 also shows that the primary factor which determines $a(h)$ is the function $\dfrac{\beta(h)}{v_1}$. We have used this fact in our discussion in §4.1.2.2.2 and §4.1.2.2.3 (Fournet (1955)).

4.1.2.3. Conclusions

We have just demonstrated the complicated factors regulating the positions of the maxima of the scattered intensity. Let us now summarize the information of this section by considering the two following cases:

1. The intensity maximum is not very sharp. This means that the

corresponding maximum of the function $a(h)$ is also not very sharp, and consequently the constitution of the matter is quite different from that of a crystal. The theoretical calculation of the position h_1 of the maximum of $a(h)$ is then often difficult. The structure factor of the particle, $F(h)$, will contribute strongly to the form of the curve of the intensity, $I(h)$. The maximum of $I(h)$ will be found at a position, h_M, which is often quite different from h_1. No simple significance is attached to this one parameter, h_M. Two procedures can be followed:

If precise information is wanted, a complete study must be made of the family of curves of $I(h)$ as a function of concentration and then an attempt must be made to compare this group of curves with theoretical results obtained from some suitable model.

If only approximate information is wanted, we can simply apply Bragg's law to the diffuse peak and determine an order of magnitude (to within 30 to 50 per cent) of some geometrical dimension characteristic of the matter being studied. It is *impossible* to determine the meaning of this geometrical dimension by this one measurement (an example is shown in §6.4.3.1 for Al–Ag alloys).

2. The observed intensity maximum is sharp. Although it is not rigorous, we are probably justified in considering the sample being studied as a paracrystalline substance, and there will probably be a simple interpretation of the maxima of $a(h)$. Since these maxima are very sharp, the factor $F^2(h)$ will have very little influence on the positions of the intensity maxima (h_M is almost exactly h_1) and will affect only the magnitude of the intensity (see Fig. 14).

This section has been deliberately developed at length in order to show clearly how easy it is to make rather serious errors in interpretation. The introduction of X-ray techniques into the studies of large molecules has not always succeeded in clarifying the ideas. This is due to the fact that the non-specialists in the scattering of X-rays have often been deceived by the dangerously precise results that have been published (certain authors have not hesitated to correct Bragg's law with a coefficient with three significant figures) and have thus by inference been able to obtain information (forms of particles, number of layers of water with which each is surrounded, etc.) which really has no serious justification and which can be completely erroneous. It should always be remembered that Bragg's law, so familiar in crystallography, applies only to good crystals.

4.2. GROUPS OF NON-IDENTICAL PARTICLES

We shall now consider the case where it is not possible to assume that all the particles are identical. The theoretical calculations of §2.3 show

that there is only one case for which a useful result can be obtained—
particles separated far enough so that interparticle interferences are
negligible. Let us state immediately that we cannot give a rigorous
method of interpretation when the particles are of several types and are
closely packed. Section 6.3 gives the uses that can be made of the
experimental results by adopting an empirical point of view.

4.2.1. DETERMINATION OF THE AVERAGE RADIUS OF GYRATION FOR THE GROUP OF PARTICLES

The curve of $\log I(h^2)$ is generally concave, with a positive second
derivative. If it is found that at small angles the curvature diminishes
enough so that the tangent at the origin can be determined with reasonable
accuracy, by applying equation 6 to the slope of this tangent a mean
radius of gyration R_{0M} can be obtained. This parameter represents a
mean value defined by the following relation:

$$R^2_{0M} = \frac{\sum_k p_k R^2_{0k} F_k^2(0)}{\sum_k p_k F_k^2(0)} = \frac{\sum_k p_k n_k^2 R^2_{0k}}{\sum_k p_k n_k^2} \qquad (27)$$

where n_k represents the number of electrons contained in the particle
of type k and p_k represents the proportion of this type.

Equation 27 can be simplified if it can be assumed that all the particles
are geometrically similar, the number of electrons n_k being proportional
to R^3_{0k}. With this assumption we find

$$R^2_{0M} = \frac{\sum_k p_k R^8_{0k}}{\sum_k p_k R^6_{0k}} \qquad (28)$$

It is easy to generalize these formulas for the case of a continuous
distribution of particle sizes by first introducing a probability density
function, $p(R_0)$, where $p(R_0) \, dR_0$ designates the probability that a
particle has a radius of gyration contained between R_0 and $R_0 + dR_0$,
and then replacing the summation by an integration.

We can employ equally well a mass distribution function, $m(R_0)$,
where $m(R_0) \, dR_0$ gives the total mass of particles whose radius of gyration
is contained between R_0 and $R_0 + dR_0$. With this approach we find

$$R^2_{0M} = \frac{\int m(R_0) R_0^5 \, dR_0}{\int m(R_0) R_0^3 \, dR_0} \qquad (29)$$

These equations show that *large radii of gyration are favored in the
experimentally determined average.* This fact can be illustrated rather
easily by considering the very simple model composed of two different

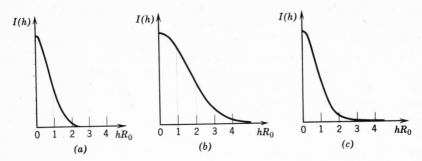

Fig. 47. Scattered intensity for dilute systems of particles: (a) Identical particles of radius of gyration R_{01}; (b) identical particles of radius of gyration $R_{02} = \frac{1}{2}R_{01}$; (c) a mixture of equal proportions of the particles of a and b.

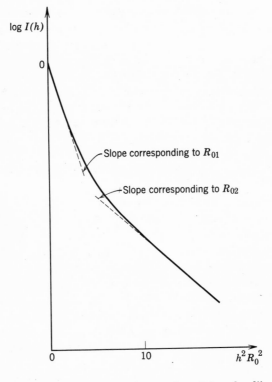

Fig. 48. Log I vs. $h^2 R_0{}^2$ for a mixture of particles of radii of gyration R_{01} and R_{02}, where $R_{02} = \frac{1}{2}R_{01}$. Same sample as for Fig. 47c.

types of particles (1 and 2) with R_{01} greater than R_{02}. Figure 47 shows three scattering curves: curve a is that for particles 1 only, curve b is that for particles 2 only, and curve c is that for a mixture of 50 per cent of particles 1 and 50 per cent of particles 2 (by weight). At very small angles, the variation of the intensity for the mixture is almost entirely due to curve a, since curve b shows only a very slight variation in this region; thus large radii are favored in the experimentally measured radius of gyration. The influence of the small particles is only perceptible at larger angles, where the intensity scattered by the large particles is practically reduced to zero.

This example will also permit us to demonstrate another important aspect characteristic of mixtures. Let us assume that the structure factors of the different particles follow the law of Guinier exactly. At very small angles we have seen that the apparent radius of gyration is effectively R_{01}; at larger angles (h_1) the curve c is due almost entirely to curve b, since the contribution from curve a is effectively zero, and the apparent radius of gyration, as defined by the slope of $\log I_c(h^2)$ at $h_1{}^2$, is practically equal to R_{02}. The curve of $\log I_c(h^2)$ is thus characterized by a decided concavity, as is shown in Fig. 48. We may generalize this remark to say that the curve of $\log I(h^2)$ for a mixture will usually present such a concave appearance. Let us make quite clear that this is only a general observation and is not a proof of a one-to-one correspondence; for example, the curve of $\log I(h^2)$ for a group of identical homogeneous rods demonstrates the same concavity.

4.2.2. ATTEMPTS AT DETERMINING THE STATISTICAL DISTRIBUTION OF THE PARTICLES

It is easy to calculate the intensity curve by means of equation 2.93,

$$I(h) = I_e(h)\overline{N}\sum_k p_k \overline{F_k{}^2(h)}$$

if the distribution of particles is given, that is, if the form, the size, and the relative fraction p_k of the particles of each type are given.

Conversely, several authors (Hosemann [79], [81]; Shull and Roess [155]) have tried to deduce the distribution of the particles from the experimental curve. But *this problem does not have a unique solution.* Hypotheses must be made, and *the results depend on these hypotheses.* Several of the methods that have been proposed will be discussed in this section.

Hypotheses are not made on the form of the particles, but it is assumed that they are all geometrically similar, so that the number of electrons n_k in a particle of type k, defined by a radius of gyration R_{0k}, is proportional to $R^3{}_{0k}$.

It is assumed that the particles of type k give a scattering curve represented by the exponential law, $e^{-(h^2 R^2_{0k})/3}$. We have already discussed the validity of this (p. 26). This approximation must be valid for the *largest particles* of the group for all values of the parameter h at which the scattered intensity is important; if small particles are present this scattering will extend to large angles, and in this case the complete calculations are correct only if the shapes of the particles are such that the exponential relation is a very good approximation up to rather large values of hR_0.

Next it is assumed that the distribution of the radii of gyration of the particles is represented by a Maxwellian distribution of the form (Whittaker and Watson (1927))

$$m(R_0) = \frac{2}{r_0^{n+1} \, \Gamma\left(\dfrac{n+1}{2}\right)} R_0^n e^{-R_0^2/r_0^2} \tag{30}$$

where $m(R_0)dR_0$ represents the proportion of the particles whose radius of gyration is between R_0 and $R_0 + dR_0$. By means of the two parameters, r_0 and n, we can satisfactorily describe a wide range of distributions. The arithmetic mean of the radii of gyration is given by

$$R_{0M} = r_0 \frac{\Gamma\left(\dfrac{n}{2} + 1\right)}{\Gamma\left(\dfrac{n}{2} + \dfrac{1}{2}\right)}$$

and the fractional standard deviation of this value, $\sqrt{\overline{\Delta R_0^2}}/R_0$, is $1/\sqrt{2(n+1)}$.

The scattered intensity is given by equation 2.93 as proportional to the integral

$$\int \frac{m(R_{0k})}{R^3_{0k}} n_k^2 e^{-\frac{h^2 R^2_{0k}}{3}} dR_{0k}$$

As a result of the form chosen for $m(R_{0k})$ the integration can be carried out, giving

$$I(h) = \frac{\text{constant}}{\left[1 + \dfrac{(hr_0)^2}{3}\right]^{(n+4)/2}} \tag{31}$$

The problem is now to determine r_0 and n in such a manner that this equation will suitably represent the experimental curve.

Several methods of calculation have been given. The method due to Hosemann is based on the use of a curve of $h^2 I(h)$ as a function of h. This curve always presents a maximum at some position h_M greater than zero. A second position, h_T, is defined by the intersection with the h-axis of the tangent to the curve at the inflection point W on the high-angle side of the curve (Fig. 49).

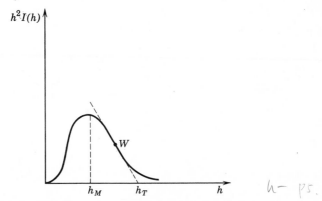

Fig. 49.   The Hosemann method for analyzing the intensity distribution from a mixture of particles [84].

Hosemann derived the following relation:

$$\frac{h_T}{2h_M} - 1 \cong \frac{1}{\sqrt{2(n+1)}}$$

From this equation the parameter n can be determined. Then the arithmetic mean of the radii of gyration can be found by the relation

$$R_{0M} = \frac{1}{h_M} \sqrt{\frac{6}{n+2}} \frac{\Gamma\left(\dfrac{n+2}{2}\right)}{\Gamma\left(\dfrac{n+1}{2}\right)}$$

The mathematical proof of these results, as drawn from equations 30 and 31, will be found in an article by Hosemann [84].[1]

In the method of Shull and Roess, equation 31 is first written in the form

$$\log I = \text{constant} - \frac{n+4}{2} \log\left(h^2 + \frac{3}{r_0^2}\right) \tag{32}$$

---

[1] Hosemann considers systems of spheres instead of general particles defined by their radius of gyration. His formulas have been changed accordingly.

Then the experimental intensity curve is constructed with the coordinate system $\log I$, $\log (h^2 + \alpha)$, and a value of α is sought for which the curve of $\log I(h^2 + \alpha)$ is a straight line. Then the parameters, r_0 and n, are determined from this constant ($r_0{}^2 = 3/\alpha$) and from the slope of the line (slope $= (n + 4)/2$).

One can also construct the family of curves of $\log I$ as a function of $\log (hr_0)^2$ for different values of n and then try to superpose the curve of $\log I(h^2)$ on one of these. When this is done, the translation of the origin along the h-axis gives r_0.

It can be stated that, although it may be easy to determine the average dimension of the particles, it is difficult to select the form of the distribution law, because the difference between theoretical curves for groups with the same average dimensions but with different distribution laws are very small (see Fig. 50).

Roess and Shull [148] have made calculations for spherical particles and particles in the form of ellipsoids of revolution with a variable axial ratio, v, in which they employed the true structure factor instead of the exponential law. They obtained exact results by expressing them in terms of generalized hypergeometric functions. They were thus able to obtain a family of curves (Fig. 50) plotted with the coordinates $\log I$ and $\log a^2h^2$, in which each curve was defined by two parameters, n and v. The parameter v described the form of the particles; n, the statistical distribution; and a, the dimensions of the average particle. The important conclusions of this distinguished work are that there is little variation in the form of the curves and also that the same forms are found for different pairs of the parameters n and v. If then we consider the experimental uncertainty of measurements, particularly at high angles, it appears that it is difficult to choose from the family of curves that particular one which gives the best coincidence with the experimental curve. Therefore the parameter n and, consequently, the statistics of the distribution are poorly determined. Again, very different values can be found, depending on the choice of v, that is, the form of the particle. This demonstrates the important limitations of low-angle scattering methods when the particles are not homogeneous.

Let us now briefly mention other contributions to this subject. Shull and Roess have repeated their calculations using a "rectangular" distribution (uniform distribution between a minimum and a maximum size). It has also been shown (Riseman [145]) that, for a system of spherical particles, it is mathematically possible to determine the statistical distribution of sizes from the experimental curve without imposing a priori some form on this intensity curve. However, there seems to be little physical interest in such calculations.

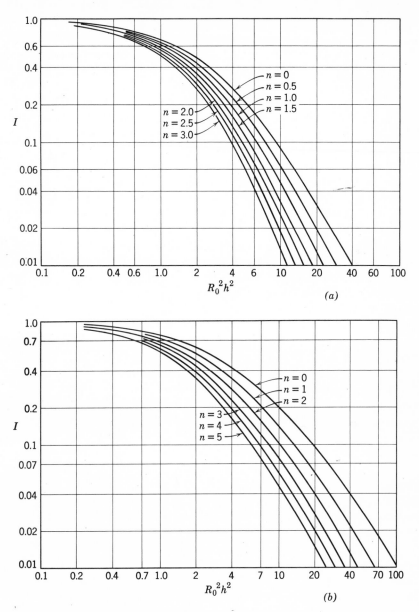

Fig. 50. Calculated curves of I vs. $(hR_0)^2$. (a) Maxwellian distributions of spheres characterized by the parameter n; (b) Maxwellian distributions of oblate ellipsoids (axial ratio: $v = 0.25$). (Roess and Shull [148].)

4.2.3. DETERMINATION OF THE SPECIFIC SURFACE

In the preceding sections we have tried to use the low-angle part of the scattering curve. But in systems composed of particles of various sizes, that low-angle part which can be represented by an exponential approximation is often inaccessible to experiment. Also, if the particles are packed together the low-angle part is perturbed by interference effects. It is therefore more advantageous under these conditions to exploit the other possible approximation, that for the *tail of the scattering curves.* It would undoubtedly be possible to determine the characteristic function $\gamma(r)$ (§2.4.3) from the experimental curve without making any hypotheses, for, mathematically, $r\gamma(r)$ is the Fourier transform of $hI(h)$. But in practice the function $\gamma(r)$ can be used to obtain one important quantity, *the value of the specific surface of the specimen,* and this is determined by the tail of the scattering curve.

The fundamental equation, equation 2.108, is valid both for systems composed of arbitrary particles distributed in an arbitrary manner and for an arbitrary distribution of matter of constant density ρ. This equation shows that, *for large values of h, the quantity* $\dfrac{h^4 I(h)}{2\pi\rho^2 I_e(h)}$ *approaches the value of S, the total free surface of the scattering body.* If the scattering body has unit volume or unit mass, then S represents the specific surface per cubic centimeter or per gram of the sample. The method requires that the measurements of the scattered intensity be extended up to rather large angles, where the intensities are rather weak. That the product $h^4 I(h)$ becomes constant must be verified. Finally, the intensity of the direct beam should be measured in order to obtain an absolute value for S. However, if samples of the same matter but of different structures are compared, then, by examining samples all of which have the same mass, *the ratio of the products $h^4 I(h)$ gives the ratio of the specific surfaces of the specimens.*

The assumption is made in these equations that the electronic density in the interior of the particles is rigorously constant, and this, by virtue of the atomic structure of matter, is never the case. This atomic structure gives rise to a high-angle scattering pattern such as that for an amorphous body, for example. The intensity to be expected from this effect in the low-angle scattering region is weak but not zero. It is negligible in the small-angle part of the region of scattering arising from the heterogeneity of the sample, but it can become perceptible towards the outer part of the curve, the part in which we are interested at this point. Other sources of extraneous radiation must also be added: fluorescence radiation, Compton scattering, thermal scattering by crystals, various parasitic scatterings, etc. The product $h^4 I(h)$ thus will begin to increase when h becomes too large. The asymptotic law is also not valid for too small values of h. There is therefore only a certain range of validity, whose extent depends on the particular sample, in which this relation can be used in making measurements of specific surfaces. *These measurements have significance only if it is verified that the product $h^4 I(h)$ remains constant* over a reasonable interval.

If the cross section of the incident beam is not pointlike but rather has a large height, then it is the product $h^3 \mathscr{I}_1(h)$ which should be constant at large values of h (equation 3.11b).

We can avoid the measurement of the intensity of the direct beam in determining the absolute value of the specific surface by making use of the normalization relation, equation 2.111. If V is the total volume of the specimen and c is the fraction of this volume occupied by matter (of electronic density ρ),

$$\int_0^\infty h^2 I(h)\,dh = 2\pi^2 I_e(h)\rho^2 V c(1-c) \tag{33}$$

If S_{sp} is the specific surface per unit volume, then $S = V S_{sp}$, and

$$S_{sp} = \frac{\lim [h^4 I(h)]}{V 2\pi \rho^2 I_e(h)} = \pi c(1-c) \frac{\lim [h^4 I(h)]}{\displaystyle\int_0^\infty h^2 I(h)\,dh} \tag{34}$$

When the scattering experiment is made with an incident beam of large height and $\mathscr{I}_1(h)$ is the measured intensity, equations 3.11b and 3.11c give

$$\lim [h^3 \mathscr{I}_1(h)] = \frac{\pi}{2} \lim [h^4 I(h)]$$

and

$$\int_0^\infty h^2 I(h)\,dh = \frac{1}{2} \int_0^\infty h \mathscr{I}_1(h)\,dh$$

Therefore

$$S_{sp} = 4c(1-c) \frac{\lim [h^3 \mathscr{I}_1(h)]}{\displaystyle\int_0^\infty h \mathscr{I}_1(h)\,dh} \tag{35}$$

The difficulty in evaluating the integrals $\int_0^\infty h^2 I(h)\,dh$ or $\int_0^\infty h \mathscr{I}_1(h)\,dh$ is that $I(h)$ or $\mathscr{I}_1(h)$ is known only beyond a certain minimum value of h. The contribution of the unknown small-angle part of the curve is certainly relatively small, particularly in the integral $\int_0^\infty h^2 I(h)\,dh$, since here the measured intensity is multiplied by h^2. Nevertheless, there is still some uncertainty which causes this method to be less precise than the method employing the intensity of the direct beam.

In interpreting certain results, Porod introduced the length

$$l_0 = 4Vc/S$$

which he designated as a "range of inhomogeneity." This length represents an average[1] of the diameters of the parts of the specimen occupied by matter; for instance, for a collection of spheres of radius R, $l_0 = \frac{4}{3}R$.

Another parameter derived from the characteristic function of the specimen which can be rather easily determined experimentally is the distance of heterogeneity or extent of coherence, l_c (Porod [137]), given by the integral $2\int_0^\infty \gamma(r)\, dr$. Equations 2.109 and 2.110 determine l_c respectively in terms of the integral $\int_0^\infty hI(h)\, dh$ and the total scattered energy E, the quantity obtained by measuring all the small-angle scattering outside of the direct beam in a counter or ionization chamber. These relations are the following:

$$l_c = \frac{1}{2\pi V \rho^2 c(1-c)I_e(h)} \int_0^\infty hI(h)\, dh \tag{36}$$

and

$$l_c = \frac{1}{V\rho^2 c(1-c)I_e(h)} \frac{E}{\lambda^2 p^2} \tag{37}$$

where p is the distance from the sample to the receiver.

By making use of the normalization relation, equation 33, these become:

$$l_c = \pi \frac{\displaystyle\int_0^\infty hI(h)\, dh}{\displaystyle\int_0^\infty h^2 I(h)\, dh} \tag{38}$$

and

$$l_c = \frac{2\pi^2}{\lambda^2 p^2} \frac{E}{\displaystyle\int_0^\infty h^2 I(h)\, dh}$$

[1] There are several ways of calculating the "average value" of the diameters of a particle. The average value considered here is not the same as the average used in §2.1.2.4 ($\frac{3}{2}R$ for the sphere).

For incident beams of large height, equations 38, 3.11c, and 3.11d give

$$l_c = 2 \frac{\displaystyle\int_0^\infty \mathscr{I}_1(h)\,dh}{\displaystyle\int_0^\infty h\mathscr{I}_1(h)\,dh} \tag{39}$$

Direct measurements of the total scattered energy have not yet been employed, but, if the sample scatters rather strongly, the method devised by Warren (§3.3.7) could be used. The evaluation of the integrals

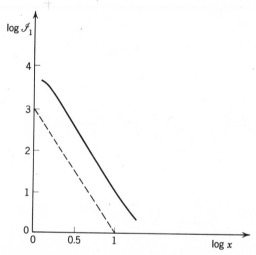

Fig. 51. Log $\mathscr{I}_1$ vs. log x for a sample of naphthalene-black. $\mathscr{I}_1$ is the scattered intensity for an incident beam of infinite height, and x is the distance on the film. The dashed line indicates a line of slope, -3. (L. Kahovek, G. Porod, H. Ruck [97'].)

$\int h\mathscr{I}_1(h)\,dh$ and particularly $\int\mathscr{I}_1(h)\,dh$ cannot be made very accurately because of the unknown small-angle part of the curve. If the small-angle scattering increases rapidly with decreasing angle (Fig. 51) the extrapolation of the curve to zero-angle is very uncertain.

As an illustration of the application of these methods let us discuss the results obtained by Kahovek, Porod, and Ruck [97'] for a sample of naphthalene-black in which $c = 0.12$. The experiments were made with monochromatized Cu $K\alpha$ radiation. The vertical dimensions of the slits defining the primary beam were large, so the beam could be considered as infinitely high. The intensity measurements were made with a Geiger counter. Figure 51 shows the curve of the variation of $\log\mathscr{I}_1$ as a function of $\log x$, where x is the distance between the point of observation and the direct beam. The curve verified the relation $\lim x^3\mathscr{I}_1(x) = A$, a constant.

In addition the following quantities were determined:

$$\int \mathscr{I}_1(x)\, dx = E$$

$$\int x \mathscr{I}_1(x)\, dx = Q$$

From these it was found that for this sample,

$$\frac{S}{V} = 4\,\frac{h}{x}\,c\,(1-c)\,\frac{A}{Q} = 7.5 \text{ m.}^2/\text{cm.}^3$$

$$l_0 = \frac{4Vc}{S} = 650 \text{ A}$$

$$l_c = 2\,\frac{x}{h}\,\frac{E}{Q} = 600 \text{ A}$$

An electron-microscope study of this specimen showed spherical grains with a diameter of approximately 1000 A.

REFERENCES FOR CHAPTER 4

Debye, P., and Menke, H. (1931), *Physik. Z.*, *31*, 797.

Ehrenfest, P. (1915), *Proc. Amsterdam Acad.*, *17*, 1132 and 1184.

Fournet, G. (1955), *J. phys. radium*, **16**, 395.

Perutz, M. F. (1946), *Trans. Faraday Soc.*, *42*, 187.

Verwey, E. J. W., and Overbeck, J. T. G. (1945), *Theory of the Stability of Lyophobic Colloids*, Elsevier, Amsterdam.

Whittaker, E. T., and Watson, G. L. (1927), *A Course of Modern Analysis*, Cambridge, London.

5. COMPARISON OF THE RESULTS FROM SMALL-ANGLE SCATTERING WITH THE RESULTS OF OTHER METHODS OF MEASUREMENT OF SMALL PARTICLES

In verifying these theories and the experimental methods which arise from them, it is very important to compare the results of small-angle scattering analyses with the data from other methods, particularly those methods which yield results more directly. Furthermore, in order to judge the possible applications of X-ray methods, it is necessary to compare their advantages and disadvantages with those of other physical methods.

With this intent, Shull and Roess [155] and Van Nordstrand and Hach [126'] studied the size of particles of a very fine powder (alumina) by X-rays and then determined the total surface of the same sample by absorption methods. The results were in reasonable accord, particularly in the experiments of Van Nordstrand and Hach. The method of these authors (§4.2.3) is independent of the rather arbitrary hypotheses demanded by the first method (§4.2.2). Nevertheless these results do not give the desired direct verification.

The real verifications have been obtained by working with particles that are visible to the *electron microscope* or by working with crystals whose dimensions can be determined from *the width of their Debye-Scherrer diffraction lines*.

5.1. COMPARISON WITH THE ELECTRON MICROSCOPE

A good, well-handled electron microscope has a resolving power of the order of 20 to 30 A. It is therefore capable of giving reasonably accurate images of particles having diameters of several hundreds of angstroms. This is precisely the size of particles that can be studied by small-angle scattering. Therefore such images are the best means of checking the X-ray results, provided that a sample has been chosen for which a rather accurate calculation of the scattering can be made.

The discussion of Chapter 4 has shown that it is necessary to choose a suspension containing *identical* particles if the calculations are to be

161

accurate. Now very regular preparations of latex spheres[1] exist which are actually used for calibration of electron microscopes. The mean diameter of these particles is 2780 A. Yudowitch [192] studied the small-angle scattering of these particles and, from measurements on five successive rings of the observed secondary maxima (§2.3.6) (Fig. 41), determined a diameter of 2740 A. Measurements of these particles were repeated in three different laboratories, with the following results: $D = 2750$ A, 2732 A, 2692 A. These numbers give an indication of the accuracy that can be obtained with the X-ray method.

Testing the validity of the determination of the radius of gyration from the slope of the curve of $\log I(h^2)$ is much more important because of the greater generality of this method. This also has been verified several times. As an example, let us cite the result obtained by Turkevitch, Hubbell, and Hillier [162] for particles of colloidal gold which were prepared so that the variation in size was a minimum, about 10 per cent. The X-ray results gave a diameter of 824 A, and the electron microscope, 700 A. Fournet [48] studied much smaller particles of colloidal silver and found a diameter of 130 A with X-rays and 120 A with the electron microscope. In this last case there was a somewhat larger variation in particle sizes than in the first.

Thus it can be concluded that the validity of the formulas used in Chapter 4 has been proved experimentally. Let us also point out that periodicities in images of fibers (collagen) have been found with the electron microscope that had already been determined by small-angle X-ray diffraction. Direct images could be compared in a straightforward way with the models that had been determined by calculations from the diffraction patterns. This is an interesting result and one which cannot be achieved in the ordinary domain of X-ray diffraction, since the structure models that are determined in the ordinary domain are on a scale of the order of angstroms, completely outside the range of even the most powerful imaging apparatus.

If the electron microscopy method is compared to that of the small-angle scattering, the advantages of the first are quite evident. Both the *form* and the *size* of the visible particles can be determined, regardless of the heterogeneity or of the compactness of the specimen. The accuracy of the results of the electron microscope is thus much greater than that of the X-ray results when a good sample preparation can be made.

A shortcoming of the microscope is that the specimen must be dried before it can be placed in the vacuum. This drying may cause either the destruction of or a serious, unpredictable modification in the sample. The X-ray technique, however, can be applied directly to suspensions

---

[1] Dow Latex 580 G.

or colloidal solutions. Certain other difficulties can often occur during the preparation of samples for the microscope; quite often the particles will agglomerate, so that the elementary particle can be isolated only with great difficulty. The image observed on the screen is the shadow of the apparent contour of the grain, and this size is a function not only of the nature of the sample but also of the condition of its preparation.

In addition, if we consider a grain that contains numerous cavities, these cavities will produce a scattering of X-rays although they are invisible to the electron microscope. An example of this type of specimen is carbon after an activation treatment; the grain has an unchanged exterior form, but the activation has resulted in the emptying of internal cavities, considerably modifying properties that are related to the total surface of the carbon.

On the whole, if there is disagreement between the X-ray results and those of the microscope, it can be predicted that the numbers obtained with the X-ray technique will probably be the smaller.

5.2. COMPARISON WITH THE METHOD OF DEBYE-SCHERRER LINE WIDTHS

If the sample is composed of very small crystallites, it is known that the diffraction lines are broadened and that, from a study of their widths, or, more exactly, of the form of the lines, the dimensions of the crystallite can be determined (Wilson (1949), Bertaut (1950)). The line broadening is accompanied by the appearance of scattering at small angles, which can be considered as arising from the broadening of the (000) diffraction point. There is a very close relation between these two phenomena. For instance, let us consider the diffraction by a crystallite having a *lattice that is assumed to be perfect.* We can apply the general formulas (equations 1.2, 1.3) to determine the scattered amplitude. Now in this case $\rho(\mathbf{x})$ is periodic, so its transform, $A(\mathbf{h})$, has a non-zero value only when $\mathbf{h}$ coincides with one of the vectors of the reciprocal lattice. The interpretation of equation 1.3 is thus the following: each point of the reciprocal lattice is surrounded by the same region of scattering as is found around the (000) point (the origin of reciprocal space), each of these regions being determined by the "form factor" of the crystal, that is, by the transform of $s(\mathbf{x})$ (Ewald (1940)). In this case there is no difference between studying the small-angle scattering and studying the broadening of the high-angle reflections.

When the sample is composed of many crystallites arranged at random, Bertaut (1950) has shown that the width of a Debye-Scherrer line can be used to determine the root mean square thickness of the crystallite in a direction perpendicular to the corresponding lattice planes. The low-angle scattering gives the radius of gyration of the particle and, thus, a mean square value of atomic distances from the center of the particle. There is thus a significant analogy between the results of the two methods, but the averaging is made in a particular direction when the reflection from a well-defined set of crystallographic planes is used, whereas there is no such privileged direction operating in low-angle scattering.

There are several important differences between the two methods. First, the complete profile of a diffraction line can be determined, since nothing prevents measurements at the center of the line, whereas in low-angle scattering the undeviated direct beam prevents measurements from being made down to zero angle. Therefore the methods of analysis of the patterns are different. When studies are made of larger particles, which give only slightly broadened reflections, it can be predicted that the same difficulties will not be encountered with the line broadening measurements as with the low-angle scattering. Actually, the line broadening technique can detect crystallites whose size is greater than 500 A with ordinary, small-diameter cameras, while such a particle dimension requires systems with large sample-to-film distances for an effective study of the small-angle scattering.

The small-angle scattering is much more intense than the scattering around the lines, because all the crystallites of the powder contribute to this, regardless of their orientations, whereas only the small number of particles which are correctly oriented will contribute to the scattering at a point on the diffraction line; also, the atomic scattering factor is a maximum at low angles.

Comparisons have been made between low-angle scattering results and those from line broadening, wherein an "average" dimension of the crystallite was determined by means of approximate formulas such as that due to Scherrer (Wilson (1949)), and the agreement between them is satisfactory. At present much more accurate methods, based on a Fourier analysis of the profile of the line, are known, but to our knowledge they have not been used for a comparison with the low-angle scattering analysis.

Such a study could reveal differences arising from two sources:

1. It is possible that the grains of the material would be made up of more than one crystal (Fig. 52). Now the width of a line depends on the size of the individual crystallite; if this is joined to crystallites of other orientations, the line width is not affected. It can thus be predicted that the small-angle scattering would give a larger crystallite size than that found from the line widths. It is possible that the sample would not even be made up of separate grains; an example would be a deformed

metal in which there were no appreciable density fluctuations. The small-angle scattering would then disappear completely, and the diffraction lines would still be broadened.

2. If the crystallite is not perfect, the lattice perturbations would produce a broadening of the lines. The separation of particle-size effects from those of lattice distortions is a difficult problem and has been widely discussed. Let us recall, for example, the long controversy over the origin of the broadening of the diffraction lines of a cold-worked metal.

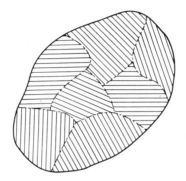

Fig. 52.   Sketch of a polycrystalline grain. The solid line outlines the grain as revealed by small-angle scattering, and the inner boundaries are those revealed by Debye-Scherrer line widths.

In any event, the relative influence of the two factors varies with the order of the reflection, while the *influence of disorder is negligible in the low-angle scattering pattern*, as we have shown in the introduction. If, therefore, the line broadening is attributed only to the influence of the crystallite size, the crystallite dimension that is so determined will be smaller than that found from the low-angle scattering pattern. For example, certain authors have calculated the particle dimensions in several varieties of carbon from the widths of the lines. Their results are not correct, since there is considerable distortion in the crystallites. The correct method, used by Franklin (1951), requires the use of the entire curve of diffracted intensity, including the low-angle scattering.

We shall see in Chapter 6 an example of the separation of the effects due to the size and to the imperfections of the crystallite that is based on a comparison of the scattering at small angles with that around a Bragg reflection (Al–Ag alloy).

When the degree of disorder increases, the material passes from the crystalline state to an amorphous state, and then the various diffraction rings are completely independent of the size of the particles. However, the particle size can still be determined from the low-angle scattering.

For example, a high polymer, such as Perspex, gives the same diffraction ring when it is in a solid state as when it is dissolved in acetone. The solution, however, gives in addition a small-angle scattering pattern from which the size of the micelles of the colloidal solution can be determined.

Consequently the method employing the widths of lines can furnish the same information as that found from small-angle scattering only if the particles are practically perfect crystallites. If this is the case, it can be more easily and more accurately employed when the crystallites have a rather large volume.

REFERENCES FOR CHAPTER 5

Bertaut, E. F.   (1950), *Acta Cryst.*, *3*, 14.
Ewald, P. P.   (1940), *Proc. Phys. Soc.* (*London*), *52*, 167.
Franklin, R. E.   (1950), *Acta Cryst.*, *3*, 158.
Franklin, R. E.   (1951), *Acta Cryst.*, *4*, 253.
Wilson, A. J. C.   (1949), *X-Rays Optics*, Methuen, London.

6. THE APPLICATIONS OF THE SMALL-ANGLE SCATTERING OF X-RAYS

We shall review in this chapter the principal problems to which the methods described in the preceding chapters have been applied.

We would like to show how these methods have been employed in relation to the known facts of a problem and the objectives of the investigation. Without summarizing all the different investigations, a list of which is given in the bibliography, we shall try to give a general picture of the results that have been obtained and of the possibilities of the methods at their present state of development, both for fundamental and applied research.

We shall distinguish two classes of problems.

1. The first will concern the study of well-defined particles, either large molecules or the grains of a finely dispersed substance.

2. The other series of problems will concern the study of a solid that contains heterogeneities on a submicroscopic scale; these can be so complex that a particle model cannot be employed.

6.1. LARGE MOLECULES

A conclusion of the theoretical study of small-angle scattering was that such scattering can be most favorably exploited when the particles are identical and widely separated from one another. If the particle is a molecule that is chemically well defined, we can be sure that the first hypothesis is verified, and it is always possible to disperse the molecules in a solution or suspension dilute enough to satisfy the second.

6.1.1. DILUTE SOLUTIONS

The experimental conditions are good if the particles have a radius of gyration[1] of the order of 10 to 50 A, or a volume of approximately 8×10^3 to 2×10^5 A^3. The corresponding weight of the particle is from 1 to 50×10^{-20} g. if the density is between 1 and 2. The gram-molecular weight of such molecules is between 5,000 and 250,000. This is the

---

[1] The introduction of this parameter, the radius of gyration, is found on p. 24, where it was defined as the root mean square of the distances of atoms from the center of gravity of the particle, each distance being modified by a coefficient equal to the atomic number of the atom.

order of magnitude of the molecular weights of many important biological compounds, as, for example, the proteins.

These remarks explain why the study of proteins offers one of the best applications of this method. As a matter of fact a large number of investigations have already been carried out on proteins, as is shown in the bibliography at the end of the text. We believe that it is in this field that small-angle scattering can give the most valuable and most important results from a general point of view.

The experimental work begins with the preparation of a dilute solution in which the molecule to be studied is found in a pure state (within several per cent).

It is essential that the electronic density of the solvent be as different as possible from that of the molecule, because the smaller this difference, the weaker will be the low-angle scattering.

Frequently aqueous solutions produce a rather intense scattering, so that solutions down to a concentration of only a few per cent can be studied.

The object of the experiment is to determine the curve of the scattered intensity as a function of scattering angle. A photographic determination of the scattering pattern must therefore be followed by a microphotometering of the film. It is certain that *Geiger-Müller counter measurements can be made to a higher degree of accuracy than photographic measurements*, and this accuracy is very desirable, particularly for solutions of molecules, since the theoretical interpretation of this case is on a rather sound basis.

The measurements of the radius of gyration of the molecules can be made by the method of §4.1.1.1. If the shape of the molecules is not too far from spherical, the description of the experimental curve as an exponential in $-kh^2$ is a sufficiently accurate approximation over a large angular region. Here an incident beam of large height can be employed without having to make corrections before interpreting the curves of $\log I(h^2)$ (see p. 114). This is important from the point of view of rapidity of measurement. As we have already indicated, the radius of gyration does not completely define the form and the size of the molecules, but (and here is a point of view on which we must insist) *it is a well-defined geometrical parameter which can be considered as a characteristic of a molecule of any shape.*

The experimental techniques, as illustrated, for example, in the counter-equipped apparatus of Beeman (Fig. 25, p. 95), have reached such a degree of simplicity and accuracy that one can envisage a broad program of systematic measurements of radii of gyration of different proteins or other large molecules in biochemical laboratories.

There are many services which these measurements could render. We have already seen how a knowledge of the radius of gyration, together with other data, can give indications of the shape and the real dimensions of the molecule.[1]   Figure 53a gives the curves of log $I(h^2)$ for a series of proteins, and it can be seen that the straight lines are defined well enough to permit an accurate determination of the radius of gyration.   In Fig. 53b the curves of log I vs. log h are plotted for two ellipsoids of the same radius of gyration with axial ratios of 2 and 3.   The experimental points for ovalbumin fall just between these two curves, indicating that the

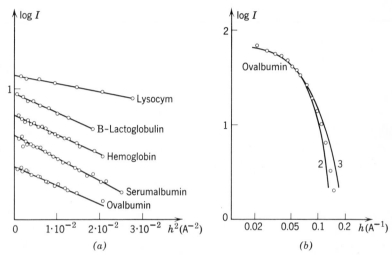

Fig. 53.   (a) Log I vs. h^2 for solutions of different proteins; (b) log I vs. log h for ellipsoids of axial ratios 2 and 3 (theoretical). The small circles ◯ show the experimental points obtained for a solution of ovalbumin. (Ritland, Kaesberg, and Beeman [492].)

ovalbumin molecule has an axial ratio of about 2.5.   With the latest improvements in experimental techniques (use of a powerful X-ray tube for studies of dilute solutions in which interparticle interferences are negligible, correction of the curves for the effect of beam height), the error in a determination of the radius of gyration is of the order of 2 to 3 per cent.   This parameter could also be used as a means of identification, if no simpler method were possible.   Finally, the single aspect of the linearity of the curve of log $I(h^2)$ is an indication of the uniformity of size of the particles and thus constitutes a means of inspection of the purity of preparations.   For example, the curves of log $I(h^2)$ for euglobulin and pseudoglobulin extracts from the serum of horse blood are strongly

[1] In addition to the other data previously mentioned (p. 130),the sedimentation and diffusion constants can be used toward this end (Ritland, Kaesberg, and Beeman (492]).

convex (Fournet [48]), and other techniques have shown that the globulins are complex mixtures.

Dervichian, Fournet, and Guinier [419] have studied the denaturing of hemoglobin and albumin serums with urea. When the small-angle scattering characteristic of the molecules disappears, the molecules have been broken up into small fragments. If all the molecules are not

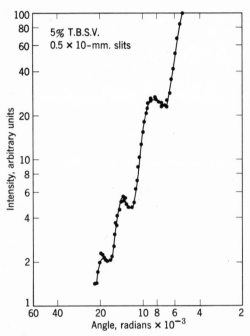

Fig. 54. Scattered intensity for a 5 per cent solution of tomato bushy stunt virus. The dotted curve is the theoretical curve for spheres of 310-A radius. (Leonard, Anderegg, Shulman, Kaesberg, and Beeman [478].)

destroyed, the patterns decrease in intensity without changing their appearance. A change of appearance of the patterns occurs when new particles are formed.

Beeman and coworkers have obtained especially accurate results for virus macromolecules [376]. The experimental curve showed several peaks which the authors were able to make coincide with the successive peaks in a scattering pattern of homogeneous spheres. They thus demonstrated that these viruses were spherical and found their diameters (Fig. 54); for example, the diameter of the tomato bushy stunt virus was 310 A. Then, by a comparison of this diameter with other molecular constants, they were able to determine the degree of internal hydration of the molecules.

It is quite evident that the information drawn from the low-angle scattering concerns only *the exterior form and not the structure of the molecule,* while much more information on the structure is contained in the diffraction patterns of crystallized proteins.

By comparing the work of Fournet on hemoglobin in solution [48] with that of Perutz and coworkers on crystallized hemoglobin [407], it can be seen that these two methods are undertakings of a completely different order of difficulty. The crystallographic method requires a considerable amount of work (and sometimes only for an uncertain result) both in the preparation of a usable crystal and in the interpretation of the patterns, whereas a low-angle scattering investigation of a solution can now be considered a routine operation.

6.1.2. CONCENTRATED SOLUTIONS

Another field of investigation in the study of large molecules such as proteins has been opened by the progress of more recent theoretical approaches. This is the study of the *spatial distribution of molecules in solutions* at high concentrations.

The organization of the molecules in a solution can be successfully determined. The method to be applied for this purpose has been described in §4.1.2.1. Without repeating the details of the technique, let us recall only that, if a solution is very concentrated and if the particles show a high degree of organization, the uniformly decreasing scattering curve of the dilute solution is deformed, showing a bump or even a maximum.

A practical consequence of this shape of the curve is that for a quantitative study either the correction for the slit height must be made or else beams used that are as small as possible. Obviously this complicates the determination of the curves. Here again only Geiger-Müller counter measurements can convey the accuracy required for the theoretical calculations. However, photographic patterns can often give immediately qualitative information which will help to decide whether a precise study is worth being undertaken.

The theoretical study showed that very carefully performed experiments made on a series of solutions of various concentrations can lead to the determination of the *mutual potential energy of a pair of molecules* as a function of the separation of their centers, if it is assumed that the molecules are spherically symmetric.

As an example of studies of this type, we cite those carried out by Beeman and his collaborators for various solutions of spherical viruses. Figure 55 gives the low-angle part of the scattering curves for solutions of turnip yellow mosaic virus of various concentrations (Schmidt, Kaesberg, and Beeman (1954)). A maximum is observed on the curves for concentrations greater than 5 per cent. Now, theoretical calculations

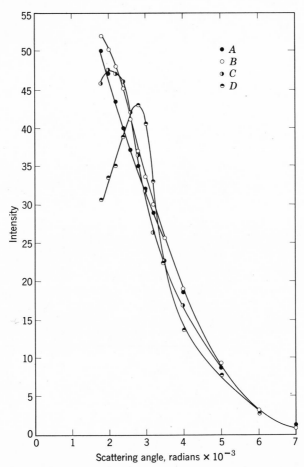

Fig. 55. Interparticle interference effects in the low-angle scattering from concentrated turnip yellow mosaic virus solutions. The ordinates are adjusted so that the curves would coincide if scattering were proportional to concentration at all angles. Curves A, B, C, and D refer to concentrations of 1.6, 3.2, 6.3, and 12.8 per cent, respectively. (Schmidt, Kaesberg, and Beeman (1954).)

based on the hard sphere model (§2.2.3.4 and Fig. 12) show that this maximum is perceptible for $8v_0\epsilon/v_1 > 2$, where ϵ is a constant approximately equal to unity, v_0 is the volume of the molecule, and v_1 is the reciprocal of the number of molecules per unit volume. By applying this theoretical result to the observations on the virus solutions, a volume v_0 is found which is 4 times as great as that determined from the experimental scattering curves of dilute solutions. From this it is concluded that the molecules do not behave as hard spheres which can come in

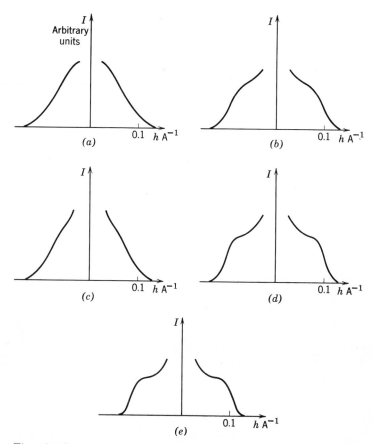

Fig. 56. Scattering from red corpuscles in various preparations. (a) Artificial hemoglobin solution; (b) normal red cells prepared with heparin; (c) sickle cells prepared with heparin; (d) fetal red cells prepared with heparin; (e) normal red cells prepared with sodium citrate.

contact with one another. Instead, there must be repulsive forces which give the molecule an effective collision diameter of about 1.6 times their actual diameter.

Differences in the form of the scattering curves have been observed between hemoglobin in normal human red corpuscles and hemoglobin in abnormal corpuscles (fetus blood, blood affected by the sickle-cell disease)

[420]. Hemoglobin extracted from these various cells and put in dilute solutions gives the same scattering curve, independent of its source. All these hemoglobin molecules therefore have the same radius of gyration, but the red corpuscles themselves give different curves in which the bump is more or less accentuated, depending on the type of corpuscle (Fig. 56). From this qualitative observation we can deduce that the organization of the molecules is less for the sickle cells than for the normal corpuscles but is greater for the fetus corpuscles.

Let us point out also the work of Riley and Oster [371] on hemoglobin and on ovalbumin serum in concentrated solutions that was based on the

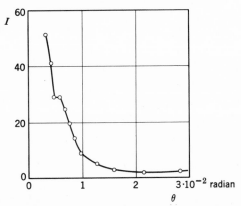

Fig. 57. Scattering from a *dilute* solution of hemocyanine. The intensity in arbitrary units is plotted against $\theta = \lambda h/4\pi$ (Cu $K\alpha$ radiation). (Kratky, Sekora, and Friedrich-Freska [474].)

method of interpretation discussed in §4.1.2.2.1. The same method of interpretation was used by Bateman, Hsu, Knudsen, and Yudowitch [382] in a series of experiments on red cells swollen to different degrees in solutions of variable tonicity. Their results confirm those of Riley and Oster but are not in accord with the works previously cited. A basic assumption whose correctness is not proved in these works is that the molecules form a sort of paracrystalline structure, which expands without appreciably changing the nature of the molecular arrangement when the concentration decreases.

Hemocyanine molecules [416], [474] are peculiar in that their scattering curve shows a maximum even for very dilute solutions (2 per cent), the position of the maximum being independent of the concentration of the solution (Fig. 57). It is therefore improbable that this maximum can be explained in terms of interparticle interferences. Isolated particles can give such patterns if it is admitted that the particles are complex, each being made up, for example, of an agglomeration of a certain number of molecules joined together.   This hypothesis agrees with the description suggested by observations with an electron microscope (Fournet [48]).

As a last example, a considerable number of investigations have been devoted to aqueous soap solutions in the presence of electrolytes (see Bibliography).   These solutions give a small-angle pattern containing rather sharp rings, often designated as I and M bands.   In the majority of the investigations the two rings have been interpreted in terms of "distances" having simple physical meanings.   For example, the M band was related to the spacing between two layers of molecules and the I band to an intermicelle distance by means of an equation analogous to 4.24.

It is certainly not permissible to separate the two peaks in this way or to apply to these micelles relations that are valid for crystalline arrangements.   The complexity of the patterns of the soaps arises from the fact that the micelle has an internal structure, so that the curve of its structure factor shows peaks.   In addition, the micelles are rather ordered, so that there are strong interferences that deform the scattering curves of the individual micelles.   An *a priori* analysis of the data is practically impossible.   We can only assume different models on which calculations can be based (Corrin [359]), but as Hughes has pointed out [362], [363], there are many widely different models that can explain certain experimental facts.

It seems, therefore, that it is necessary at the present time to reconsider the majority of the "quantitative" results for soap solutions that have been arrived at by overly simplified reasoning.   It is necessary to retain only those results that have been obtained by a restrained application of a correct theory to the patterns, leading to a modest but sure interpretation.

There is no doubt that often the numbers that are given are not even approximately correct, and *the so-called "conclusions" from the X-ray patterns can only bring confusion into questions that have not yet been cleared up if these conclusions are adopted by non-specialists.*

In several cases the tendency to order among the large molecules becomes so strong that they tend towards a regular arrangement, and it becomes legitimate to adopt a crystalline model.   The dimensions of the basic units are such that these lattices have very large cells, so that diffraction lines appear at very small angles.   Bernal and Carlisle [9] found that the molecules of wet turnip yellow virus form a cubic, diamond-type lattice.   The distance between molecules is 304 A and the layer of water between neighboring molecules is 70 A thick.   In this case the intermolecular forces succeed in bringing about good regularity over long distances.

Another example is furnished by the red corpuscles of a rat. After being subjected to a special treatment (Ponder (1945)), these give a small-angle pattern containing a series of extremely sharp lines that coincide with those from hemoglobin crystals prepared from pure solutions. The organization of the molecules has here resulted in crystallization. At this stage the interpretation of the pattern becomes simple, because the classical procedures of crystallography can again be applied. However, we wish to repeat that it is justifiable to apply these procedures only if the experimental results permit it; the indispensable condition is that the pattern contain many well-marked lines.

Despite the difficulties we have not hesitated to stress, it is certain that the results already obtained show the chemist and biochemist interested in large molecules that small-angle scattering patterns should no longer be neglected, as has generally been done. It is obviously in this region of a diffraction pattern in which the forms of scattering are found that show the organization of matter on the scale of large molecules. Even if a complete interpretation is not possible, the pattern can serve to characterize a product; therefore it can be a tool for following and checking preparations or fractionations. For example, lipides extracted from egg yolk give rise to two rather sharp diffraction lines. When these lipides are dissolved in alcohol a separation into two phases is observed; the upper phase always gives rise to two lines, while nothing is observed for the lower phase.

6.2. HIGH POLYMERS
6.2.1. STUDY OF SOLUTIONS

The large molecules formed by polymerization offer a natural field of application for small-angle scattering. But here a difficulty is found that did not exist for proteins; in general, the particles are not all identical, since the number of elementary monomeric units can vary from one polymer to another. It should therefore be expected (§4.2) that quite often the X-ray results cannot be very precise. If there is only a small variation in the sizes of the polymers in the mixture, an average radius of gyration can be determined, as defined in §4.2.1. When a large range of sizes is present and when the mixture contains some very large particles, this measurement is difficult. It must not be forgotten that, from its definition, the "average" radius that is found is near that of the largest particles. Consequently this radius can be determined only if an apparatus is used that allows measurements at very small angles. If the shape of the particles is known and if it is assumed that they are all similar, it is possible to derive the distribution function for the sizes of the particles from the experimental measurements (§4.2.2). In order that the experiments be accurate, the concentration of particles must be small, and *it is essential that they be contained in a medium of very different electronic density so that there will be sufficient scattered intensity.*

Kratky and Wurster [476], in a study of cellulose fibers submitted to a series of swelling agents, verified that the intensity of scattering at a given angle was proportional to the square of the difference of the electronic density between the crystallized cellulose and the liquid in which the micelles were immersed. An unknown electronic density in particles can thus be determined by finding the solvent that cancels the small-angle scattering.

The result of such small-angle scattering experiments could be the determination of molecular weights of high polymers. Actually, to the best of our knowledge, there has not yet been a systematic employment of X-rays towards this end, either because of difficulties in the method for particles that are too large or of too heterogeneous a distribution, or because other physical methods are simpler and more certain.

Kratky and Porod [469] have studied the scattering from coiled chain molecules in solution. Calculations predicted a small-angle scattering curve of the form e^{-kh^2}, but this part is not visible since the radius of gyration of the molecule is too large. They further predicted that for increasing angles the intensity would vary first as h^{-2} followed by a curve in h^{-1}. Thus, if a plot of the measured intensity multiplied by h^2 were made, we would obtain a horizontal straight-line section followed by another straight line of negative slope. The transition point between the two parts of the curve would be related to the mode of coiling of the molecule, or, more exactly, to the "distance of persistence" in which on the average the molecule does not change its orientation appreciably. An experiment was made on polyvinylbromide in methylnaphthalene. The theoretical results were not verified very clearly, but nevertheless the measured distance of persistence was of the expected order of magnitude.

6.2.2. STUDY OF FIBERS

X-rays have been used to a great extent in the study of polymers in the form of fibers (see Bibliography). In fibers the particles have a common average orientation, and this, by simplifying the interpretation of the scattering patterns, increases the interest in them considerably. Thus it was noticed a long time ago that ramie fibers gave a low-angle scattering spot that was elongated in the direction perpendicular to the fiber axis. In the direction parallel to the fiber axis (the fiber is then placed perpendicular to the height of the beam if this is defined by slits), the scattering is not perceptible if measurements cannot be made at extremely small angles. This is immediate proof, in advance of any quantitative measurements, of the existence of elementary particles that are very

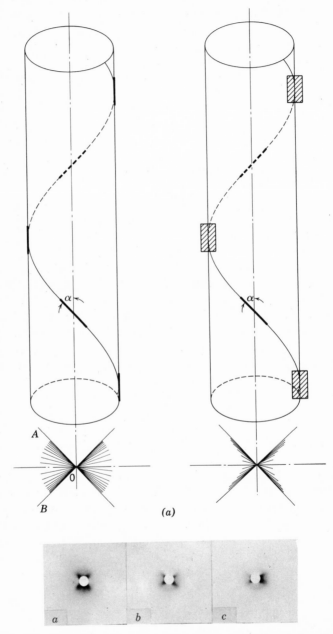

Fig. 58. (a) Small-angle scattering from cylindrical and lamellar micelles on a helix about the fiber axis; (b) small-angle patterns of vegetable fibers: a, coir; b, Tula ixtle; c, Jaumave ixtle. (Heyn [446].)

elongated in the direction of the fiber axis.   Hosemann [80] has succeeded
in estimating the length of these cellulose micelles as being greater than
3000 A.

The first result to be obtained from the patterns is therefore the demon-
stration of the form and orientation of the elementary particles in a very
simple, qualitative manner.   Heyn [442] has studied vegetable fibers, in
which the micelles are arranged in spirals around the fiber axis.   The
pattern is composed of a cross, the angle between the branches being
twice the angle that the axis of the micelles makes with the fiber axis.
This pattern can be explained by assuming that the micelles are not
cylindrical but are rather in the form of lamella.   To show this, let us
consider a cylindrical particle making the angle α with the fiber axis,
which is normal to the X-ray beam (see Fig. 58).   This causes a streak of
scattering elongated in the direction OX, the line of intersection with the
film of the plane normal to the axis of the micelle.   When the particle
rotates around the fiber axis, OX sweeps out $\angle AOB = 2\alpha$.   But the
variation of the intensity along OX will maintain itself more or less
constant throughout the interior of this angle because the average
inertial distance of the cylindrical particle in the direction of OX is
independent of the position of the particle.   On the other hand, if the
particle is a thin plate, the direction OX is parallel to the direction of
minimum thickness only for the limiting directions, OA and OB.   Therefore a cross rather than a fan-shaped pattern should be observed if the
particles have the form of lamella, and this is the result given by experiment.

Heyn [446] has also used small-angle scattering to show the orientation
phenomenon in fibers of viscose drawn under different conditions.

The fiber that has been studied the most with X-rays is cellulose, for
which the existence of a low-angle scattering in the form of a streak
perpendicular to the fiber axis was long ago observed (Mark (1932);
Kratky [466]; Hosemann [452]; P. H. Hermans [440]; etc.).   But it
cannot yet be said that a clear picture of the micelle structure of cellulose
has been achieved.   This structure is certainly very complex, and the
different investigators have tried to interpret the scattering patterns by
means of predetermined models which were necessarily oversimplified.
This has led to quite varied results which do not agree among themselves.

A method of quantitative interpretation of such a pattern, based on the
assumption of no interparticle interferences, was given in §4.1.1.2.   An
"average inertial distance" with respect to the fiber axis is obtained
(equation 4.11) that plays the role of a radius of gyration for disoriented
particles and that is a characteristic of the breadth of the particle perpendicular to its axis.   Heyn [447], in a study of different fibers in a wet,

swollen state, found quite linear curves of $\log I(h^2)$ and determined inertial distances of the order of 8 A for jute and 12 A for ramie. If the particles are cylindrical, these correspond to diameters of 22 and 35 A, respectively.

Many fibers give curves of $\log I(h^2)$ having a curvature too accentuated to allow a valid determination of the radius of gyration. Attempts have been made to determine the combination of particles of various sizes that would give the observed pattern. Hosemann [80], by applying the methods of §4.2.2, has determined the statistical distribution of the diameters of particles of acetylcellulose.

Nevertheless, the question arises whether it is legitimate to apply methods to cellulose fibers that are valid theoretically only for a system of particles of low concentration, since the known, rather high density of this fiber leads to the prediction that the micelles should be very tightly packed (see Bibliography for numerous papers by Kratky and Heyn). Actually this approximation is perhaps not as bad as could be feared, since the individual particles are not of uniform size. It has been shown (§2.3.3) that irregularity of sizes considerably diminishes the influence of interparticle interferences for random-shaped particles. It is just as true, however, that there are certainly cases in which the appearance of the scattering curve proves that interferences are playing a part (see §6.2.3).

A supplementary item of information, the *absolute value* of the scattered intensity, can also be used, as was done in comparing dry and wet cellulose (Fournet and Antzenberger [434']). This is not useful in finding *a priori* the structure of the cellulose, but it enables a decision to be made on whether a model of the structure is acceptable. As a result of this work, cellulose can no longer be considered as made up of particles isolated by empty spaces; rather we must assume the existence of dense particles having an ordered internal structure, each surrounded by amorphous, cellulosic matter of slightly lower density. The volume occupied by the "particles" is of the order of 25 per cent of the total volume, so that it is legitimate, for dry cellulose, to use the approximation of a dilute system. When the cellulose is swollen by water, the density of the intermediate regions becomes smaller and the contrast of the "particles" increases. This causes the very definite increase in the intensity scattered by the system that is observed experimentally. At the same time the particles become more organized (§6.2.3).

Kratky and his collaborators take as a base for their interpretation a model drawn from general knowledge about the structure of fibers. The micelles are taken to be in the form of thin platelets having large surfaces. These platelets are stacked on one another in an approximately parallel manner like pages in a book, but these "pages" are of irregular thicknesses and are separated from their neighbors by intervals that are also more or less irregular. The complete fiber is formed of groups of micelles having in common a general direction of the fiber but with slight misorientations. We have seen in a previous section that micellar plates of thickness d and random orientation in a system of low concentration give a scattered intensity in the region accessible to experiment which is proportional to

$$\frac{1}{h^2} d \left(\frac{\sin (hd/2)}{hd/2} \right)^2$$ (equation 2.41).[1] Furthermore a group of lamellar

micelles will give an intensity proportional to $h^{-2}\Phi$, where Φ is a one-dimensional function which depends on the distribution of empty and occupied segments on the normal to the plane of the lamellas. The method of Kratky and Porod [137] is thus to *multiply the observed intensity by h^2* and to interpret the resulting function Φ as the scattering pattern of a linear structure. This pattern depends not only on the distribution of thicknesses of the micelles but also on their arrangement. We have already pointed out (p. 70) that the importance of interferences is particularly great for linear structures. The controversies that have arisen between the partisans of the theory of isolated particles (which neglects interparticle interferences) and those who give these interferences a dominant place in the explanation of small-angle scattering phenomena have been obscured by the fact that the two groups are working from different models.

Zernicke and Prins [309], J. J. Hermans (1944), Porod [137], and Hosemann [276], [278] have calculated the scattering from different models of linear structures for given statistical distributions of segments and the intervals which separate them. One of these models is the following: Segments of equal length or with small fluctuations around an average length are separated by intervals such that the *degree of expansion*, that is, the ratio of the total length of the structure to the total length of the segments, is fixed. The total length of the intervals between segments is given, but the division of this length into individual intervals is randomly made. For an infinite degree of expansion we observe the scattering from isolated particles (Fig. 59), and as the density of the system increases the curve becomes deformed, just as was found for the closer packing of spherical particles (Fig. 12). The difference between these cases is that the intensity scattered by dense linear systems decreases in absolute value until it becomes zero when there is no interval between segments, whereas spheres in a compact structure still give a crystalline diffraction

[1] This expression describes equation 2.41 in a slightly modified form, where $1/R^2$ has been replaced by d; this follows from the fact that $R^2 d$ is proportional to n, the total number of electrons in the particle.

pattern.   Janeschitz-Kriegl [457] has studied the small-angle scattering pattern of threads of viscose in various degrees of distention.   By comparing the experimentally determined curve of $h^2I(h)$ with the group of curves of Fig. 59, he concluded that the micelles had an average thickness of 50 A with a fluctuation of 50 per cent, but the determination was not very accurate.

Another model is one of segments whose distribution of lengths follows a Gaussian curve, these segments being separated by *small, equal* intervals.

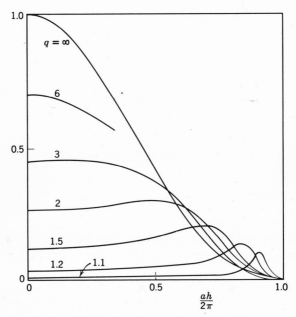

Fig. 59.   Scattered intensity from a linear structure composed of segments of uniform length, a, separated by intervals which follow the distribution law for perfect disorder, $H(y) = (1/b)e^{(-y/b)}$, where b is the average interval.   The degree of expansion, q, is equal to $(a + b)/a$.

This is therefore a very dense system.   The scattering curve is similar to that for a liquid or, rather, a paracrystal.   The intensity is very weak at very low angles, and there are large maxima in the neighborhood of the angles at which would be found the maxima from a linear lattice of period equal to the average micelle thickness.   When the fluctuations of thickness are large, only the first two such maxima are observable.   The experimental curve of $h^2I(h)$ for non-distended fibers of viscose [457] is of this type and gives a mean micelle thickness of 40 A.   However, the agreement between theoretical and experimental results is rather qualitative.

6.2.3. ORDERED ARRANGEMENTS OF MICELLES

Certain high polymers give a completely different type of small-angle scattering pattern. Instead of a scattering that decreases regularly from the center, bumps or maxima are observed that are more or less pronounced. These patterns are similar to those already pointed out in

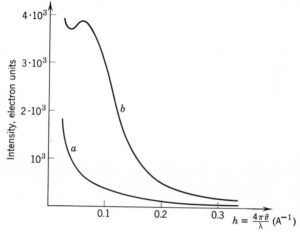

Fig. 60. Absolute measurements of the intensity per $C_6H_{10}O_5$ group scattered by ramie fiber. Curve a: dry fiber; curve b: wet fiber.

connection with concentrated solutions, but with the added complication that the pattern no longer has circular symmetry, showing lines or diffuse spots instead of rings.

This effect has been noted on patterns of substances such as moist cellulose (Figs. 60 and 61), the polyamides (nylon), and the polyethylenes

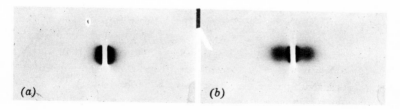

Fig. 61. Small-angle scattering pattern of "Fortisan" rayon. (a) Fiber in the dry state; (b) fiber swollen in water. Natural size of photograph; sample-to-film distance 20 cm.; Cu $K\alpha$ radiation. (Heyn (1953).)

[442], [441'], [441''], [480]. Although complete use has not yet been successfully made of the data, these observations apparently are the origin of an important application of small-angle scattering methods.

Figure 63 gives an idea of the effects that are observed. It should be noted that *the use of the photographic method is almost indispensable* in this kind of study. The general appearance of the pattern that will be found is not known *a priori*, and a correct interpretation of a Geiger-Müller counter measurement without previous photography would be practically impossible.

The explanation of these phenomena is based on the existence of an order among the particles, or, in a more general manner, on the existence of certain large-scale regularities in the density of matter.

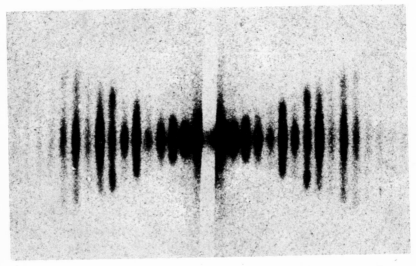

Fig. 62. Small-angle diffraction pattern from a plain, dry fiber of kangaroo tail tendon. Fundamental period of sample: $b_0 = 627$ A. (Bear and Bolduan [397].)

As we have already pointed out, the problem is simple when the sample can be considered in terms of a well-defined, true periodicity. The most typical example is provided by the fibers of collagen (kangaroo tail) (Bear and Bolduan [397]) (Fig. 62) or fibers of myosin, in which the periods along the fiber axis are respectively 700 and 146 A and in which the periodicity is so perfect that the pattern contains several tens of lines, up to very high orders (40th). In other substances periodicity exists in the plane perpendicular to the fiber axis. This structure is manifested by quite sharp lines, small in number (often only two), on the equator of the pattern. This is exemplified by chrysotile (Fankuchen and Schneider [434]) and by the tobacco mosaic virus. These can be explained by assuming that the molecules show a crystalline type of arrangement (hexagonal). The different molecules of tobacco mosaic virus are separated by a fixed distance; Bernal and Fankuchen [402] found this to be equal to 152 A for the dry state and 450 A when the virus is in solution. The arrangement is rather imperfect, resulting in a broadening of the reflections.

These viruses are exceptional cases. Generally the degree of regularity is much smaller, which seems natural, given the weak forces that can be exerted between the large basic units. The difficulties in interpreting the observed facts are consequently greater, and a complete explanation of the facts is still far from being achieved. Two methods of approach

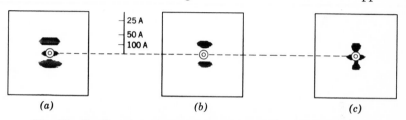

Fig. 63. Small-angle pattern of synthetic fibers. (a) Copolamide, stretched, $T = 20°$ C; (b) same material, stretched, $T = 200°$ C; (c) same material drawn from the melt, unstretched, $T = 20°$ C. Fiber axis vertical. Scale given in terms of $\dfrac{\lambda}{2 \sin \theta} = \dfrac{2\pi}{h}$ A. (Hess and Kiessig [441'].)

are generally adopted: the use of either a model of a perturbed crystal in which there is no long-range order (a paracrystal) or a model of a gaseous arrangement in which the disposition of neighboring molecules is somewhat ordered. At present we can only repeat the conclusions offered in the discussion of ordering between molecules of proteins or soaps. It is dangerous to apply results valid for crystalline arrangements to these cases without caution. The application of Bragg's law should be distrusted, even when it is believed to be "corrected" by the use of a factor somewhat larger than unity (1.23, 1.22, 1.16, 1.05, etc.).

It is certainly regrettable that these negative remarks cannot be followed by a correct general interpretation, but this has not yet been developed.

As an example of the general case, let us consider the patterns of synthetic polyamide fibers (Hess and Kiessig [441'], [441"]). In addition to a central spot elongated perpendicular to the fiber axis, the pattern also contains two other regions of scattering whose aspect and position vary according to the treatment given to the fiber (Fig. 63). For example, a copolamide gives rise to two rather diffuse streaks perpendicular to the fiber axis. The centers of these streaks are found by Bragg's law to correspond to a distance of the order of 80 A. Hess and Kiessig proposed as a model of this structure a regular arrangement of micelles with a periodicity of 80 A along the fiber axis. The smearing out of the spots was interpreted as being the result of the small number of micelles coherently grouped together. When the temperature of the fiber is raised, the distance of the spots from the center of the pattern diminishes a little, which, according to the above model, would mean that the periodicity increases by a lengthening of the elementary micelle. But, in trying to take account of all the observations, this model leads to contradictions, as Hosemann [84] has pointed out. If it were true that the width of the spot, interpreted as a crystalline reflection, is due to the limited size of the crystallite, a diffuse spot of the same size should be found around the center of the pattern, the (000) reflection, as was pointed out on p. 163. This is not the case; although different treatments of the fiber can modify the two other spots, the central spot does not vary. Moreover, no spots corresponding to higher orders of reflection have been detected. Thus the "crystalline" model is not a useful approximation. The starting point for a correct explanation is to suppose that the fiber contains micelles between which there is a lower density of matter. These micelles are distributed with a certain *degree of order*, particularly in the direction of the fiber axis. This organization of the micelles among themselves will cause the large scattering maxima that are observed. It may be possible to define this organization quantitatively but only on two conditions: (1) We must begin with a scattering curve that has been well determined experimentally. This means that a counter should be used to determine precisely the shape of the scattering distribution that the photographic technique has revealed. (2) We must consider the complete curve of the scattering. *The simple determination of the position of the maximum has no significance.* This maximum, in fact, can be displaced either by a change in the organization of the micelles, as, for example, when the organization becomes more regular (see p. 140), or by the agglomeration of a larger number of micelles *without the micelles themselves changing dimensions.* These effects are opposite to those foreseen by Hess and Kiessig. This shows, for example, that the theory of the effect of temperature can be completely changed.

A detailed quantitative study of the large-scale organization of polymers in fibers has not yet actually been approached. Not only are the experimental data merely qualitative (the observations of Heikins, Hermans, and Weidinger [439] on the fiber G, moist "Fortisan," and those of Kratky, Schauenstein, and Sekora [470] on natural silk), but also the theoretical difficulties have not yet been fully resolved. The progress already accomplished in the study of imperfect crystalline structures leads to the hope that this new aspect of the structure of polymers, the importance of which cannot be questioned, will soon be taken up. In any event the experimental techniques are already sufficient to undertake this kind of work.

6.3. FINELY DISPERSED SOLIDS. CATALYSTS

We shall now consider the case in which the particle is no longer a molecule but is instead a grain of matter of very small dimensions, as for example those found in colloidal suspensions or in extremely fine powders such as certain catalysts. The problem is to carry out a granulometric measurement with X-rays when the grains are too small to be studied by other methods. The particle dimensions most favorable to an X-ray study are from several tens to a thousand angstroms. This upper limit can certainly be exceeded with X-rays, but the experimental difficulties involved in a measurement of a dimension of, let us say, 5000 A (0.50 μ) are not justified in practice, since other methods are much simpler for particles of this size.

The major difficulty limiting the effectiveness of X-ray measurements is that in general the particles are not uniform in either size or form. Also, if the sample is in the form of a powder, the particles are generally packed closely against one another. This represents therefore the least favorable case for the interpretation of small-angle scattering. Realizing the complexity of the data, there is no hope of drawing from the *single* scattering curve $I(h)$ a complete description of the distribution of forms and sizes of the particles being studied. Calculations such as those made for molecules in concentrated solutions are not at all applicable.

Nevertheless, there is an important favorable element in this problem, which is that the non-uniformity in the sizes of the particles diminishes the influence of interferences even between nearest neighboring particles (p. 70). It is therefore not unreasonable to assume that the observed intensity is the sum of the intensities diffracted by the individual particles.

The first studies of fine powders based on theories for the low-angle part of the scattering curve have been able to give only qualitative results. There are almost always large particles in the mixture for which these theories are not valid, so that it is only rarely that an average radius of gyration can be obtained which has real significance (§4.2.1). The attempts at determining the distribution of grain sizes depend so greatly on the initial hypotheses that the results should be applied only with many precautions.

The methods of analysis based on theories for the tails of the scattering curve (§4.2.3) seem capable of giving more interesting results. In no case can a complete picture of the structure be given by small-angle scattering experiments, but a parameter whose definition is quite precise, the *specific surface* of the specimen, can be successfully obtained without resort to arbitrary hypotheses. Likewise, the radius of gyration can be determined accurately and without arbitrary hypotheses from experiments on dilute systems of particles of uniform size. Since the specific surface is a very important property of fine powders, the methods of analysis of §4.2.3 should give rise to very interesting applications. These methods, however, are too new for a sure judgment of their practical value to be given.

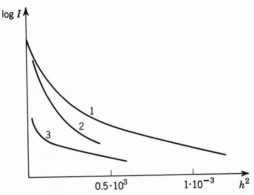

Fig. 64. Log $I(h^2)$ for three samples of carbon black: 1. Standard grade 6, channel black. 2. Sample P33; large particles formed by thermal decomposition. 3. Carbolac 1; channel black of extremely fine particle size. (Biscoe and Warren [10].)

6.3.1. CARBONS

Several varieties of carbon, both artificial and natural, are found in very fine grain sizes. As a matter of fact, it was on these substances that small-angle scattering was first observed and immediately attributed to the state of division of the matter. The pattern of small-angle scattering is very dependent on the type of carbon. Practically invisible for anthracite, it is intense and contained within small angles for lampblack; it becomes more or less enlarged for the different preparations of carbon black, and, finally, it is very intense and extends over a large angular region for certain active carbons. A typical example is given by the comparison of three carbon blacks used as a charge in the rubber industry. Figure 64 reproduces the curves obtained by Biscoe and Warren [10], represented as curves of log $I(h^2)$. The characteristic of each of these, the general rule in studies of powders, is that *the curves of log $I(h^2)$ are not linear* but are curved in such a way that the slope increases with decreasing scattering angle. The intensity increases so rapidly as the small angles are approached that it is not possible to obtain the complete curve by photometry of a single film; a series of films of different exposures must be made and their results combined. Two situations can occur. As in curve 1, the variation in slope may become small enough near the low-angle limit so that an extrapolation of the curve to zero-angle is possible. This means that the largest particles in the sample do not have a radius of gyration too large to escape the measurement (p. 149). The slope at the origin then gives the average radius of gyration as defined in §4.2.1 ($R_0 = 210$ A). In the other case (curves 2 and 3), the curvature of the curve at small angles is such that an accurate extrapolation cannot be made. The average radius of gyration cannot be measured without extending the measurements to smaller scattering angles. All that can be said is that there is a lower limit to the average radius. The interpretation of these curves can only be qualitative. The general aspect of the curves shows that sample 2 contains many large particles and only a few small ones. In sample 3 there is apparently a mixture of large particles with a large proportion of very small particles, the large particles giving rise to the very steep initial part of the curve and the small particles causing the only slightly inclined tail of the curve.

If the statistical methods described in §4.2.2 are applied, it is necessary to make use of a very precise experimental curve extended down to very small angles. It is necessary, furthermore, to apply corrections to this curve for the effects of slit height (§3.4.2), and these corrections are not negligible for curves of $\log I(h^2)$ that are very non-linear.

6.3.1.1. Practical Study of Carbon Blacks

Although it is difficult to obtain a rigorous description of the grains of a sample, the X-ray data can nevertheless have useful technical applications. The scattering curve by itself characterizes the state of division of the matter and often can be used to distinguish the various qualities of carbon blacks and even to classify them qualitatively as to degree of fineness. Such information is simple to obtain. The intensity scattered by carbons is very high; it is not necessary to *monochromatize* the radiation, and the Geiger-Müller counter measurements, which are preferable to photography, are very rapid.

It has been reported [126'] that satisfactory results can be obtained with a commercial spectrometer to which only very simple modifications and adjustments have been made (it is necessary to use small slits and to place the sample holder so that the powder sample, in the form of a plate of appropriate thickness, is normal to the incident beam). The results of the measurements are much more interesting if care has been taken to insure that the scattering mass has been held constant for a series of samples. To illustrate this, let us consider the following schematic example: one carbon black is made up entirely of fine particles, and a second is made up of 50 per cent of the same particles and 50 per cent of grains which are so large that they produce no scattering in the accessible angular region. The two scattering curves will be superposable, but, if the scattering masses are the same, the intensity from the second sample will be only one-half the absolute value of that given by the first. Therefore, if only fine particles are active particles, the quality of the sample is directly characterized by the absolute value of the scattered intensity.

The proper execution of such an experiment requires that the X-ray tube input and the geometry of the scattering apparatus be held constant. The constancy of the scattering mass, also necessary, can be easily maintained, as, for example, by the following technique: a *fixed mass of powder* is placed in a small cylindrically shaped cup with a mica bottom. The powder is spread into a uniform layer and then compressed by a cover that also has a mica window. In this manner the mass per unit surface will be the same for all the samples, and, since the cross section of the beam is invariant, the scattering mass is then constant from one experiment to the next.

6.3.1.2. Structure of Different Varieties of Carbon

Brusset [13], [18] has used small-angle scattering to compare natural carbons of various origins and has shown that they are differentiable from the point of view of their granular structure. Riley [141] found an anthracite from Wales that gave a very singular pattern containing a ring of scattering. Riley compared this pattern to those of liquids and suggested that in the carbon there were particles in contact with one another. Let us point out that analogous patterns have been found for age-hardening alloys (p. 204) and that a different interpretation has been given them. This interpretation involved particles which were isolated but showed internal density variations. It would be interesting to see whether an analogous explanation could be valid for these carbons.

R. E. Franklin [56'], [56″] has studied the structure of carbon blacks obtained by carbonization of organic substances. She obtained an atomic distribution function such as is obtained for liquids by a Fourier inversion of the complete intensity curve, including both the small-angle scattering and the high-angle diffraction maxima. In this way she determined at the same time both the structure of the carbon and the dimensions of the particles. These particles were for the most part isolated layers of the graphite structure, the particle produced by pyrolysis of polyvinylidene chloride at 1000° C. having a diameter of only 16 A. The size of the particles increased with the temperature of carbonization. Franklin also used a Fourier transformation to interpret only the curve of small-angle scattering. However, this transform, analogous to the characteristic function of Porod [137] (§2.4.3), does not have a simple physical significance because of the non-uniformity of the particles and because of their interactions.

Another interesting example is that of activated charcoal. Cocoanut charcoal, before activation treatment, gives only a rather limited and weak, low-angle scattering. However, after activation the scattering is extremely intense and extends out to angles of several degrees. Actually, this is the substance that gives the strongest low-angle scattering observed.

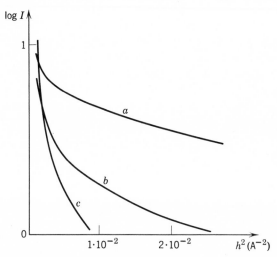

Fig. 65. Log $I(h^2)$ for activated charcoals: (a) activated cocoanut charcoal; (b) and (c) charcoal activated by two different treatments. (Brusset [13].)

The curve of log $I(h^2)$ for this sample shows a very pronounced curvature followed by a long linear part of small slope (Fig. 65). It might then be said that the sample is made up of a mixture of particles of very different sizes, the smallest particles having a radius of gyration not larger than 10 A. Yet, given the method of activation of the charcoal, this model is not satisfactory, for it is known that the activation does not have the effect of producing a fine powder but rather that it produces cavities in the interior of a grain by dissociation of the tarry substances that fill it. The active surface is thus increased, which gives large absorbing properties to the charcoal.

The model of isolated material particles is, therefore, completely inadequate in this problem. We could more validly adopt the opposite point of view, the small holes in the interior of grains of large dimensions playing the role of small scattering particles. The important factor in the scattering is the difference in density between the particle and the surrounding medium; two complementary objects (Fig. 66) in which the holes of one correspond to the solid parts of the other give exactly the same scattering pattern in the region accessible to experiment (§2.2.2.2). The 10 A radius of gyration would accordingly correspond to the smallest pores of the active charcoal.

It would certainly be quite interesting to undertake measurements of the specific surface of carbons by the method of §4.2.3. This would be a precise and probably convenient method for characterizing the porosity of a carbon.

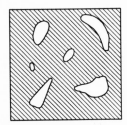 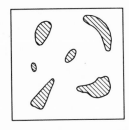

Fig. 66.   A sketch of the structure of two complementary objects.

6.3.2. CATALYSTS

This is a domain in which the applications of small-angle scattering are the most immediate since the granulometry of a catalyst is an important factor in the value of the product.

Pulverized catalytic nickel is obtained by various processes. It is known that Raney nickel is more active than Sabatier nickel, and small-angle scattering shows immediately that the first is made up of much smaller grains than the second [65].

The difficulties of interpretation already pointed out for the carbons are found again for the catalysts. Nevertheless, determinations of the statistical distribution of grain sizes have been successfully made. Elkin, Shull, and Roess [41] applied the method of §4.2.2 to desiccated silica and alumina gels as well as to oxides of nickel and iron. Then, from the measured distribution of grain sizes, they calculated the specific surface of the catalyst and obtained good agreement with the result given by classical gas adsorption methods. This very interesting result gives some confidence in the hypotheses used in the calculations and shows that at least in certain cases a precise analysis of the patterns deserves to be made.

As has been done for the carbon blacks, certain laboratories are beginning to use small-angle scattering to characterize a catalyst from a technical standpoint. The following example makes the most of the advantages of this method.

Van Nordstrand and Hach [126'] showed that the form of the scattering curve was progressively modified as an alumina catalyst was subjected to heating at higher and higher temperatures, the small particles disappearing by partial fusion. If a catalyst has partially lost its activity after

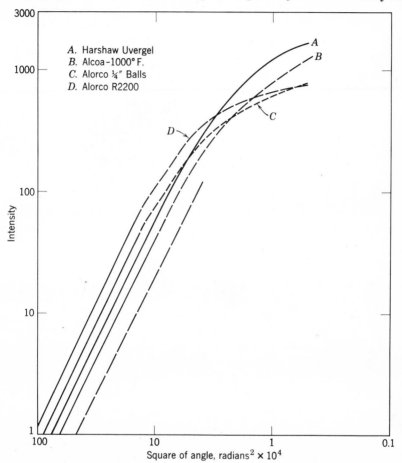

Fig. 67. Log I vs. log h^2 for different samples of alumina catalysts. The dotted line shows the theoretical h^{-4} dependence. (Van Nordstrand and Hach [126'].)

use, this can arise from two causes: either a part of the product has been rendered completely inactive, the rest still being good, or else the whole catalyst has been slightly modified. The remedies to be considered are different in the two cases. Small-angle scattering will allow a sure diagnosis: in the first, the form of the curve will not have varied, but its absolute intensity will have decreased; in the second, the form of the curve is modified.   The same authors found empirically that the intensity scattered at rather large angles varied as h^{-4} (Fig. 67) and that in this region the intensity at a given angle for a given mass of catalyst was proportional to the specific surface of the catalyst as determined by the nitrogen adsorption method (Fig. 68).   This is an excellent verification of Porod's theory (§2.4.3), though it was apparently unknown to these authors.   After a preliminary calibration a measurement of the specific surface could be made with X-rays in five minutes with a very simple

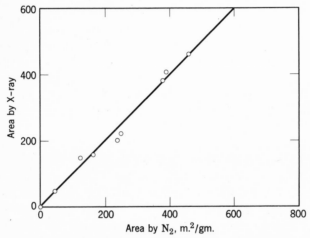

Fig. 68.   Specific surface areas as measured by X-rays and by nitrogen adsorption. (Van Nordstrand and Hach [126'].)

apparatus such as a commercial Geiger counter spectrometer (p. 95). They found also that the measurement of small-angle scattering curves could sometimes advantageously replace the determination of gaseous adsorption-desorption isotherms.

6.3.3. COLLOIDAL SOLUTIONS

Colloidal micelles generally are of a size favorable to study by X-rays, and when colloids of high atomic weight, such as certain metals, are considered, the very high intensity of the small-angle scattering makes the measurement easy to carry out.

Fournet [48] studied a solution of colloidal silver and obtained a curve of log $I(h^2)$ which had a long linear part; from this the radius of gyration could be easily determined, the result being 50 A.   The same colloid after flocculation gave a curve of log $I(h^2)$, which could be superposed almost exactly with the curve of the first solution except at very small angles. This shows that, although flocculation has caused a drawing together of the particles, only a small percentage of them at the most have clustered into larger units. This experiment shows also that it is legitimate to apply the theory of widely separated particles to systems of a rather high density if the particles of the system are only slightly non-uniform.

The results of this experiment were confirmed by a measurement with the electron microscope. The micelles appeared as approximately spherical particles with a rather uniform diameter of about 120.A. The sphere of radius of gyration of 50 A has a diameter of 130 A.

Porod [137] found that colloidal molybdic acid in the dry state gave a different pattern from that of the solution, the pattern showing a ring of scattering rather than the pattern of isolated particles. The difference in the behavior of this colloid as compared to silver may be associated with the fact that, whereas flocculation of silver is irreversible, it is reversible for molybdic acid.

6.4. SUBMICROSCOPIC HETEROGENEITIES IN SOLIDS. APPLICATIONS TO PHYSICAL METALLURGY

The existence of small-angle scattering is in a very general way characteristic of the existence of submicroscopic heterogeneities in the scatterer. The example in which the scatterer is composed of small, separate particles is only a particular case of which we have seen numerous applications (solutions, suspensions, and powders). A continuous solid can also give rise to low-angle scattering if its *electronic density shows fluctuations*, the particular conditions having been analyzed in §2.4.1. We have already mentioned several examples in which the sample was not composed of distinct particles (certain fibers of high polymers). We shall now consider certain metals and alloys that offer interesting examples of heterogeneities. Often these heterogeneities have been disclosed only by the phenomenon of small-angle scattering.

6.4.1. HETEROGENEITIES IN PURE METALS

We shall not consider here either metals in the form of fine powders or metals in the form of colloidal grains, since these problems have already been discussed.

Several experiments (Blin and Guinier [11']; Blin (1954); Hayes and Smoluchowski [74''']) have shown that a piece of metal that to the eye or even to the microscope is pure, sound, and homogeneous can give rise to small-angle scattering. Since this is very weak in intensity, its study requires a well-designed apparatus from which all parasitic scattering has been eliminated. A Geiger-Müller counter must be used as the detector, since photographic techniques are not of high enough sensitivity. The sample should be in the form of a thin plate whose thickness is approximately the optimum thickness for transmission experiments (p. 88), that is, of the order of some hundredths of a millimeter.

This scattering appears when the metal has been severely cold-worked, particularly by tensile elongation. It has been observed on nickel, copper, aluminum, and zinc. The scattering is of the continuous type, the intensity decreasing with increasing distance from the center of the pattern. The curve traced with the usual coordinates ($\log I(h^2)$) shows a rather long linear part that corresponds to a radius of gyration of the order of 6 A. When the cold-worked metal is annealed, the scattering at small angles is not modified until recovery has been completed. Then the scattered intensity becomes stronger at very small angles and decreases much more rapidly with increasing scattering angle, so that the curve of $\log I(h^2)$ corresponds to a much larger radius of gyration.

Thus far we have not tried to interpret these observations in terms of the structure of the sample. The values of the radii of gyration serve only to summarize the facts in a rather convenient form that allows us to contrive probable models of the structure. Lattice defects, such as dislocations, introduced by deformation of the metal, produce at the most only very small variations in density, and these are certainly so localized that they cannot be invoked to explain this scattering phenomenon. Moreover, such defects produce a broadening of the Debye-Scherrer lines, and actually there is no positive correlation between this broadening and the observed scattering at small angles. Vacancies or missing atoms in the lattice also correspond to a radius of gyration that is too small. We are therefore led to the assumption that the heterogeneities found in a deformed metal are submicroscopic cavities formed by the coalescence of vacancies, these cavities, *if they are spherical*, having a diameter of the order of 15 A. It is natural to assume that the form of the cavities would depend on the directions of the stresses experienced by the metal. Their shapes, therefore, would not be spherical, but it is difficult to describe them more precisely.

These cavities are not sensitive to anneals at low temperatures at which the atomic mobility is small, since the lattice could then become more perfect only by local rearrangement of the atoms. At high temperatures, at the point at which the metal is transformed by the appearance of new recrystallized crystals, these cavities either disappear or are eventually fused together to give a smaller number of much larger cavities retained in the recrystallized metal.

The hypothesis of the existence of cavities in the deformed metal is confirmed by the slightly smaller density of the metal after cold-working. However, such measurements of density are very critical and are not sufficiently precise, so that apparently this new aspect of imperfections in metals can be more easily studied with X-rays.

6.4.2. HETEROGENEITIES IN SOLID SOLUTIONS

The schematic structure of a solid solution is the following: the atoms of the various constituent metals are distributed on the lattice points of a single lattice.   Such a solution is certainly homogeneous on a microscopic scale but is not so on an atomic scale.   The heterogeneities can become important if the distribution of atoms is not perfectly random, as, for example, if the atoms of one type tend to agglomerate into clusters.   In such circumstances, moreover, the predominance of one type of atom in a cluster can lead to a deformation of its lattice, the atoms being displaced more or less from the lattice points of the average lattice of the solid solution.   These irregularities or defects in periodicity, arising both from the nature of the atoms and from their positions, modify the crystalline reflections and cause abnormal diffuse scattering outside the positions of the Bragg reflections.   In particular, small-angle scattering can appear.

The study of the real structure of a solid solution requires a knowledge of the complete pattern of scattering and diffraction and not solely a knowledge of the small-angle region of the pattern.   Nevertheless, in the following paragraphs we shall consider only the consequences of small-angle scattering in order to show how simply this furnishes conditions that have to be satisfied by the structure models contrived to explain the total pattern.   It is therefore essential that the small-angle part of the X-ray pattern be not neglected in any such study.   It is impossible to explore the very-small-angle region with standard large-angle diffraction apparatus, and consequently investigators who have limited themselves to such equipment have often been led to propose structure models that are in contradiction with the results drawn from the simple appearance of the small-angle scattering patterns.

6.4.2.1. Equilibrium Solid Solutions

When an alloy is at a temperature such that the solid solution is the only equilibrium phase and at which there is no ordered state, as, for example, all dilute solid solutions, it was thought for a long time that the equilibrium state of the solid solution was one of perfect disorder.   More precisely stated, this means that the nature of an atom has no influence at all on the nature of the atoms that occupy neighboring sites in the lattice.

The number of atoms of one type in a volume containing a given number of lattice sites will undergo statistical fluctuations about the mean value required by the composition of the alloy. There is a certain probability, therefore, that a group of atoms of one type can be accidentally produced on a group of neighboring sites. This probability can be easily calculated, and it of course rapidly becomes very small when the number of sites in the group increases. These fluctuations of composition correspond to local fluctuations of electronic density and thus cause a *scattering at small angles*.

A simple calculation shows that this scattering is independent of the scattering angle.[1] If the sample is a binary alloy, AB, containing p

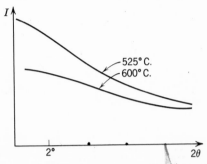

Fig. 69. Scattered intensity from an equilibrium solid solution of Al-Ag (20 per cent Ag by weight) at two temperatures. (Walker, Blin, and Guinier [169].)

atomic per cent of atoms of type B, the scattered intensity per atom of the solid solution is: $I = I_e p(1 - p) (f_A - f_B)^2$, where f_A and f_B designate the scattering factors of the two types of atoms, equal to the atomic numbers at zero angle, and where I_e is the intensity scattered by one electron. This formula, first deduced by Laue, is a particular application of the general relation, equation 2.72.

The intensity of this scattering is very weak. Even in the favorable circumstance of an equiatomic mixture of atoms of very different atomic numbers, it is just at the limit of the intensity measurable with a very sensitive Geiger-Müller counter-equipped apparatus.

Walker, Blin, and Guinier [169] measured the scattering from an Al–Ag alloy containing 20 weight per cent Ag at a temperature at which the solid solution is in equilibrium ($T > 450°$ C.). The scattered intensity shows a maximum at zero-angle and is considerably stronger than the intensity predicted by Laue's equation. The maximum in the scattering at zero-angle becomes less pronounced at higher temperatures (Fig. 69). These experiments show that the atoms are not distributed completely at random. The atoms of silver have a tendency to bunch

[1] Aside from the slow decrease with angle due to the variation of the atomic scattering factors.

together and form very small nuclei rich in silver. As we have already stated, such nuclei can be produced in a perfectly disordered crystal by statistical fluctuations, but the experiment proves that there are more such nuclei than would be predicted by the statistics of an ideally disordered state. These results are in agreement with the theoretical discussion of binary solid solutions given by Fournet (1953a). The very slow decrease of the scattered intensity with increasing angle allows the inference that the nuclei are very small.

The value of a radius of gyration would not have much meaning, since these nuclei are certainly non-uniform both in size and shape. There is a special method for interpreting the experimental data in this case which was first used to determine the degree of short-range order in solid solutions. By means of a Fourier transformation of the experimental curve we can determine the probability of finding two atoms of silver at distances equal to those of first neighbors, second neighbors, etc., in the lattice. This is related to the function $\gamma(r)$ introduced in §2.4.3. This method, however, requires a knowledge not simply of the scattering curve at small angles but of the total scattering curve. Another method consists of calculating the function $I(h)$ theoretically and comparing this with the experimental curve (Fournet (1953b)). The complete solution of the problem thus extends beyond our particular subject. Nevertheless, from the small-angle scattering we can obtain qualitative proof of the existence of clusters of atoms, and it can be immediately seen that these clusters can only be of small size.

6.4.2.2. Supersaturated Solid Solutions: Age-Hardening

The heterogeneities that we have discussed so far have been rather small and, consequently, have produced a small-angle scattering that is very weak in intensity and difficult to study. Intense scattering phenomena have been observed, however, for certain supersaturated solid solutions, that is, solutions that are out of the region of single-phase equilibrium.

Let us consider a binary solid solution, AB, for which the limit of solubility of B in A increases with temperature. The solid solution at a given composition is in equilibrium above a temperature T_0 (Fig. 70); it is in this region of temperature that the experiments described in the preceding section have been made. When this solid solution is brought to room temperature by quenching, it is no longer in the equilibrium state; indeed, the room-temperature equilibrium state consists of two phases, a solid solution α of normal concentration and a β phase in which the excess dissolved B atoms are assembled.

By thermal treatments at fairly low temperatures ($T < T_0$) the solid solution can be made to evolve towards the stable state. Generally the most stable state, corresponding to the precipitation of the β phase, is not produced directly. The precipitation is preceded by intermediate stages in which the excess atoms are clustered together but do not yet form the true final precipitate. These structural transformations are shown by a betterment of the mechanical properties of the alloy called age-hardening.

The heterogeneities of the hardened alloy are too small in size to be visible to the microscope, but they can cause observable small-angle

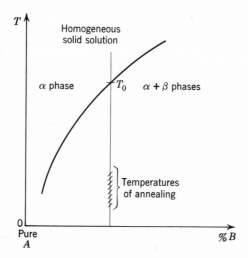

Fig. 70.   Schematic phase diagram of an age-hardening alloy.

scattering. This scattering plays a fundamental role in the study of age-hardening, a phenomenon that is not only of scientific interest in the development of the physics of metals but also of considerable technical interest, in that it affects many applications of light alloys. As we have already pointed out, it is somewhat artificial to isolate the study of scattering at small angles from the rest of the pattern. However, we shall stress particularly the direct information that the small-angle scattering can provide, especially when the simplicity of the phenomena makes the method useful for technical applications.

6.4.2.3. Structural Characteristics Directly Related to the Small-Angle Scattering

The difficulty in studies of the structure of hardened alloys arises from the simultaneous presence of lattice deformations and local changes in composition produced by the clustering of the dissolved atoms. It is for precisely such a condition that an interpretation is facilitated by the consideration of small-angle phenomena. This follows from two properties of small-angle scattering which, in view of their importance in this matter, we shall recall at this time.

1. *Small-angle scattering depends primarily on heterogeneities of composition and little, if at all, on deformations of the lattice.* A schematic example will demonstrate this.

Let us suppose that in the lattice of a solid solution the dissolved *B* atoms assemble in irregularly arranged small clusters or *zones* without

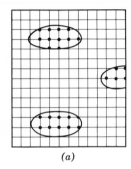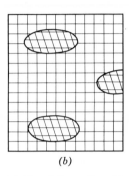

(a)   (b)

Fig. 71. (a) Structure of a zone without lattice deformation. Foreign atoms have clustered on the matrix lattice sites. (b) Inclusion in the matrix lattice of a grain with a different lattice but with the same composition.

producing any deformation of the general lattice (Fig. 71). The local heterogeneities, in which the electronic density is different from that of the surrounding medium, will cause small-angle scattering similar to that produced by small, isolated particles of the same exterior form. But, in addition, the small particles in this case are small crystals; they will therefore produce high-angle diffraction spots also, these being somewhat enlarged as a result of the small particle size. It can be shown (§5.1) that each point in the reciprocal lattice, including the origin or (000) point, is replaced by a small diffracting region centered on each point. This is the explanation of the broadening of Bragg diffraction spots. The essential conclusion to be drawn from this calculation is that the regions around each of the points are identical, any one being derivable from any other by a simple translation. Thus, if the alloy shows heterogeneity without deformation, the study of the scattering in the neighborhood of the center gives all the information that can be furnished by X-ray diffraction.

Now let us consider as a second example the opposite case, deformation in a lattice of uniform composition. Let us suppose that the lattice of a homogeneous solid solution includes regions in which the lattice has slightly different parameters from those of the matrix. The fluctuations of the parameters are necessarily small, since metals always have a compact structure, so that the density of the medium can undergo only very small variations. Therefore, since the whole metal has a quasi-constant density, there is no scattering at the center of the pattern. On the other hand, the Bragg angle of a given high-angle reflection will vary for the regions with different lattices, the variations in parameters producing an effect which is greater, the larger the Bragg angle of the reflection (the higher the indices of the reflection). The primary reciprocal lattice points will be surrounded by a region of diffraction whose extent will increase in proportion to the distance of the point from the center. *The center itself is not surrounded by any scattering region.*

Another type of deformation that is often found in face-centered cubic metallic structures is the slippage of (111) planes over one another. This causes the formation of more or less extended regions with a hexagonal close-packed structure which are called stacking faults (Barrett (1952), p. 259). These stacking faults produce regions of scattering around certain reciprocal lattice points that are elongated along the [111] lines of the reciprocal lattice normal to the (111) planes showing the faults. *There is no scattering around the center*, since, regardless of the mode of stacking of the (111) planes, the density remains rigorously constant at all points of the metal lattice.

2. The two simple examples discussed above form extreme cases between which are those structures generally found in practice, where a variation in composition is connected with a deformation of the lattice, either in that the B atoms have a different diameter from the A, or in that there is a tendency of the cluster to form a crystalline structure different from that of the original lattice. The distribution of the regions of scattering in reciprocal space can then become very complex, but to a first approximation *the scattering in the neighborhood of the center depends only on the exterior surface of the heterogeneous regions and not on their internal structure.* Hence, if in the example of Fig. 71b we suppose that the atoms of the zones are B atoms or at least a mixture containing a large proportion of B, the small-angle scattering phenomena will be exactly the same as for the case of Fig. 71a. The variations of the parameters will have no influence on this scattering.

In order that the small-angle scattering be intense enough to be detectable, it is necessary that the variations in electronic density be large and, consequently, that there be a large difference between the atomic numbers of the alloying elements. When these elements are adjacent or near neighbors in the periodic table, *the method is not applicable.* This is true for alloys such as Al–Mg or Al–Si, and also for Cu–Zn and Ni–Fe.

6.4.3. EXAMPLES OF SMALL-ANGLE SCATTERING BY AGE-HARDENING ALLOYS

It is found that, in the different systems of age-hardening alloys that have been studied, the small-angle scattering patterns present quite varied appearances, showing that the process of precipitation varies according to the nature of the atoms. We shall give examples corresponding to two quite distinct types, stressing only the manner in which the X-ray technique is utilized, and not the results pertinent to the field of physical metallurgy.

6.4.3.1. Aluminum-Silver Alloy: First Stage of Hardening

The metal is an alloy containing 20 weight per cent of silver. After an anneal at a temperature greater than 450° C. (the temperature at which the alloy becomes homogeneous) the sample is brought to room temperature by a rapid quench and then studied after anneals of various lengths at temperatures of the order of 50 to 200° C.

The sample is prepared in the form of a thin foil of suitable thickness (0.04 mm. for Cu $K\alpha$ radiation). It is preferable, as we have already pointed out, to begin the investigation with the use of photographic techniques, since it is not possible to predict *a priori* the appearance of the low-angle scattering in these cases.

Two facts can be drawn from the first observations ([170], Walker and Guinier (1953), Belbéoch and Guinier (1954)):

1. The patterns are the same regardless of the state of crystallization of the metal, whether it be in a microcrystallized state (cold-worked) or whether it be a single crystal of arbitrary orientation.

2. The scattering does not decrease continuously from a maximum at zero-angle (Fig. 72). Instead, when the height of the beam has been reduced sufficiently, the pattern has the form of a rather sharply defined ring whose diameter varies according to the thermal treatment given the sample. The mean scattering angle of the ring corresponds by Bragg's law to a distance of the order of magnitude of 50 A. We have already called attention to other low-angle scattering patterns that contained a ring of scattering (§4.1.2.2), but the ring is more sharply defined in this case, and, more important, the intensity of the scattering inside the ring is very weak near the center.

It is obvious that one must try to interpret these observations in terms of the formation of clusters of silver atoms. Since the orientation of the crystal has no effect on the appearance of the pattern, it can be concluded that these clusters are isotropic and have a symmetry which at least on the average is rigorously spherical. But, in order that the scattering not be a

maximum at zero-angle, it would be necessary that the particles show
a very strong interaction between themselves, analogous to the interaction between the molecules of a liquid.   This was the interpretation
advanced by Riley [141] for the ring observed on the small-angle patterns

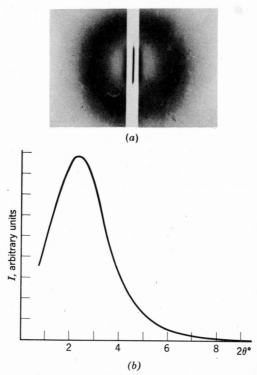

(a)

(b)

Fig. 72.   (a) Small-angle scattering from Al-Ag (20 per cent Ag by
weight) water-quenched from 520° C.   (b) A graph of intensity vs.
scattering angle for this sample.

of certain carbons.   However, this model of a structure does not seem
very probable for an alloy.   A ring of such sharpness could only come
from close-packed particles of a very uniform size.   How can this
regularity be justified?   In addition, when the alloy is annealed, the ring
remains sharply defined and contracts.   This would mean that the
clusters become uniformly larger and change into another close-packed
arrangement in which the interparticle distances are somewhat greater.
Such a transformation is difficult to imagine.

Another model, which is more acceptable, has been proposed by Walker
and Guinier (1953).   It is assumed that there are independent particles
that do not give rise to interparticle interferences, and that the single

particle has such an internal structure as to give a ring-type pattern instead of the classical continuous scattering curves. We have already called attention to an analogous interpretation for hemocyanine (p. 174). Actually, if the particles we considered in Chapter 2 have continually decreasing scattering curves, it is because their structure can be assumed to be of effectively uniform density. The scattering curve can become much more complex, however, if there are regions of different electronic density in the interior of each particle.

When the silver atoms cluster around a particular point in the solid solution, they migrate by diffusion, but as the annealing temperature is not very high the atoms are not very mobile. It is therefore easy to imagine that the silver atoms clustered into a nucleus leave a shell-like region emptied of silver atoms. Thus the schematic particle would be made up of a spherical nucleus of high electronic density ρ_1 surrounded by a spherical shell of a density ρ_2 that is less than the average density ρ_0 of the medium in which the particle is immersed. This concept requires the supplementary condition that $\int \rho \, dv = \rho_0 V$, since all the atomic movements have taken place at the interior of the total volume V of the particle.

Let us consider the following simple model: the two parts of the particle are defined by two concentric spheres of radii R_1 and R_2. The condition relating ρ_1, ρ_2, and ρ_0 is:

$$\rho_1 R_1{}^3 + \rho_2(R_2{}^3 - R_1{}^3) = \rho_0 R_2{}^3$$

or

$$(\rho_1 - \rho_2)R_1{}^3 = (\rho_0 - \rho_2)R_2{}^3$$

In a calculation of the scattering, the particle can be replaced by a set of two superposed concentric spheres, one of radius R_1 and density $(\rho_1 - \rho_2)$, and the other of radius R_2 and negative density, $-(\rho_0 - \rho_2)$. The scattered intensity will be the square of the algebraic sum of the amplitudes scattered by these two spheres. The amplitudes at zero-angle are equal and opposite, as is seen from equation 2.10, but the scattering due to the small sphere R_1 decreases more slowly with angle than that of the large sphere R_2. The curve of the intensity, therefore, starts from zero at zero-angle, and it obviously again becomes zero at large angles, so that it shows a maximum quite similar to the one found experimentally (Fig. 73).

This model is obviously arbitrarily chosen, but a better model of a spherically symmetric, heterogeneous particle can be obtained by quantitatively determining the electronic density distribution $\rho(r)$ that would produce the observed scattering curve.

Equation 2.13 gives the scattered intensity as

$$I(h) = I_e(h)\left[\int_0^\infty \rho(r)\,\frac{\sin hr}{hr}\,4\pi r^2\,dr\right]^2$$

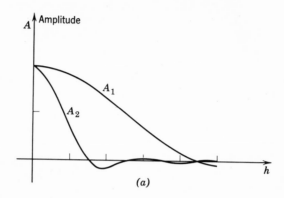

(a)

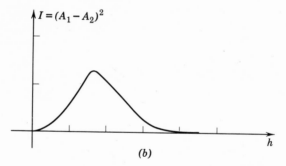

(b)

Fig. 73. (a) The amplitude of scattering for two spheres: A_1, a sphere of radius R_1 and density ($\rho_1 - \rho_2$); A_2, a sphere of radius R_2 and density ($\rho_0 - \rho_2$). (b) Scattered intensity for the concentric spheres model: $I = (A_1 - A_2)^2$.

where $h = (4\pi \sin \theta)/\lambda$. The density $\rho(r)$ can be obtained from the experimental curve $I(h)$ by a Fourier transformation:

$$\rho(r) = \frac{1}{2\pi^2 r}\int_0^\infty h\sqrt{\frac{I(h)}{I_e(h)}}\,\sin hr\,dh$$

A second method of approach, which does not require the assumption of spherically symmetric particles, is to use equation 2.21 and the Fourier transform of $hI(h)$,

$$r\gamma_0(r) \propto \int_0^\infty hI(h)\sin hr\,dh$$

If $I(h)$ is normalized so that $\gamma_0(0) = 1$, then $\gamma_0(r)$ is related to the probability of finding an atom of silver a distance r away from another atom
of silver (Fig. 74).

In reality the distribution of matter in the interior of the particles is not
continuous. The aluminum and silver atoms are situated on sites of the

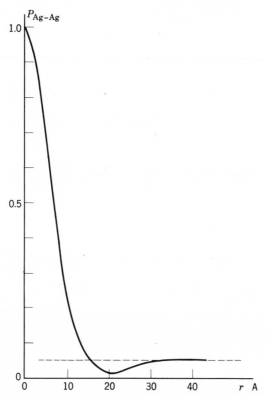

Fig. 74.   The probability of finding an Ag atom at a distance r from
another Ag atom in the quenched Al-Ag alloy.

known lattice, and the problem is to find their statistical distribution.
The solution to this problem given by Cowley (1950) leads to similar
equations.

Theoretically, the same results about the structure of the solid solution
could be obtained by using the phenomena of the scattering around any
Bragg reflection of the crystal, but *it is much easier experimentally to use
the low-angle part of the pattern.* The principal advantage of this is that
the metal can be used directly regardless of its state of crystallization.
The method can thus be applied to cold-worked metals or to metals in

the form of very fine crystals such as are used in metallurgical techniques. A determination of the structure of a hardening alloy of this type can be made even on samples usually employed for other physical or mechanical tests.

6.4.3.2. Aluminum-Silver Alloy: Second Stage of Hardening

When the same Al–Ag alloy is given anneals at higher and higher temperatures, the ring decreases in size until only an intense blur at very small angles is observed; then finally a completely different phenomenon

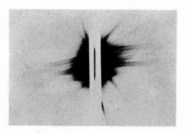

Fig. 75. Small-angle scattering from Al-Ag, water-quenched from 520° C. and annealed 10 days at 140° C.

appears. When the sample is polycrystalline, with not too fine a crystal size, the pattern contains several streaks of scattering, the direction and number depending on the orientation of the crystals (Fig. 75). A displacement or rotation of the sample will modify the number and orientation of the observed streaks. A study of this effect should be made with a monocrystal whose axes can be oriented at will with respect to the incident beam.

The object of the experiment is to find the form and extent of the scattering regions around the center of reciprocal space and to determine their orientations with respect to the axes of the reciprocal lattice of the solid solution (this is a face-centered cubic crystal with parameters practically equal to those of aluminum). The result of the study is shown in Fig. 76. The regions of scattering are directed along [111] axes. They are very narrow, and their length depends on the thermal treatment of the alloy. More exactly, the intensity decreases with increasing angle, the scattering for Cu $K\alpha$ being perceptible up to scattering angles of the order of 2° or 3° for the longest streaks.

The observations on the polycrystalline samples mentioned above are then explained in the following manner: The reciprocal space of the sample contains a number of scattering regions in the form of straight lines centered on the origin, the number being equal to 4 times the number of crystals irradiated by the incident beam. It is known that the pattern for a given position of the sample can be depicted by the cut through reciprocal space of the Ewald sphere of reflection. Near the center of the pattern this spherical surface can be replaced by the plane normal to the direction of the incident beam. If there are a sufficient number of crystals and if these are randomly oriented, there are always a certain number of scattering regions that are very near this plane normal to the beam. In order that a streak may appear, it is necessary theoretically that the scattering regions be in this plane. In practice, as a result of the divergence of the rays of the primary beam, it is sufficient that these

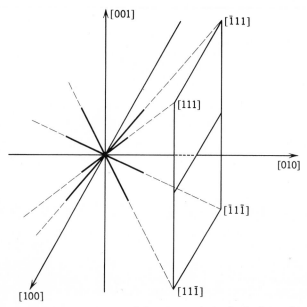

Fig. 76. The representation of the observed streaks in the reciprocal lattice of the matrix Al-Ag crystal.

domains be close to the plane. A certain number of streaks will be observed whose directions cannot be predicted *a priori*, since the orientations of the crystals are unknown. If the number of irradiated crystals is too large, as in a cold-worked material, the streaks will be very numerous and very weak, since the individual crystals will be quite small. As a result the streaks will merge to form a continuous scattering that is spread out but too weak to be detectable by photography.

Let us return to the consideration of a single crystal. What are the particles that can explain the small-angle scattering in reciprocal space shown in Fig. 76. The anisotropy of the pattern proves that, unlike the particles in the first stage, these are anisotropic and are oriented with respect to the matrix crystal.   In §2.1.3.4 and §4.1.1.2, it was shown that a wide, thin platelet gives a pattern of scattering that is elongated along the normal to the platelet.   The data of Fig. 76 are then explained by supposing that the matrix crystal contains four series of particles in the form of platelets parallel to the four sets of (111) planes.   This is a particularly acceptable supposition, since the precipitates visible to the microscope at a later stage also have the form of platelets parallel to the (111) planes (Widmanstätten structure) (Barrett (1952), p. 542).

The *diameter of the platelet* determines the thickness of the scattering region, or the width of the streak on the film.   This measured width appears to be determined uniquely by the experimental conditions, such as crystal dimensions and beam dimensions.   Consequently all that can be said is that the diameter of the platelet is at least of the order of a thousand angstroms.   The *thickness of the platelet* determines the length of the streak.   If the curve of the variation of intensity along the streak were known, theoretically we could apply equation 2.44 to determine a mean inertial distance with respect to the plane of the platelet.   It is more simple and satisfactory to evaluate the length of the streak, ϵ, in angular units and then to obtain the thickness of the platelet by means of the following reasoning: The scattering by a thin, wide platelet of thickness d will become zero at an angle equal to $\epsilon = \lambda/d$.   Therefore the order of magnitude of the thickness of the platelet is $d = \lambda/\epsilon$.   In the case described above, the thickness is determined in this way to be $\sim$30 to 50 A.   The platelets become thicker as the annealing continues.

Here again the consideration of the small-angle scattering has given no information about the internal structure of these platelets.   The large-angle patterns show that these are *grains of a precipitate* with a hexagonal structure in which the lattice is derived from that of the solid solution by a slippage of (111) planes over one another.   The diffraction spots of these precipitates are surrounded by regions of scattering that are also directed along the [111] axes.   These regions are much longer than the region around the center of the pattern.   In order to explain these high-angle scattering phenomena we must suppose that the platelets of precipitate parallel to (111) planes do not have a thickness of more than 10 A, a figure that is in contradiction with the small-angle scattering data.   The correct interpretation, which explains all the observations, is that the platelets have the dimensions determined from the small-angle scattering but that their crystalline lattice is not perfect.   The principal cause of the high-angle streaks of scattering along the (111) directions is the presence of "stacking faults" in the precipitates (Barrett (1952)).

Although the complete study required that the investigation be carried out on a single crystal, let us observe that, once the facts just established are known, a simple small-angle scattering experiment on a metal without special preparation allows us to determine the actual state of the alloy, to distinguish between the two stages of hardening, and to obtain in a simple manner quantitative results on the dimensions of the clusters or sub-microscopic grains of precipitate.

6.4.3.3. Aluminum-Copper Alloy

Several other systems give phenomena analogous to those of the aluminum-silver system, but this is not a general precipitation process. Frequently the low-angle scattering patterns are very different in appearance, and often they are less easy to measure and interpret than in the example we have just discussed.

An aluminum-copper age-hardening alloy in not too fine a crystalline form gives a pattern of streaks coming from the center even in the first stage of hardening [64], [274]. These streaks are directed along the [100] axes of the crystal of the solid solution; they can be very long (from 10° to 15° with Cu $K\alpha$ radiation) and they are of rather low intensity. In order to study them in practice, it is necessary to work with a single crystal. We can deduce from the form and orientation of these streaks that *the heterogeneous regions are very thin platelets parallel to the three sets of* (100) *planes*. The simplest region that could be imagined would be formed of clusters of copper atoms on one or two (100) planes of the solid solution lattice in zones having a diameter of several hundred angstroms. Figure 77 reproduces the low-angle part of the pattern corresponding to an alloy annealed at 100° C. for 100 hours and oriented so that the [100] axis is parallel to the incident beam; the two other fourfold axes are horizontal and vertical, respectively. The two branches of the cross correspond to two of the three series of zones; the third, oriented normal to the beam, should theoretically give a circularly symmetrical scattering, but it is too limited in diameter to be visible. It is easy to calculate the distribution of scattering from a thin platelet parallel to the direct beam.[1] We can thus obtain the dimensions of the platelet that gives a low-angle scattering identical to that observed. It is by this type of calculation, which we shall not reproduce here, that the zone dimensions reported in the first papers [64] were obtained. But this model of zones of clustered copper atoms does not allow an explanation of the other abnormal and complex scattering phenomena observed at high angles. In order to explain these it is necessary to assume that the lattice of the zones is deformed. Since the copper atom is much smaller than the aluminum

---

[1] It is curious to discover that in this very particular case we cannot make the approximation usually made in Chapter 2, which was to neglect the variation of the direction of the vector **h** with the scattering angle.

atom, it seems reasonable that a clustering of copper would cause such a contraction in the spacing of the crystalline planes.

The low-angle scattering of this alloy extends to rather large angles, actually joining the other regions of scattering. Thus the single "cross" of Fig. 77 cannot be isolated from the other regions of scattering that were not represented there. The procedure for separation of the effect of the heterogeneity from the effect of the lattice deformation is not applicable here. An attempt at a more complete explanation is no longer within

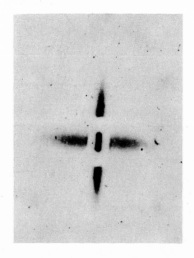

Fig. 77. Small-angle pattern from a single crystal of an Al-Cu alloy (4 per cent Cu by weight). The [100] axis is parallel to the incident beam and normal to the film, and the [010] axis is vertical. Mo $K\alpha$ radiation; sample-to-film distance, 4 cm. Enlarged 2 ×.

the compass of a discussion of small-angle scattering but rather is in that of crystalline imperfections in general.

It is no less true, however, that, qualitatively and even semiquantitatively speaking, *an examination of the small-angle scattering gives the orientation, the form, and the order of magnitude of the dimensions of the heterogeneous regions.*

The examples treated above show the capabilities of small-angle scattering in a study of a *solid state reaction.* We could also find applications to non-metallic substances. When the presence of heterogeneities of a dimension less than several hundred angstroms is suspected, the X-ray method should be attempted. Let us point out that the zones of clustering in hardening alloys have been demonstrated only by X-ray methods; they are not visible to the electron microscope, even though they are of a size greater than the resolving power of this instrument. This is due to the fact that the zones are not sensitive to the methods of etching that have so far been employed.

6.5. ABSOLUTE MEASUREMENTS OF THE INTENSITY OF SCATTERING AT ZERO ANGLE. MEASUREMENTS OF THE COMPRESSIBILITY OF A FLUID

In the majority of the applications cited up to this point only a knowledge of the form of the scattering curve is required. In several cases we have seen that a comparison between two scattering curves had to be made (p. 190), but the only requirement was that the incident intensity be constant, the absolute magnitude not being needed.

It is possible to determine experimentally the ratio of the scattered intensity to the incident intensity. These absolute measurements (§3.5.3) are difficult because of the disproportion between the two quantities to be measured. We have shown, nonetheless, how these measurements can be successfully made with a reasonable accuracy, of the order of 5 per cent.

The formulas employing the absolute value of the limiting intensity were established in Chapter 2 and the possible applications follow from these.

In the case of identical, widely separated particles, the equation for the limiting intensity is

$$I(0) = I_e N n^2$$

I_e, the intensity scattered by one electron, can be calculated as a function of the incident intensity by means of Thomson's equation (p. 6) ($I_e(0) = 7.9 \times 10^{-26} I_0 p^{-2}$); N is the total number of particles, and n is the number of electrons per particle. $I(0)$ can certainly not be determined directly by experiment, but if the curve of $\log I(h^2)$ is linear at low angles it can easily be obtained by extrapolation. The total mass of the scattering particles gives the value of the product, Nn. The small-angle scattering experiment will therefore give the value of n, which, let us recall, can be used to describe the form of the particle more precisely (§4.1.1.1).

If, on the other hand, the form of the particle is known, the volume of the particle, and thus n, can be determined from the radius of gyration. In such a case the X-ray measurement gives the value of N. In this way the number of particles or the concentration of particles in a sample can be determined. There are certain cases in which this method, complex though it is, is the only possible method. Let us cite as an example the case of microcavities in cold-worked metals, in which Blin (1954) determined the total volume of the cavities by X-ray measurements. The number of clusters of atoms in a hardening alloy can also be determined in this way.

Another expression for the absolute value of the scattered intensity was given in §2.2.3.3 for the example in which the particles were molecules of a fluid (this expression is *not* restricted to macromolecules only). The relation (equation 2.74, p. 47) is

$$I(0) = I_e(0)n^2\overline{N}\,\frac{kT}{v_1}\,\beta$$

$\overline{N}$ is the average number of molecules irradiated; T is the temperature of the fluid; v_1, the average volume offered to each molecule ($v_1 = V/\overline{N}$); and β is the isothermal compressibility,

$$\beta = -\frac{1}{V}\left(\frac{\partial V}{\partial P}\right)_T$$

An interesting application of equation 2.74 is the experimental *measurement of the coefficient of compressibility of a fluid by X-rays*. This measurement has recently been made for liquid helium at temperatures above and below the λ-point (Tweet [162']). The intensity scattered by helium is very weak. However, since the intensity varies very little with scattering angle, the Geiger-Müller counter detector can be adjusted to receive very divergent beams, and this, together with the use of a powerful source (a rotating anode tube), makes the measurement possible. The container for the scatterer was filled successively with helium and with a gas that scattered as a perfect gas. The value of β could be derived from the ratio of the measured intensities and from the ratio of the densities.

At 4° K. the scattered intensity showed a rather marked maximum at zero-angles (Fig. 78), just as is observed for all fluids in the neighborhood of their critical point (see Fig. 11 for argon). The value of β determined from these X-ray measurements agreed well with the value of the compressibility as measured by completely different methods.

At 2° K., below the λ-point, the intensity does not vary perceptibly with the scattering angle, and is slightly higher than the value of $(kT/v_1)\beta$ by an amount greater than the experimental uncertainty. These experiments show that the statistics of the helium atoms at this temperature are different from those of the normal gas, and they will serve as a test of theoretical predictions.

REFERENCES FOR CHAPTER 6

Barrett, C. S.   (1952), *Structure of Metals*, McGraw-Hill, New York.
Belbéoch, B., and Guinier, A.   (1954), *Compt. rend.*, *238*, 1003.
Blin, J.   (1954), Thèse Ing. Doct., Univ. Paris.

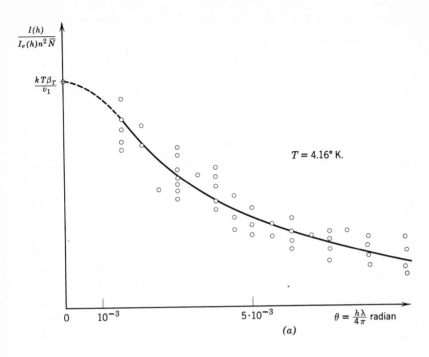

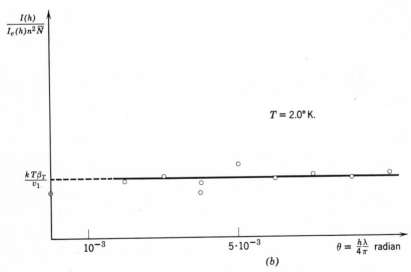

Fig. 78. The scattered intensity in absolute units for liquid helium above and below the λ-point, at 4.16° K. and 2.0° K., respectively. The point ⊕ indicates the theoretical value of the scattered intensity at zero-angle derived from equation 2.74. (Tweet [162'].)

Cowley, J.   (1950), *J. Appl. Phys.*, *21*, 24.
Fournet, G.   (1953*a*), *Acta Met.*, *1*, 383.
Fournet, G.   (1953*b*), *Compt. rend.*, *237*, 75.
Hermans, J. J.   (1944), *Rec. trav. chim.*, *63*, 5.
Heyn, A. N. J.   (1953), *Textile Research J.*, *23*, 782.
Mark, H.   (1932), *Physik und Chemie der Cellulose*, Springer, Berlin.
Ponder, E.   (1945), *J. Gen. Physiol.*, *29*, 89.
Schmidt, P., Kaesberg, P., and Beeman, W. W.   (1954), *Biochim. et Biophys. Acta*, *14*, 1.
Walker, C. B., and Guinier, A.   (1953), *Acta Met.*, *1*, 568.

BIBLIOGRAPHY

This compilation of 569 titles on small-angle X-ray scattering is a revision of the 398-title bibliography issued in March 1952 by the American Crystallographic Association. It is divided for convenience into seven sections as follows:

The division into these sections is arbitrary; many of the references might well be listed in more than one section. However, each reference is listed only once in the section considered most appropriate. Sections I–III were made as complete and up to date as possible. Sections IV–VII are incomplete, as the definition of what is properly associated with small-angle scattering is here somewhat indefinite.

Within each section the arrangement is alphabetical by first author, and chronological under each author. The numbering of references is continuous through all seven sections. The author index is alphabetical and notes all references to each author by number. The type of reference is coded as follows:

A. Published article or letter.
P. Presented paper.
a. Published abstract.
B. Book.
T. Thesis.

For *articles* or letters the information includes the authors, journal, volume, inclusive pages, year, and title. If only one page number is given, the reference is complete on that page. For *papers* the information includes the authors, society, paper number, place and date of meeting, and title. Papers *abstracted* in a journal have the same information as articles. For *books* the information includes the authors, publisher's name and location, the year of publication, the title, and usually the pages of interest. *Thesis* information includes the author, institution, degree, year, and title.

For a few items the above information is not complete. Often a brief annotation is appended to the reference. The language of the title indicates the language of the paper. It was necessary to translate a few titles back to the approximate original from English; and the Russian names were transliterated and titles translated.

The compound and transliterated names have been alphabetized as follows:

Boyes-Watson	B	von Nardroff	N
DeVore	D	Van Nordstrand	N
Danilov	D	Nowacki	N
DuMond	D	Phillipovich	P
Frey-Wyssling	F	Porai-Koshits	P
Friedrich-Freska	F	Serikov	S
Janeschitz-Kriegl	J	Shishakov	S
Kachkurzov	K	Sokolov	S
Kalinina	K	Todes	T
LaMer	L	Toraldo Di Francia	T
Lennard-Jones	L	Van de Hulst	V
MacArthur	M	Van Rijssel	V
McBain	M	van der Wyk	W
McReynolds	M	Zubko	Z
McRoberts	M		

To avoid tedious renumbering and reindexing, 66 late additions to the bibliography were incorporated into appropriate positions and numbered with primes.

I. GENERAL

1 Bale, H.   T
Univ. N. Dakota, M.S. (1953). "Acetic Acid near the Critical Point,"
See No. 180.

1' Banerjee, K.   P
Intern. Union Cryst., No. B-8, Cambridge, Mass. (July 1948). "Method for Studying Extremely Low-Angle Scattering of Monochromatic X-Rays." Not presented.

2 Banerjee, K., and Maitra, J. C.   A
Indian J. Phys., 25, 141–144 (1951). "On a Method of Studying Small-Angle Scattering of Monochromatic X-Rays." Single crystal spectrometer.

3 Barton, H. M., Jr.   T
Polytechnic Inst., Brooklyn, M.S. (1950). "A Study of Electron Density by Low-Angle X-Ray Scattering." Electron density of carbon blacks from total power in small-angle scattering.

4 Barton, H. M., Jr.   Pa
Am. Phys. Soc., No. H-6, Washington (April 1950). *Phys. Rev.*, 79, 211 (1950). "Average Electron Density Measurements by Low-Angle X-Ray Scattering."

5   Barton, H. M., Jr., and Brill, R.   A
    J. Appl. Phys., *21*, 783–785 (1950).   "Average Electron Density Measurements
    by Low-Angle X-Ray Scattering."   See No. 174.
6   Bauer, S. H.   A
    J. Chem. Phys., *13*, 450–451 (1945).   "Inversion of Low-Angle Scattering Data
    for Particle Size Distribution."   See Nos. 145, 147, 155.
7   Baule, B., and Kratky, O.   A
    Z. physik. Chem., *B–52*, 142–152 (1942).   "Die Dehnung der amorphen Bereiche
    bei affiner Verzerrung eines micellaren Netzes."
8   Beeman, W. W., and Kaesberg, P.   A
    Phys. Rev., *72*, 512 (1947).   "X-Ray Scattering at Very Small Angles."
    Use of double crystal spectrometer.   Comparison of multiple refraction and
    scattering.   See Nos. 173, 206, 208, 209, 212, 226, 230, 238.
8′ Beeman, W. W., and Neynaber, R. H.   Pa
    Am. Phys. Soc., No. 17, Washington (April 1954).   *Phys. Rev.*, *95*, 617 (1954).
    "Equipment for the Measurement of Very Small X-Ray Scattering Cross
    Sections."
9   Bernal, J. D., and Carlisle, C. H.   PA
    Discussions Faraday Soc., *11*, 227–229 (1951).   "The Place of X-Ray Diffraction
    Methods in the Estimation of the Size and Mutual Arrangements of Colloidal
    Particles."
10 Biscoe, J., and Warren, B. E.   A
    J. Appl. Phys., *13*, 364–371 (1942).   "An X-Ray Study of Carbon Black."
    Particle size of carbon black from small-angle scattering compared with
    crystallite size from line broadening.
11 Blin, J., and Guinier, A.   A
    Compt. rend., *233*, 1288–1290 (1951).   "Diffusion des rayons X aux très petits
    angles par les métaux écrouis."   Cavities in Ni and Cu of about 18 A.
11′ Blin, J., and Guinier, A.   A
    Compt. rend., *236*, 2150–2152 (1953).   "Étude expérimentale des cavités
    submicroscopiques au sein des métaux écrouis."
11″ Bowman, J. C., Hayes, S., and Smoluchowski, R.   Pa
    Am. Phys. Soc., No. Z-1, Chapel Hill, N. Carolina (March 1953).   *Phys. Rev.*,
    91, 244 (1953).   "X-Ray Study of Graphitization."
12 Brentano, J. C. M.   P
    ASXRED, No. 17, Philadelphia (December 1949).   "Small-Angle Diffraction
    from Compact Powders."   Theory of scattering from irregular discontinuities
    related to structure breaks.
13 Brusset, H.   T
    Univ. Paris, D.S.P. (1947).   "Contribution a l'étude du carbone et des charbons
    minéraux."   Comprehensive study of structure of solids by small-angle X-ray
    scattering, with special application to carbons.
14 Brusset, H.   A
    Compt. rend., *225*, 1002–1003 (1947).   "Diffusion centrale des rayons X et
    microscopie électronique."   Six samples of C black examined by small-angle
    scattering and electron microscopy.   Sizes by electron microscopy several
    times those from X-ray measurements.   It is concluded that in electron
    microscopy the particles usually observed are aggregates.
15 Brusset, H.   A
    Compt. rend., *228*, 323–327 (1949).   "Étude par la diffusion centrale des rayons
    X de l'activation du carbone."

16 Brusset, H.   A
Bull. soc. chim. France, 16, 319–323 (1949). "Étude de l'état de division fine des gels de silice."

17 Brusset, H., Devaux, J., and Guinier, A.   A
Compt. rend., 216, 152–154 (1943). "Étude de quelques charbons par la diffusion des rayons X sous très petits angles." Carbons alike in wide angle patterns distinguished by their small-angle scattering.

18 Brusset, H., and Kikindai, T.   A
Compt rend., 231, 858–860 (1950). "La diffusion centrale des rayons X produite par quelques colloides minéraux." Particle sizes of several minerals.

18' Buttrey, J. W.   T
Univ. Mo., Ph.D. (1953). "Small-Angle Scattering from Liquid Paraffins near Their Critical Points."

19 Carroll, B., and Fankuchen, I.   A
J. Chem. Phys., 16, 153–154 (1948). "Small-Angle X-Ray Scattering from Metal Deposits Made by Evaporation." Black deposits of evaporated Al and Cu show small-angle scattering characteristic of colloidal particles.

19' Charlesby, A.   A
J. Polymer Sci., 10, 201–211 (1953). "Investigation of Halo Patterns of Amorphous Polymers." Debye formula for several molecular models to explain halos.

20 Christman, A. C., Jr.   T
Penn. State College, M.S. (1950). "X-Ray Determination of Particle Size of Mercuric Oxide."

21 Clark, G. L.   B
McGraw-Hill, New York (1947). *Applied X-Rays.* Third edition, p. 504. Brief discussion of Guinier's method. Fuller treatment in fourth edition (Jan. 1955).

22 Clark, G. L., Eckert, A. C., Jr., and Burton, R. L.   A
Ind. Eng. Chem., 41, 201–208 (1949). "Commercial and Experimental Carbon Blacks. An X-Ray Comparison." No two carbons give identical X-ray patterns. The scattering at small angles increases with temperature of heat treatment at low temperatures, indicating a growth of clusters.

23 Daams, H., and Arlman, J. J.   A
Appl. Sci. Research, B–2, 217–226 (1951). "Design of and Measurements with a Simple Double Crystal Spectrometer for Small-Angle Scattering." Latex peaks. MgO correlated with electron microscopy. See Nos. 25, 115, 192.

24 Danielson, W. E.   T
Calif. Inst. Tech., Ph.D. (1952). "Application of the Point Focusing X-Ray Monochromator to the Study of Low-Angle Diffraction."

25 Danielson, W. E., Shenfil, L., and DuMond, J. W. M.   A
J. Appl. Phys., 23, 860–865 (1952). "Latex Particle Size Determination Using Diffraction Peaks Obtained with the Point Focusing X-Ray Monochromator." See Nos. 23, 115, 192.

26 Danilov, V. I., and Serikov, A. S.   A
Doklady Akad. Nauk, SSSR, 83, 71–74 (1952). "The Scattering of X-Rays at Small Angles and the Pore Structure of Activated Carbon." (In Russian).

27 Danilov, V. I., and Zubko, A. M.   A
Doklady Akad. Nauk, SSSR, 82, 385–388 (1952). "On the Fine Structure of Activated Carbons." (In Russian.)

28 Davis, B. **A**
J. Franklin Inst., **204**, 29–39 (1927). "Refraction of X-Rays." Experimental central scattering attributed to refraction.

29 Davis, B., and Slack, C. M. **Pa**
Am. Phys. Soc., No. 8, Washington (April 1926). *Phys. Rev.*, **27**, 796–797 (1926). "Refraction of X-Rays in Prisms." Broadening of beam by granular materials.

30 Dexter, D. L. **T**
Univ. Wisc., Ph.D. (1950). "Studies in Small-Angle Scattering of X-Rays and in Solid State Physics."

30′ Dexter, D. L. **Pa**
Am. Phys. Soc., No. FA-10, Washington (May 1953). *Phys. Rev.*, **91**, 448 (1953). "Small-Angle Scattering of X-Rays from Cold-Worked Crystals."

30″ Dexter, D. L. **A**
Phys. Rev., **90**, 1007–1012 (1953). "The Small-Angle Scattering of X-Rays from Cold-Worked Solids." Scattering from either cavities or edge-type dislocations.

31 Dexter, D. L., and Beeman, W. W. **A**
Phys. Rev., **76**, 1782–1786 (1949). "Multiple Diffuse Small-Angle Scattering of X-Rays." Multiple scattering from large spheres. Particles sizes are determined from the variation of the width of the scattering curve with sample thickness. Same as Part III of No. 30.

32 Dexter, D. L., and Beeman, W. W. **P**
Conf. Small-Angle X-Ray Scattering, No. 7, Columbia, Mo. (October 1949). "Multiple Diffuse Small-Angle Scattering of X-Rays."

33 Dexter, D. L., and Beeman, W. W. **Pa**
Am. Phys. Soc., No. V-3, Chicago (November 1949). *Phys. Rev.*, **77**, 761 (1950). "Multiple Diffuse Small-Angle Scattering of X-Rays.

34 Donnay, J. D. H., and Shull, C. G.
ASXRED Bibliography (1946). "X-Ray Small-Angle Scattering Annotated Bibliography," Sixty-nine references arranged by year to 1945. Indexed as non-Laue reflections, small-angle scattering, large Bragg spacings, and non-Bragg reflections.

34′ Dorgelo, H. B., and Daams, H. **A**
Ned. Tijdschr. Natuurk., **17**, 209–233 (1951). "De Bespaling van Grootte, Vorm en Grootte-Distributie van Submicroscopische Deeltjes."

35 Dragsdorf, R. D. **T**
Mass. Inst. Tech., Ph.D. (1948). "Small-Angle X-Ray Scattering." Refraction versus scattering discussed. Interparticle interference peaks noted. See Nos. 87, 168, 254, 256, 355.

36 Dragsdorf, R. D. **P**
ASXRED, No. 31, Columbus (December 1948). "Small-Angle X-Ray Scattering."

37 Dragsdorf, R. D. **P**
Conf. Small-Angle X-Ray Scattering, No. 12, Columbia, Mo. (October 1949). "Small-Angle X-Ray Scattering." Refraction versus scattering. Interparticle interference.

38 Eisenstein, A. S. **T**
Univ. Mo., Ph.D. (1942). "The Diffraction of X-Rays by Argon in the Liquid, Vapor, and Critical Regions."

39 Eisenstein, A. S., and Gingrich, N. S.   A
Phys. Rev., *58*, 307–309 (1940). "The Diffraction of X-Rays by Liquid Argon."

40 Eisenstein, A. S., and Gingrich, N.S.   A
Phys. Rev., *62*, 261–270 (1942). "The Diffraction of X-Rays by Argon in the Liquid, Vapor, and Critical Regions." Small-angle scattering from argon near saturated vapor curve. See Nos. 49, 59, 180.

41 Elkin, P. B., Shull, C. G., and Roess, L. C.   A
Ind. Eng. Chem., *37*, 327–331 (1945). "Specific Surface and Particle Size Distribution in Silica Alumina Gels." Correlations given between specific surface and particle size distribution obtained from small-angle scattering.

42 Fankuchen, L., and Jellinek, M. H.   B
Academic Press, New York (1948). *Advances in Catalysis*. Chapter on X-ray diffraction.

43 Firth, F. G.   A
Rubber Age and Synthetics, London, *57*, 561–564 (1945). Use of Low-Angle X-Ray Scattering in the Study of Catalysts, Viruses, and Other Materials." Changes indicating growth of Al_2O_3 particles. Lines of diffuse maxima along meridian with nylon at angles corresponding to Bragg period of 100 A. Review and discussion of developments.

44 Fournet, G.   A
Compt. rend., *228*, 1421–1423 (1949). "Diffusion des rayons X aux petits angles par des systèmes denses de particules identiques." Small-angle scattering equation including interparticle interference derived for gases, based on Born and Green's partition function. See Nos. 56, 120, 126, 128, 137, 186, 268, 284.

45 Fournet, G.   A
Compt. rend., *228*, 1801–1803 (1949). "Application de la théorie de Born et Green au calcul de l'intensité diffuse par les gaz et les liquides." Extension of equation including interparticle interference to apply to liquids as well as gases. See Nos. 259, 260, 261, 273.

46 Fournet, G.   A
Compt. rend., *229*, 1071–1073 (1949). "Generalisation de la théorie des fluides de Born et Green aux mélanges du plusieurs espèces de molécules. Calcul de la diffusion par les rayons X." Extension of equation including interparticle interference to fluids of two sizes of spheres.

47 Fournet, G.   TB
Paris, Doctorat d'État-Sciences (1950). Masson et c, Paris (1951). "Étude théorique et expérimentale de la diffusion des rayons X par les ensembles denses de particules."

48 Fournet, G.   A
Bull. soc. franç. minéral. et crist., *74*, 39–113 (1951). Same as No. 47.

49 Fournet, G.   A
Acta Cryst., *4*, 293–301 (1951). "Diffusion des rayons X par les fluides." Intensity from Born and Green—argon. See Nos. 40, 59, 180.

50 Fournet, G   PA
Discussions Faraday Soc., *11*, 121–125 (1951). "Influence of the Size and Shape of Particles on the Interpretation of the X-Ray Diffuse Diagrams." Critical discussion of validity of relating interparticle intensity maximum to a "mean" distance.

51 Fournet, G.   A
J. phys. radium, *12*, 592–595 (1951). "Generalisation de la théorie cinétique des fluides de Born et Green aux ensembles de particules de plusieurs espèces différentes." Effects due to proximity of particles and interparticle forces are separated. Particles of several kinds.

52 Fournet, G.   PA
Intern. Union Chem., Strasbourg (June 1952). *J. Polymer Sci.*, *9*, 539–545 (1952). "Interprétation des diagrammes de diffusion des rayons X par des systèmes denses de particules."

53 Fournet, G., and Guinier, A.   A
Compt. rend., *228*, 66–68 (1949). "Interprétation de la valeur limitée de la diffusion des rayons X aux très faibles angles." Scattered intensity at zero angle attributed to density fluctuations which may be treated thermodynamically.

54 Fournet, G., and Guinier, A.   A
J. phys. radium, *11*, 516–520 (1950). "L'état actuel de la théorie de la diffusion des rayons X aux petits angles." See No. 74.

55 François, J.   A
Compt. rend., *230*, 1282–1284 (1950). "Influence de la temperature sur la dimension des particules d'oxyde de nickel." Usual slope analysis correlated with electron microscopy.

56 Frank, R. M., and Yudowitch, K. L.   A
Phys. Rev., *88*, 759–760 (1952). "Small-Angle X-Ray Scattering from Compact Identical Particles." Novel treatment using an average radial electron density. See Nos. 44, 120, 126, 128, 137, 186, 268, 284.

56′ Franklin, R. E.   A
Acta Cryst., *3*, 107–121 (1950). "The Interpretation of Diffuse Diagrams of Carbon."

56″ Franklin, R. E.   A
Proc. Roy. Soc. (London), *A-209*, 196–218 (1951). "Crystallite Growth in Graphitizing and Non-Graphitizing Carbons."

57 Gingrich, N. S.   P
Conf. Small-Angle X-Ray Scattering, No. 1, Columbia, Mo. (October 1949). "Introductory Remarks." Brief review.

58 Glocker, R.   A
FIAT Rev. Ger. Sci., *1939-1946*, I, 1–14 (1948). "Physik der festen Körper." Review of German work to 1946. Crystal monochromators. Fibers.

59 Graham, W., and Lund, L. H.   A
J. Chem. Phys., *19*, 1380–1382 (1951). "Small-Angle X-Ray Scattering from Argon." See Nos. 40, 49, 180.

60 Gray, J. A.   A
Can. J. Research, *12*, 408–409 (1935). "Note on the Scattering of X-Rays at Small Angles."

61 Gray, J. A., and Zinn, W. H.   A
Can. J. Research, *2*, 291–293 (1930). "New Phenomena in X-Ray Scattering." Early observation of small-angle scattering by charcoal, related to particle size. See No. 130.

62 Guinier, A.   A
Compt. rend., *206*, 1374–1376 (1938). "La diffusion des rayons X sous les très faibles angles appliqués a l'étude de fines particules et de suspensions colloidales."

63   Guinier, A.   A
Compt. rend., 206, 1641–1643 (1938). "Un nouveau type de diagrammes de
rayons X." Particle size determination from small-angle scattering. Central
streaks.

64   Guinier, A.   T
Univ. Paris, Doctorat (1939). "La diffraction des rayons X aux très petits
angles; application à l'étude de phénomènes ultramicroscopiques." Basic
discussion of X-ray scattering at small angles by small discrete particles.
Considers effect of particle shape but not of size distribution.

65   Guinier, A.   A
Ann. phys., 12, 161–237 (1939). "La diffraction des rayons X aux très petits
angles; application à l'étude de phénomènes ultramicroscopiques." Same as
No. 64.

65' Guinier, A.   A
Compt. rend., 208, 894–896 (1939). "La diffusion des rayons X par les
cristaux et les corps microcristallisés."

66   Guinier, A.   A
J. phys. radium, 2, 124–136 (1942). "Le mécanisme de la précipitation dans
un cristal de solution solide métallique. Cas des systèmes aluminum-cuivre et
aluminum-argent."

67   Guinier, A.   A
J. chim. phys., 40, 133–150 (1943). "Détermination de la taille des particules
submicroscopiques par les rayons X." Summary of work by Guinier, Hosemann, and Kratky.

67' Guinier, A.   A
Métaux, corrosion, usure, 18, 209–213 (1943). "Étude du mécanisme de la
précipitation d'une solution solide sursaturée aluminium-zinc." Clusters in
Al-Zn age-hardened alloy.

68   Guinier, A.   B
Dunod, Paris (1945). Radiocrystallographie. Chapter 12 and Appendix 8.
See No. 72.

69   Guinier, A.   A
Proc. Phys. Soc. (London), 57, 310–324 (1945). "Imperfections of Crystal
Lattices as Investigated by the Study of X-Ray Diffuse Scattering." Small-
angle method mentioned.

70   Guinier, A.   PA
Colloq. très grosses molécules, Liege (April 1948). Bull. soc. chim. Belges, 57,
286–297 (1948). "Détermination de la taille et de l'arrangement mutuel des
grosses molécules par la diffusion des rayons X aux petits angles." Two
curved crystals. Hemoglobin, hemocyanine in solution.

71   Guinier, A.   PA
Discussions Faraday Soc., 8, 344–347 (1950). "Study of Catalysts by Scattering of X-Rays at Small Angles." Use of small-angle scattering supplementing
other data to determine size, shape, and dispersion of catalysts.

72   Guinier, A.   B
Hilger and Watts, London (1952). X-Ray Crystallographic Technology.
Translation of No. 68 by T. L. Tippell.

72' Guinier, A   A
Z. Metallkunde, 43, 217–223 (1952). "Les données de la diffusion des rayons
X aux petits angles sur la structure des alliages durcissants. Cas de l'alliage
aluminium-argent." Clusters in Al-Ag.

73 Guinier, A.   PA
    Intern. Union Chem., Strasbourg (June 1952). *J. Polymer Sci.*, *9*, 557–563
    (1952). "Les possibilités de la diffusion des rayons X aux petits angles dans
    l'étude des grosses molécules."
73′ Guinier, A   Pa
    Am. Phys. Soc., No. V–1, Chapel Hill, N. Carolina (March 1953). *Phys. Rev.*,
    91, 239 (1953). "Possibilities of X-Ray Small-Angle Scattering for Study of
    Crystal Imperfections."
74 Guinier, A., and Fournet, G.   P
    Conf. Small-Angle X-Ray Scattering, No. 6, Columbia, Mo. (October 1949).
    "L'état actuel de la théorie de la diffusion des rayons X aux petits angles."
    Review of scattering by systems of dilute and compact, uniform and non-
    uniform particles. Read in English translation. Same as No. 54.
74′ Guinier, A., and Jacquet, P.   A
    Rev. mét., *41*, 1–16 (1944). "Étude du durcissement des alliages cuivre-
    glucinium." Clusters in age-hardened alloys of Cu-Be.
74″ Gupta, N. N.   A
    Proc. Natl. Inst. Sci. India, *A-18*, 379–388 (1952). "The Optical Principles of
    the Low-Angle Scattering of X-Rays."
74‴ Hayes, S., and Smoluchowski, R.   Pa
    Am. Phys. Soc., No. Z-2, Chapel Hill, N. Carolina (March 1953). *Phys. Rev.*,
    91, 244 (1953). "Small-Angle X-Ray Scattering in Proton Irradiated Dia-
    mond."
74⁗ Hayes, S., and Smoluchowski, R.
    Appl. Sci. Research, *B-4*, 10–24 (1954). "Small-Angle X-Ray Scattering
    Study of Imperfections in Copper."
75 Hayes, S., Smoluchowski, R., and Turner, R. W.   Pa
    Am. Phys. Soc., No. H-4, Cambridge (January 1953). *Phys. Rev.*, *90*, 350
    (1953). "Small-Angle X-Ray Scattering in Deformed Crystals."
76 Hendricks, S. B.   A
    Z. Krist., *A-83*, 503–504 (1932). "Die Glanzkohle, eine andere Kohlenstoff-
    form." Diffuse scattering approximately uniform in density between central
    image and interference maxima.
76′ Henke, B.   T
    Calif. Inst. Tech., Ph.D. (1953). Total reflection focusing of copper L lines.
    Latex application.
76″ Henke, B.
    Calif. Inst. Tech., *Special Tech. Rep.* 24, O.N.R., No. 3, A.E.C. (June 1953).
    "Diffraction of Long Wavelength X-Rays."
76‴ Henke, B.   Pa
    Am. Phys. Soc., No. B-1, Albuquerque, N.M. (September 1953). *Phys. Rev.*,
    92, 1079 (1953). "The Size Determination of Submicroscopic Particles by
    Long Wavelength X-Ray Diffraction."
76⁗ Henke, B., and DuMond, J. W. M.   A
    Phys. Rev., *89*, 1300 (1953). "Low-Angle X-Ray Diffraction with Long Wave-
    lengths."
77 Henry, N. F. M., Lipson, H., and Wooster, W. A.   B
    Van Nostrand, New York (1951). *The Interpretation of X-Ray Diffraction
    Photographs.* (P. 217.)
78 Heywood, H.   A
    Nature, *159*, 717–718 (1947). "Particle Size Analysis." Report on February
    1947 Conf. Inst. Chem. Engrs. and Soc. Chem. Ind.

79 Hosemann, R. A
Z. Physik, 113, 751–768 (1939). "Theorie der Röntgenstrahlenstreuung und Partikelhaufen. Aufstellung des Aggregationsdiagrammes." Theory developed for small-angle scattering from single oriented rotational ellipsoids.

80 Hosemann, R. A
Z. Physik, 114, 133–169 (1939). "Neues Röntgenographisches Verfahren zur Bestimmung des submikroskopischen Feinbaues eines Stoffes. Diskussion des Zellulosemodells." Description of apparatus and cellulose data. Application of theory of No. 79.

80′ Hosemann, R. A
Z. Elektrochem., 53, 331–334 (1949). "Theorie der Röntgenstreuung an statistisch Ungeordneten linearen Gittern."

81 Hosemann, R. A
Kolloid-Z., 117, 13–41 (1950). "Röntgeninterferenzen an kolloiden Systemen. Zusammenhang zwischen Packungsdicke, Polydispersitat, und reiner Partikelstreuung." General theory for small-angle scattering for randomly and regularly packed as well as dilute systems.

82 Hosemann, R. A
Kolloid-Z., 119, 129–145 (1950). "Grossenstatistik der parakristallinen Bereiche in festen hochmolekularen Stoffen bei kontinuierlicher Kleinwinkelstreuung."

83 Hosemann, R. A
Z. Physik, 128, 465–492 (1950). "Der ideale Parakristall und die von ihm gestreute kohärente Röntgenstrahlen."

84 Hosemann, R. A
Ergeb. exakt. Naturw., 24, 142–221 (1951). "Die Erforschung der Struktur hochmolekularer und kolloider Stoffe mittels Kleinwinkelstreuung." Comprehensive, 188 references.

85 Hosemann, R. PA
Deut. Mineral. Gesell., Sektion für Kristallkunde (1951). Zur Struktur und Materie der Festkörper, 127–222 (1951). "Der statistische Charakter der Feinstruktur hochmolekularer und kolloider Stoffe." Lengthy review with 48 references.

86 Hosemann, R., and Bagchi, S. N. A
Acta Cryst., 5, 749–762 (1952). "Existenzbeweis für eindeutige Röntgenstrukturanalyse durch Entfaltung. I. Entfaltung zentrosymmetrischer endlicher Massenverteilungen."

87 Hubbell, H. H., Jr. T
Princeton, Ph.D. (1947). "X-Ray Scattering at Small Angles." Wavelength dependence checked. Secondary intensity plateaus noted. See No. 161.

88 Hubbell, H. H., Jr. P
Conf. Small-Angle X-Ray Scattering, No. 2, Columbia, Mo. (October 1949). "Observed and Expected Intensity Distribution in the Small-Angle Scattering from Carbon and Other Substances."

89 Imelik, B., and Carteret, Y. A
Compt. rend., 231, 280–282 (1950). "Étude de gel de silice par la diffusion centrale des rayons X."

90 Imelik, B., and Carteret, Y. A
Bull. soc. chim. France, 18, 864–867 (1951). "Étude de gels de silice."

91 Imelik, B., Teichner, S., and Carteret, Y.   A
    J. chim. phys., *48*, 438–446 (1951). "Étude comparative de la texture des gels
    de silice par le diffraction des rayons X aux petits angles et l'adsorption
    d'azote à basse température."

92 Jellinek, M. H.   T
    Polytechnic Inst., Brooklyn, Ph.D. (1946). "The X-Ray Examination of
    Gamma Alumina." Line breadth and small-angle studies of heat treatment
    of gamma alumina. Attempted size distribution from small-angle scattering.

93 Jellinek, M. H., and Fankuchen, I.   A
    Ind. Eng. Chem., *37*, 158–164 (1945). "X-Ray Diffraction Examination of
    Gamma Alumina." Crystal and particle size. Filtered radiation and long
    collimating system used in small-angle scattering study on heat-treated
    gamma alumina.

94 Jellinek, M. H., and Fankuchen, I.   Pa
    Am. Phys. Soc., No. D-4, New York (January 1945). *Phys. Rev.*, *67*, 201
    (1945). "Low-Angle Scattering of X-Rays." Use of Geiger counter instead of
    film for continuous recording over 1000 : 1 intensity range.

95 Jellinek, M. H., and Fankuchen, I.   A
    Ind. Eng. Chem., *41*, 2259–2265 (1949). "X-Ray Examination of Pure
    Alumina Gel." Both wide-angle and small-angle measurements indicate an
    increase in crystallite and particle size with increase in severity of heat treat-
    ment, negating structures proposed earlier in No. 93.

96 Jellinek, M. H., Solomon, E., and Fankuchen, I.   A
    Ind. Eng. Chem., *Anal. Ed.*, *18*, 172-175 (1946). " Measurement and Analysis
    of Small-Angle X-Ray Scattering." Geiger recording of small-angle X-ray
    scattering. Graphical analysis of size distribution given for alumina and
    carbon black.

97 Kaesberg, P.   T
    Univ. Wisc., Ph.D. (1949). "The Use of the Double Crystal Spectrometer in
    the Analysis of Small-Angle Scattering."

97' Kahovek, L., Porod, G., and Ruck, H.
    Kolloid Z., *133*, 16 (1953). "Röntgenkleinwinkeluntersuchungen an dichtge-
    packten kolloiden Systemen."

98 Kaufman, H. S., and Fankuchen, I   A
    Anal. Chem., *24*, 20–22 (1952). "X-Ray Diffraction." General review.

99 Kaufman, H. S., Saches, A., Alfrey, T., and Fankuchen, I.   A
    J. Am. Chem. Soc., *70*, 3147 (1948). "Side-Chain Crystallization in Alkyl
    Polyerylates."

100 Kikindai, T.   A
    Compt. rend., *230*, 1772–1774 (1950). "Taille de particules d'oxyde de cuivre
    colloidal." Slope analysis of sintered copper.

101 Klug, H. P., and Alexander, L.   B
    Wiley, New York (1954). *X-Ray Diffraction Procedures for Polycrystalline and
    Amorphous Materials*. Chapter 12. Apparatus and techniques. See Nos.
    193, 205.

102 Kratky, O.   A
    Naturwissenschaften, *30*, 542–543 (1942). "Die Berechnung von Dimensionen
    kolloider Teilchen aus der unter kleinster Winkeln abgebeugten Röntgen-
    strahlen." Cellulose measurements considering close-packing.

103   Kratky, O.   A
Beih. Z. Ver. deut. Chem., *47*, 79–80 (1943). "Untersuchung über die Kleinwinkelstreuung." Size, shape, density, and swelling interpretation.
104   Kratky, O.   Aa
Monatsh. Chem., *76*, 311–318 (1946–1947). *Anz. Akad. Wiss. Wien, Math.-
naturw. Kl.*, *83*, 29–30 (1946). "Die Struktur amorpher Festkörper." Packing
in quasi-crystals.
105   Kratky, O.   A
Monatsh. Chem., *76*, 325–349 (1947). "Die Abhängigkeit der Röntgen-
kleinwinkelstreuung von Grösse und Form der kolloiden Teilchen in verdünnten
Systemen." Scattering from non-spherical particles as a combination of
spheres. Hemocyanine.
106   Kratky, O.   A
Acta Phys. Austriaca, *4*, 502 (1951). "Teilchengrössen-bestimmungen an
Metallsolen mittels der Röntgenkleinwinkelmethode."
106' Kratky, O.   A
Österr. Chem-Z., *54*, 149 (1953). "Grösse und Gestalt von Kolloidteilchen und
Makromolekulen nach der Röntgenkleinwinkelmethode."
107   Kratky, O., and Porod, G.   A
Acta Phys. Austriaca, *2*, 133–147 (1948). "Die Abhängigkeit der Röntgen-
kleinwinkelstreuung von Form und Grösse der kolloiden Teilchen in verdünnten
Systemen." Approximations of Guinier (gyration radius), Kratky (sphere-
clusters), and Porod to determine particle form.
108   Kratky, O., and Porod, G.   A
J. Colloid Sci., *4*, 35–70 (1949). "Diffuse Small-Angle Scattering of X-Rays in
Colloid Systems." Theory for dense systems, particularly layer-packed and
sphere-clusters. Cellulose applications.
109   Kratky, O., and Porod, G.   P
12th Intern. Congr. Pure Appl. Chem., Section 9, No. 27, New York (September
1951). "Problems of Small-Angle Scattering of Densely Packed Systems."
110   Kratky, O., Porod, G., and Kahovek, L.   P
Pittsburgh Conf. X-Ray Electron Diffr., No. 4, Pittsburgh (November 1950).
"Recent Advances in the Technique and Evaluation of X-Ray Small-Angle
Scattering Investigations." Collimation technique and corrections. Particle
volume from absolute intensity.
111   Kratky, O., Porod, G., and Kahovek, L.   A
Z. Elektrochem., *55*, 53–59 (1951). "Einige Neuerungen in der Technik und
Auswertung von Röntgenkleinwinkelmessungen."
111' Kratky, O., and Schossberger, F.   A
Z. Elektrochem., *43*, 666–667 (1937). "Über den micellaren Aufbau des
Kautschuks."
112   Kratky, O., and Sekora, A.   A
Naturwissenschaften, *31*, 46–47 (1943). "Bestimmung von Form und Grösse
geloster Teilchen aus den unter kleinsten Winkeln diffus abgebeugten Röntgenstrahlen." Approximation for non-spherical particles by model of agglomer-
ated spheres.
113   Kratky, O., Sekora, A., and Treer, R.   A
Z. Elektrochem., *48*, 587–601 (1942). "Über die an kolloiden Systemen unter
kleinen Winkeln diffus abgebeugten Röntgenstrahlung." Lamellar micelles.
Camera. Solutions.

114 Kratky, O., Treiber, E., and Schurz, J.   A
    Z. Elektrochem., 56, 143–146 (1952). "Photometrierung durch automatische
    Kornzählung." Counting developed grains; usable to low densities.

114' Kratky, O., and Worthmann, W.   A
    Monatsh. Chem., 76, 263–281 (1947). "Über die Bestimmbarkeit der Kon-
    figuration gelöster organischer Moleküle durch interferometrische Vermessung
    mit Röntgenstrahlen."

115 Leonard, B. R., Jr., Anderegg, J. W., Kaesberg, P., and Beeman, W. W.   A
    J. Appl. Phys., 23, 152 (1952). "The Size of Latex Particles by X-Ray
    Scattering." See Nos. 23, 25, 192.

115' Li, Y. Y., and Smoluchowski, R.   P
    Am. Phys. Soc., No. E-2, New York (January 1954). "Diffraction of X-Rays
    by Lattice Imperfections."

115" Li, Y. Y., and Smoluchowski, R.   P
    Am. Phys. Soc., No. W-10, Detroit (March 1954). "The Fourier Analysis of
    X-Ray Small-Angle Scattering."

116 Lonsdale, K.   B
    Bell, London (1948). Crystals and X-Rays. Pp. 145–147. Brief description
    of source and application of small-angle scattering.

117 Lund, L. H.   P
    ASXRED, Columbus, Ohio (1948). "Interparticle Interference Effects in
    Small-Angle X-Ray Scattering." Interference modified intensity distribution.

118 Lund, L. H.   T
    Univ. Mo., Ph.D. (1949). "Radial Density Functions and Interference of
    X-Rays Scattered at Small Angles." Particle-to-particle interferences worked
    out for various aggregates.

119 Lund, L. H.   P
    Conf. Small-Angle X-Ray Scattering, No. 8, Columbia, Mo. (October 1949).
    "Interparticle Interference Effects in Small-Angle X-Ray Scattering."
    Intensity distribution shown for aggregates of 2 to 12 particles.

120 Lund, L. H., and Vineyard, G. H.   A
    J. Appl. Phys., 20, 593–597 (1949). "Interparticle Interference Effects in the
    Small-Angle X-Ray Scattering from Fine Powder." Interparticle interference
    significant for one-third or more close packing. Intensity distribution from
    several aggregates computed. See Nos. 44, 56, 126, 128, 137, 186, 268, 284.

121 Milligan, W. O.   P
    Am. Chem. Soc., Anal. Div., No. 34, Atlantic City (September 1952). "X-Ray
    and Electron Diffraction Examination of Colloidal Materials."

122 Müller, F. H., and Erbring, H.   A
    FIAT Rev. Ger. Sci., 1939–1946. "Physik der Flüssigkeiten und Gase."
    Review and bibliography.

123 von Nardroff, R.   Pa
    Am. Phys. Soc., No. 9, Washington (April 1926). Phys. Rev., 27, 797 (1926).
    "The Refraction of X-Rays Applied to the Determination of the Diameters of
    Small Particles." Multiple refraction theory.

124 von Nardroff, R.   A
    Phys. Rev., 28, 240–246 (1926). "Refraction of X-Rays by Small Particles."
    Theory of multiple refraction of X-rays at particle surfaces.

125 Noakes, G. E.   T
    Univ. Toronto, Ph.D. (1951). "An Investigation of the Small-Angle Scatter-
    ing of X-Rays by Small Particles."

126 Noakes, G. E., and Allin, E. J. A
Can. J. Phys., *31*, 40–48 (1953). "Interference Effects in the Small-Angle Scattering of X-Rays by Small Particles." Aluminum radiation. Colloidal gold. See Nos. 44, 56, 120, 128, 137, 186, 268, 284.

126' Van Nordstrand, R. A., and Hach, K. M. P
Catalysis Club, Chicago (May 1953). "Small-Angle Scattering of Alumina and Silica Gels." Empirical relation of scattering to adsorption measured surface.

126" Van Nordstrand, R. A., and Johnson, M. F. L. P
Pittsburgh Conf. X-Ray Electron Diffr. and *ACA*, No. 23, Pittsburgh (November 1954). "Small-Angle X-Ray Scattering of Cracking Catalysts—Comparison with Adsorption Isotherms." Slope of linear log-log plot of scattered intensity vs. angle correlated with surface measurements for several types of catalysts.

127 Nowacki, W. A
Schweiz. Chem.-Z. u. Tech. Ind., *29*, 235–238, 267–270 (1946). "Kleinwinkel-röntgeninterferenzen und submikroskopische Struktur." Review with 42 references. See Nos. 127', 130'.

127' Nowacki, W. A
Uspekhi Khim., *16*, 319–326 (1947). "The Scattering of X-Rays at Small Angles by Submicroscopic Structure. II. The Application of X-Ray Scattering at Small Angles to the Determination of Submicroscopic Structure." (In Russian.) See No. 130'.

128 Oster, G., and Riley, D. P. A
Acta Cryst., *5*, 1–6 (1952). "Scattering from Isotropic Colloidal and Macro-molecular Systems." See Nos. 44, 56, 120, 126, 137, 186, 268, 284.

129 Oster, G., and Riley, D. P. A
Acta Cryst., *5*, 272–276 (1952). "Scattering from Cylindrically Symmetric Systems."

130 Penley, H. H., and Gray, J. A. A
Can. J. Research, *A-15*, 45–47 (1937). "Scattering of X-Rays at Very Small Angles." Scattering from charcoal and powdered graphite in terms of refraction and gas-type scattering. See No. 61.

130' Porai-Koshits, Ye. A. A
Uspekhi Khim., *16*, 315–319 (1947). "The Scattering of X-Rays at Small Angles by Submicroscopic Structure. I. Concerning the Scattering of X-Rays at Small Angles." (In Russian.) See Nos. 127, 127'.

131 Porai-Koshits, Ye. A. A
Izvest. Akad. Nauk S.S.S.R., *Ser. Fiz.*, *15*, 195–201 (1951). "The Study of Matter in the Dispersed State with the Aid of Small-Angle X-Ray Scattering." (In Russian.) Uses crystal monochromatization and vacuum camera.

131' Porai-Koshits, Ye. A., Kalinina, A. M., and Phillipovich, V. N. A
Doklady Akad. Nauk, S.S.S.R., *86*, 985–988 (1952). "A Study of the Structure of Several Silica Gels by the Method of X-Ray Scattering at Small Angles." (In Russian.)

132 Porai-Koshits, Ye. A., and Sokolov, U. G. A
Doklady Akad. Nauk, S.S.S.R., *72*, 477–480 (1950). "Diffuse Scattering of X-Rays at Small Angles." (In Russian.)

133 Porod, G. T
Univ. Graz, doctoral (1947).

134 Porod, G.   A
Acta Phys. Austriaca, **2**, 255–292 (1948). "Die Abhängigkeit der Röntgen-kleinwinkelstreuung von Form und Grösse der kolloiden Teilchen in verdünnten Systemen, IV." Calculation of scattering from dilute monodispersed rods, needles, plates, ellipsoids, cylinders, and spheres.

135 Porod, G.   A
Acta Phys. Austriaca, **3**, 66–81 (1949). "Abhängigkeit der Röntgenklein-winkelstreuung von Form und Anordnung der kolloiden Teilchen in dicht-gepackten Systemen." Scattering from proposed platelet structure model for cellulose fibers.

136 Porod, G.   A
Z. Naturforsch., *A-4*, 401–414 (1949). "Theorie der diffusen Röntgenklein-winkelstreuung an kolloiden Systemen." Scattering by (1) dilute systems of globules, rods, and plates, (2) oriented and unoriented compact systems, and (3) boundaries and edges.

137 Porod, G.   A
Kolloid-Z., *124*, 83–114 (1951); *125*, 51–57, 109–122 (1952). "Die Röntgen-kleinwinkelstreuung von dichtgepackten kolloiden Systemen I, II." See Nos. 44, 56, 120, 126, 128, 186, 268, 284.

138 Posner, A.   P
Am. Dental Assoc., St. Louis (September 1952). "Discussion of the Inorganic Portion of Human Enamel."

139 Posner, A. S.   A
Natl. Bur. Standards Tech. News Bull., *37*, 85–86 (1953). "X-Ray Scattering Study of Tooth Structure."

139′ Posner, A. S.   T
Univ. Liège, Ph.D. (1954). "A Study of the Constitution of Certain Mineral-ogical, Biological, and Synthetic Calcium Phosphates."

139″ Posner, A. S., and Stephenson, S. R.   A
J. Am. Dental Assoc., *46*, 257–264 (1953). "Isomorphous Substitution in Enamel Apatite."

140 Raether, H.   A
FIAT Rev. Ger. Sci., *1939–1946*, I, 102–108 (1948). "Struktur der festen Körper, VI. Struktur der dünnen Filmen."

141 Riley, D. P.   PA
Brit. Coal Utilization Research Assoc. Conf., London (1944). "The Ultra-Fine Structure of Coals and Cokes." (Pp. 232–239.) "The Low-Angle Scattering of X-Rays by Various Coals." Coals investigated give either liquid-type or gas-type scattering—a diffuse ring or central scattering.

142 Riley, D. P.   PA
Brit. Coal Utilization Research Assoc. Conf., London (1944). "The Ultra-Fine Structure of Coals and Cokes." (Pp. 246–257.) "The Crystallinity of Certain High Ash-Content Coals." Both small- and wide-angle diffuse X-ray rings.

143 Riley, D. P.   PA
Inst. of Physics, X-Ray Analysis Group, Royal Inst. (April 1950). *Nature*, *165*, 870–872 (1950). "Production and Application of High-Intensity X-Ray Beams." Conference report includes a few small-angle applications.

144 Riley, D. P.   P
Conf. du Palais de la Découverte, Univ. Paris (1948). "La structure des charbons."

Δ√ 145 Riseman, J.   A
Acta Cryst., **5**, 193–196 (1952). "Particle Size Distribution from Small-Angle Scattering." Theoretical distribution for spheres. See Nos. 6, 147, 155.

145′ Ritland, W. N., and Beeman, W. W.   P
Pittsburgh Conf. X-Ray Electron Diffr. and *ACA*, No. 21, Pittsburgh (November 1954). "The Small-Angle Scattering of X-Rays by Several Glasses."

146 Ritter, H. L., and Erich, L. C.   A
Anal. Chem., **20**, 665–670 (1948). "Pore Size Distribution in Porous Materials. Interpretation of Small-Angle X-Ray Scattering Patterns." Theory of small-angle scattering applied to porous aggregates, and results reduced to continuous distributions of pore size. A semi-empirical method of correcting for collimation is developed and applied.

146′ Robinson, W. H., Li, Y. Y., and Smoluchowski, R.   P
Am. Phys. Soc., No. W-9, Detroit (March 1954). "Small-Angle Scattering of X-Rays by Irradiated Diamond."

146″ Robinson, W. H., Li, Y. Y., and Smoluchowski, R.   P
Pittsburgh Conf. X-Ray Electron Diffr. and *ACA*, No. 22, Pittsburgh (November 1954). "Small-Angle Scattering of X-Rays by Diamond." No vacancy clusters found, but 1500 A surface imperfections.

147 Roess, L. C.   A
J. Chem. Phys., **14**, 695–697 (1946). "A Simple Method of Obtaining a Particle Mass Distribution by Inverting the X-Ray Intensity Scattered at Small Angles." See Nos. 6, 145, 155.

148 Roess, L. C., and Shull, C. G.   A
J. Appl. Phys., **18**, 308–313 (1947). "X-Ray Scattering at Small Angles by Finely Divided Solids. II. Exact Theory for Random Distribution of Spheroidal Particles." Families of scattering curves for spheroids. Fit between experimental and calculated scattering curves for mass distribution.

149 Ruess, G.   A
Monatsh. Chem., **76**, 253–262 (1946–1947). "Über die Struktur des Glaz-kohlenstoffs." Includes small-angle scattering.

149′ Schmidt, P.   T
Univ. Wisc., Ph.D. (1953). Small-angle scattering from turnip yellow mosaic virus.

149″ Shacklett, R.   T
Calif. Inst. Tech., Ph.D. (1953). Point-focusing monochromator applications.

150 Sharrah, P. C.   P
Conf. Small-Angle X-Ray Scattering, No. 11, Columbia, Mo. (October 1949). "Surface Coating on Magnesium." Examination of surface film using small-angle scattering.

151 Shenfil, L., Danielson, W. E., and DuMond, J. W. M.
Tech. Report 15, O.N.R. Contract N6ONR–244, T.O. IV, NRO17–602. "A Point-Focusing Monochromator for the Study of Low-Angle X-Ray Diffraction; Determinations of the Size Distributions of Carbon Blacks and a Precision Determination of the Size of Dow Latex Particles." See Nos. 25, 229.

152 Shishakov, N. A.   A
Zhur. Eksptl. i. Teoret. Fiz. (*J. Exptl. Theoret. Phys. U.S.S.R.*), **19**, 431–437 (1949). "Displacement of the Interference Maxima with Variation the of Size and Shape of Very Small Crystals." (In Russian.)

153 Shull, C. G. P
ASXRED and *AAAS*, Gibson Island, Md. (August 1944). "Some Experimental Studies of Small-Angle Scattering."

154 Shull, C. G., Elkin, P. B., and Roess, L. C. A
J. Am. Chem. Soc., *70*, 1410–1414 (1948). "Physical Studies of Gel Microstructure." Pore size by adsorption and small-angle scattering.

155 Shull, C. G., and Roess, L. C. A
J. Appl. Phys., *18*, 295–307 (1947). "X-Ray Scattering at Small Angles by Finely Divided Solids. I. General Approximate Theory and Applications." Review of theory for independent particles. Procedure for obtaining mass distribution and correcting for slit geometry. Examples. See Nos. 6, 145, 147, 148.

156 Smith, A. E. Pa
Am. Phys. Soc., No. B-2, Los Angeles (January 1947). *Phys. Rev.*, *71*, 277 (1947). "Determination of Particle Size by Low-Angle Scattering of X-Rays." Effect on small-angle scattering of particle shape. Check with line broadening.
Note: item 157 is omitted

158 Stone, L. L., and Yudowitch, K. L. P
Pittsburgh Conf. X-Ray Electron Diffr., No. 11, Pittsburgh (November 1950). "Applications of a High Resolution Small-Angle Scattering Camera." Extension by fine geometry to 1/4 micron particles. Application to bacterial nuclei and latex. See No. 192.

159 Turkevich, J., and Hubbell, H. H., Jr. Pa
Am. Phys. Soc., No. G-12, New York (January 1948). *Phys. Rev.*, *73*, 1250 (1948). "Experimental Check on Intensity Distribution in Small-Angle X-Ray Scattering." Guinier formula checked on wavelength dependence. Secondary maximum detected.

160 Turkevich, J., and Hubbell, H. H., Jr. P
Am. Chem. Soc., Phys. Inorg. Div., No. 117, Atlantic City (September 1949). "Small-Angle Scattering of X-Rays by Colloidal Particles."

161 Turkevich, J., and Hubbell, H. H., Jr. A
J. Am. Chem. Soc., *73*, 1–7 (1951). "Low-Angle X-Ray Diffraction of Colloidal Gold and Carbon Black."

162 Turkevich, J., Hubbell, H. H., Jr., and Hillier, J. PA
Discussions Faraday Soc., *8*, 348–352 (1950). "Electron Microscopy and Small-Angle X-Ray Scattering." Correlation on catalysts.

162' Tweet, A. G. Pa
Am. Phys. Soc., No. W-2, Washington (May 1953). *Phys. Rev.*, *91*, 488–489 (1953). "Small-Angle Scattering of X-Rays from Helium I and Helium II."

163 Vineyard, G. H. Pa
Am. Phys. Soc., No. C-7, Washington (April 1948). *Phys. Rev.*, *74*, 1209 (1948). "The Interpretation of Small-Angle X-Ray Scattering Observed from Argon." Scattering from argon near critical point re-examined for pretransition phenomena.

164 Vineyard, G. H. A
Phys. Rev., *74*, 1076–1083 (1948). "Small-Angle X-Ray Scattering from Amorphous Materials." Derivation of scattering from inhomogeneities.

165 Vineyard, G. H. P
ASXRED, No. 29, Columbus (December 1948). "Small-Angle Scattering from Amorphous Materials."

166 Vineyard, G. H.   P
Conf. Small-Angle X-Ray Scattering, No. 13, Columbia, Mo. (October 1949).
"Ray Optics for Larger Particles?" Particle size, refractive index, and wavelength determine whether refraction or diffraction theory is valid.

167 Vineyard, G. H.   A
Phys. Rev., *82*, 453 (1951). "Concerning Certain Anomalous Small-Angle Diffraction Effects."

168 Vineyard, G. H.   A
Phys. Rev., *85*, 633–636 (1952). "Geometrical Optics and the Theory of Multiple Small-Angle Scattering." See Nos. 35, 254, 256, 355.

168′ Vineyard, G. H.   P
Am. Phys. Soc., No. E-1, New York (January 1954). "Small-Angle Scattering."

169 Walker, C. B., Blin, J., and Guinier, A.   A
Compt. rend., *235*, 254–255 (1952). "Mise en evidence des hétérogénéités d'une solution solide en équilibre."

170 Walker, C. B., and Guinier, A.   A
Compt. rend., *234*, 2379–2381 (1952). "Les phénomènes de pre-précipitation dans l'alliage aluminium-argent." Silver nuclei.

171 Warren, B. E.   A
J. Chem. Phys., *2*, 551–555 (1934). "X-Ray Diffraction Study of Carbon Black." Small-angle scattering. Interpretation without any assumption as to crystallinity—but packing density variations.

172 Warren, B. E.   Pa
Am. Phys. Soc., No. 132, Washington (April 1936). *Phys. Rev.*, *49*, 885 (1936). "Small-Angle X-Ray Scattering." C-black and SiO_2. Interpreted as scattering and interference between particles. All atoms of a particle thought in phase. Particle size measurement discussed.

173 Warren, B. E.   P
ASXRED, No. 40, Ste. Marguerite Sta., Quebec (June 1947). "Double Crystal Spectrometer Measurements of Total Energy of Small-Angle Scattering." Specimen moved from between crystals to between second crystal and counter to obtain total small-angle scattering and hence an average particle size.

174 Warren, B. E.   A
J. Appl. Phys., *20*, 96–97 (1949). "A Method for Measuring the Total Power of Small-Angle X-Ray Scattering." Total power in small-angle scattering from the difference between two settings of double crystal spectrometer for an average particle size. See No. 5.

175 West, W. J.   P
Soc. Rheology, No. 25, Chicago (October 1951). "Size Determinations of Clay Particles in Water Suspensions by Use of Low-Angle X-Ray Diffraction."

176 West, W. J.   A
J. Colloid Sci., *7*, 295–305 (1952). "Size Determinations of Clay Particles in Water Suspensions by Use of Low-Angle X-Ray Diffraction." Two crystal spectrometer. Largest particles exhibit most swelling.

177 Whitman, J.   T
Fla. State Univ., M.S. (1950). "Accurate Determination of Particle Size by the Line Broadening Method Using Soft X-Rays; Critical Examination of Corrections of Such Methods."

178 Whitman, J., and Yudowitch, K. L.   PA
     Florida Acad. Sci., No. 84 (December 1950). *Quart. J. Florida Acad. Sci., 14,*
     43–46 (1951). "X-Ray Line Breadth Corrections." Crystallite size compared
     with particle size.

179 Wild, R. L.   T
     Univ. Mo., Ph.D. (1950). "The Small-Angle Scattering of X-Rays by
     Nitrogen."

180 Wild, R. L.   A
     J. Chem. Phys., 18, 1627–1632 (1950). "The Small-Angle Scattering of X-Rays
     by Nitrogen." Compressibility and inhomogeneity size for nitrogen near
     critical point. Compressibility values check; inhomogeneous regions found
     to be only 4–8 A. See Nos. 40, 49, 59.

181 Wild, R. L.   P
     Pittsburgh Conf. X-Ray Electron Diffr., No. 1, Pittsburgh (November 1950).
     "The Small-Angle Scattering of X-Rays by Nitrogen." Evidence of inhomo-
     geneities near critical point.

182 Wood, L. A.   T
     Stanford Univ., Ph.D. (1939). "The Absolute Amount of Adsorption in the
     Surface of Solutions."

183 Yudowitch, K. L.   T
     Univ. Mo., Ph.D. (1948). "Particle Size Determination by the Scattering of
     Soft X-Rays." Secondary maxima observed. Interparticle interference
     peaks observed and theory suggested. Optimum collimation scheme outlined.
     Examples of colloidal gold with vacuum-soft aluminum X-rays.

184 Yudowitch, K. L.   Pa
     Electron Micr. Soc. Amer., No. 41, Toronto (November 1948). *Anal. Chem.,
     20,* 993 (1948). "Particle Size Correlation with X-Ray Methods." Soft X-rays
     extend small-angle technique to overlap electron microscopy range. See
     No. 186.

185 Yudowitch, K. L.   P
     Pittsburgh Conf. X-Ray Electron Diffr., No. 18, Pittsburgh (November 1948).
     "Particle Size Determination by Soft X-Ray Scattering." See No. 186.

186 Yudowitch, K. L.   A
     J. Appl. Phys., 20, 174–182 (1949). "Particle Size Determination by Soft
     X-Ray Scattering." See Nos. 44, 56, 120, 126, 128, 137, 268, 284.

187 Yudowitch, K. L.   A
     Phys. Today, 2, 33 (1949). "Measuring Colloidal Particles."

188 Yudowitch, K. L.   PA
     Florida Acad. Sci., No. 65 (December 1949). *Quart. J. Florida Acad. Sci., 12,*
     246–250 (1949). "Particle Size by X-Ray Scattering." Line broadening and
     small-angle scattering.

189 Yudowitch, K. L.   P
     Electron Micr. Soc. Amer., No. 12, Detroit (September 1950). "Latex Size by
     X-Rays." See No. 192.

190 Yudowitch, K. L.
     Final Report, Chem. Corps, Camp Detrick, Md., Contract W-18-064-CM-229
     (1950). "An Investigation of Particle Structure, Packing, and Size
     Distribution."

191 Yudowitch, K. L.
     Final Report, Chem. Corps, Camp Detrick, Md., Contract DA-18-064-CML-464
     (1951). "Investigation of Particle Structure and Size Distribution."

192 Yudowitch, K. L.   A
J. Appl. Phys., *22*, 214–216 (1951). "Latex Particle Size from X-Ray Diffraction Peaks." Particle size of spheres from series of secondary maxima. See Nos. 23, 115, 151.

193 Yudowitch, K. L.   A
Rev. Sci. Instr., *23*, 83–90 (1952). "Small-Angle X-Ray Scattering Technique." Comprehensive review of design for peak and slope analysis.

194 Yudowitch, K. L.   P
ACA, Tamiment, Pa. (June 1952). "Interparticle Interference Effects." See No. 56.

195 Yudowitch, K. L.   P
Am. Chem. Soc., Anal. Div., No. 35, Atlantic City (September 1952). "Small-Angle Scattering Technique, Interpretation, and Applications." See No. 196.

196 Yudowitch, K. L.   A
Anal. Chem., *25*, 721–724 (1953). "Low-Angle X-Ray Scattering Technique, Interpretation, and Application." Elementary review.

197 Yvon, M. J.   A
J. phys. radium, *7*, 201–202 (1946). "Le coefficient de compressibilité des fluides déduit du diagramme diffusion des rayons X." Liquid compressibility from small-angle data.

II. GEOMETRY

198 Alexander, L.   P
Pittsburgh Conf. X-Ray Electron Diffr., Pittsburgh (November 1947). Geometry.

199 Alexander, L.   A
J. Appl. Phys., *19*, 1068–1071 (1948). "Geometrical Factors Affecting the Contours of X-Ray Spectrometer Maxima. I. Factors Causing Asymmetry." 3rd dimension error.

200 Alexander, L.   A
J. Appl. Phys., *21*, 126–136 (1950). "Geometrical Factors Affecting the Contours of X-Ray Spectrometer Maxima. II. Factors Causing Broadening." The pure diffraction contour is broadened by X-ray source width, flat rather than curved sample surface, vertical divergence of the X-ray beam, penetration of the sample by the beam, receiving slit width.

200' Alexander, L.   A
Brit. J. Appl. Phys., *4*, 92–93 (1953). "The Effect of Vertical Divergence on X-Ray Powder Diffraction Lines."

201 Alexander, L., and Klug, H. P.   P
ASXRED, Ithaca, N.Y. (June 1949). Geometry.

202 Alexander, L., and Klug, H. P.   A
J. Appl. Phys., *21*, 137–142 (1950). "Determination of Crystallite Size with the X-Ray Spectrometer." Convolution analysis for effect of geometrical factors in broadening pure diffraction contour.

203 Bergman, M. E., and Fankuchen, I.   A
Rev. Sci. Instr., *20*, 696 (1949). "Modification of X-Ray Diffraction Micro-Camera to Permit Study of Long Spacings."   •

204 Bertaut, F.   A
Compt. rend., *228*, 1597–1599 (1949). "Méthode de correction de la forme des raies Debye-Scherrer." Correction of line profile.

205   Bolduan, O. E. A., and Bear, R. S.   A
J. Appl. Phys., *20*, 983–992 (1949). "Effective Use of Collimating Apertures in Small-Angle X-Ray Diffraction Cameras." Optimum conditions for pinhole and slit aperture systems are developed. Construction and performance of some cameras for periodic structures.

206   Broussard, L.   A
Rev. Sci. Instr., *21*, 399–400 (1950). "Improved Double Crystal Spectrometer for Small-Angle Scattering Measuring." Second crystal and counter rotate rigidly about specimen. See Nos. 8, 209, 212, 226, 238.

207   Clark, G. L., and Corrigan, K. E.   A
Ind. Eng. Chem., *23*, 815–820 (1931). "Industrial and Chemical Research with X-Rays of High Intensity and with Soft X-Rays." Use of longer wavelengths to increase diffraction angles: Mg target.

208   Davis, B., and Slack, C. M.   A
Phys. Rev., *27*, 18–22 (1926). "Measurement of the Refraction of X-Rays in a Prism by Means of the Double X-Ray Spectrometer." Double crystal spectrometer used to measure small angular deflection. See No. 230.

208'   Déspujols, J.   A
Compt. rend., *235*, 716–718 (1952). "Monochromateur pour rayons X à foyer ponctuel."

209   DuMond, J. W. M.   A
Phys. Rev., *72*, 83–84 (1947). "Method of Correcting Low-Angle X-Ray Diffraction Curves for the Study of Small Particle Sizes." Two crystal techniques described, correction for slit height. See Nos. 8, 173, 206, 208, 212, 226, 230, 238.

210   DuMond, J. W. M.   A
Rev. Sci. Instr., *21*, 188–189 (1950). "Point Focus Monochromators for Low-Angle Diffraction." Two types of point-focusing crystal arrangements described.

211   DuMond, J. W. M., Shenfil, L., Danielson, W., and Henke, B.   P
Pittsburgh Conf. X-Ray Electron Diffr., No. 10, Pittsburgh (1950). "Anastigmatic Point-Focusing X-Ray Monochromator for Cu $K\alpha$ Radiation for Use in Low-Angle X-Ray Diffraction Studies."

212   Fankuchen, I., and Jellinek, M. H.   Pa
Am. Phys. Soc., No. D-5, New York (January 1945). *Phys. Rev.*, *67*, 201 (1945). "Low-Angle X-Ray Scattering." Describes a double crystal method for obtaining scattering. Geiger counter. Scattering at extremely small angles can be studied. Specimen between crystals in parallel and antiparallel arrangements. See Nos. 8, 173, 206, 208, 209, 226, 230, 238.

212'   Finean, J. B.   A
J. Sci. Instr., *30*, 60–61 (1953). "A Versatile Camera for Low-Angle Diffraction Studies."

213   Fournier, F.   A
Compt. rend., *227*, 833–834 (1948). "Sur la réalisation et l'utilisation de faisceaux de rayons X très fins, de l'ordre de quelques microns." Glass capillaries.

214   Franklin, R. E.   A
Acta Cryst., *3*, 158–159 (1950). "A Rapid Approximate Method for Correcting Low-Angle Scattering Measurements for the Influence of the Finite Height of the Beam."

215   Gokhale, B. G.   A
Compt. rend., *230*, 636–638 (1950). "Sur l'effet de la largeur de fente du microphotomètre sur la largeur enregistrée des raies dans les spectres des rayons X."

216   Guinier, A., and Fournet, G.   A
J. phys. radium, *8*, 345–351 (1947). "Facteurs de correction dans les mesures de la diffusion des rayons X aux faibles angles." Consideration of error in small-angle pattern due to finite cross section of incident beam.

217   Guinier, A., and Fournet, G.   A
Nature, *160*, 501 (1947). "Correction of Measurements of Low-Angle X-Ray Scattering." The correction for the finite height of the monochromator beam is worked out for spherical and ellipsoidal particles, and shown graphically.

218   Guinier, A., and Fournet, G.   P
CSA-ASXRED, New Haven, Conn. (1948). "A Two-Curved Crystal Mono-chromator for the Study of Low-Angle Scattering."

219   Guinier, A., and Fournet, G.   A
Compt. rend., *226*, 656–659 (1948). "Emploi d'un monochromateur double pour l'étude de la diffusion des rayons X aux très faibles angles." A slit is placed at the focus of the first curved crystal monochromator, and the rays focused on the film by the second monochromator. Background is greatly reduced, at the expense of increase in exposure time. Spacings to 250 A.

219′   Hägg, G., and Karlsson, N.   A
Acta Cryst., *5*, 728–730 (1952). "Aluminum Monochromator with Double Curvature for High-Intensity Powder Photographs."

220   Hubbell, H. H., Jr.   Pa
Am. Phys. Soc., No. G-13, Chicago (December 1947). *Phys. Rev.*, *73*, 1251 (1948). "The Effect of Apparatus Geometry on Small-Angle X-Ray Scattering Curves." Smearing of secondary maxima by slits.

220′   Huxley, H. E.   A
Acta Cryst., *6*, 457–465 (1953). "Optimum Geometric Conditions in the Design and Use of X-Ray Diffraction Tubes and Cameras." See Nos. 125, 205, 241.

221   Kaesberg, P., Beeman, W. W., and Ritland, H. N.   Pa
Am. Phys. Soc., No. OB-4, New York (February 1950). *Phys. Rev.*, *78*, 336 (1950). "Double Crystal and Slit Methods in Small-Angle X-Ray Scattering." Resolution of about 10 seconds obtained using a calcite double crystal spectrometer. Wing background at larger angles makes detection of weak scattering difficult. Method inferior to a slit system for low resolution requirement. See No. 226.

222   Kahovek, L., and Treiber, E.   A
Z. Elektrochem., *55*, 437–439 (1951). "Über eine Röntgenküvette für Klein-winkelaufnahmen."

222′   Kiessig, H.   A
Kolloid-Z., *98*, 213–221 (1942). "Röntgenuntersuchung grosser Netzebenen-abstande und Untersuchung strömender Lösungen." Describes apparatus.

223   Lely, J. A., and Van Rijssel, T. W.   A
Acta Cryst., *2*, 337–338 (1949). "X-Ray Collimator Producing a Beam of Very Small Divergence and Large Intensity." Slits constructed of polished glass blocks with a critical angle less than 15′ produce strong beams of small divergence.

224 Lipson, H., Nelson, J. B., and Riley, D. P.   A
     J. Sci. Instr., *22*, 184–187 (1945). "Monochromatic X-Radiation."

225 Ritland, H. N., Kaesberg, P., and Beeman, W. W.   P
     Conf. Small-Angle X-Ray Scattering, No. 3, Columbia, Mo. (October 1949).
     "Double Crystal and Slit Methods in Small-Angle X-Ray Scattering."
     Intensity wings with double crystal spectrometer examined; reduced by third
     crystal.

226 Ritland, H. N., Kaesberg, P., and Beeman, W. W.   A
     J. Appl. Phys., *21*, 838–841 (1950). "Double Crystal and Slit Methods in
     Small-Angle X-Ray Scattering." Experimental comparison of slit vs. crystal
     collimation. Intensity wings from crystal examined. See Nos. 8, 209, 212.

227 Shenfil, L.   T
     Calif. Inst. Tech., Ph.D. (1952). "Point-Focusing X-Ray Monochromator for
     Low-Angle Scattering Studies."

228 Shenfil, L., Danielson, W. E., and DuMond, J. W. M.   Pa
     Am. Phys. Soc., No. B-5, Houston (November 1951). *Phys. Rev.*, *85*, 739
     (1952). "A Point-Focusing Monochromator for Low-Angle X-Ray Diffraction."

229 Shenfil, L., Danielson, W. E., and DuMond, J. W. M.   A
     J. Appl. Phys., *23*, 854–859 (1952). "A Point-Focusing X-Ray Monochromator
     for the Study of Low-Angle Diffraction." See Nos. 25, 151, 438.

230 Slack, C. M.   A
     Phys. Rev., *27*, 691–695 (1926). "Refraction of X-Rays in Prisms of Various
     Materials." Double crystal spectrometer for beam contour. Granular
     material. See No. 208.

231 Solomon, E., and Jellinek, M. H.   A
     Rev. Sci. Instr., *15*, 348–349 (1944). "An Inexpensive Densitometer for the
     Evaluation of Low-Angle X-Ray Scattering Films."

232 Spencer, R. C.   A
     Phys. Rev., *38*, 618–629 (1931). "Additional Theory of the Double X-Ray
     Spectrometer."

233 Spencer, R. C.   A
     Phys. Rev., *48*, 473 (1935). "The Effect of the Spectrometer on the Width of
     Spectral Lines."

234 Spencer, R. C.   A
     Phys. Rev., *52*, 761 (1937). "A Theorem on the Effect of Vertical Divergence."

235 Spencer, R. C.   Pa
     Am. Phys. Soc., No. 31, Chicago (November 1938). *Phys. Rev.*, *55*, 239 (1939).
     "The Correction of Experimental Curves for the Resolving Power of the
     Apparatus."

236 Spencer, R. C.   Pa
     Am. Phys. Soc., No. 33, Providence (June 1941). *Phys. Rev.*, *60*, 172 (1941).
     "Optimum Design of Physical Apparatus."

237 Spencer, R. C.   A
     J. Appl. Phys., *20*, 413–414 (1949). "Discussion of Geometrical Factors
     Affecting X-Ray Spectrometer Maxima."

238 Wild, R.   A
     Rev. Sci. Instr., *22*, 537–538 (1951). "Automatic Focusing Condition for
     Double Crystal Spectrometer." See Nos. 8, 206, 209, 212, 226.

239 Yudowitch, K. L.   Pa
     Am. Phys. Soc., No. B-1, Cambridge, Mass. (June 1949). *Phys. Rev.*, *76*, 455
     (1949). "Collimation Error in Small-Angle X-Ray Scattering."

240   Yudowitch, K. L.   P
      Conf. Small-Angle X-Ray Scattering, No. 4, Columbia, Mo. (October 1949).
      "Proper Design for Minimizing Collimation Error in Small-Angle Scattering."
241   Yudowitch, K. L.   A
      J. Appl. Phys., *20*, 1232–1236 (1949). "Collimation Error in Small-Angle
      X-Ray Scattering." Minimization of range of angles for rays reaching a single
      point on film leads to optimum slit shape and spacing.
242   Yudowitch, K. L.   P
      ACA, No. 1, Chicago (October 1951). "Powder Pattern Geometry."
243   Yudowitch, K. L.   A
      J. Opt. Soc. Amer., *42*, 437–440 (1952). "Diffraction Geometry."
244   Yudowitch, K. L.   A
      J. Opt. Soc. Amer., *43*, 50–52 (1953). "Recording Radially Symmetric
      Scattering."

III.   NEUTRONS

245   Halpern, O.   Pa
      Am. Phys. Soc., No. H-3, Houston (November 1947). *Phys. Rev.*, *73*, 653
      (1948). "Small-Angle Diffraction in Lattices." Theoretical paper on small-
      angle scattering of light and material waves.
246   Halpern, O.   P
      Pittsburgh Conf. X-Ray Electron Diffr., No. 2, Pittsburgh (November 1950).
      "Small-Angle Diffraction of Neutrons." Theoretical consideration of scatter-
      ing cross sections for neutrons,
247   Halpern, O., and Gerjouy, E.   Pa
      Am. Phys. Soc., No. H-5, Pasadena (June 1948). *Phys. Rev.*, *74*, 1562 (1948).
      "On Diffraction under Small Angles by Three-Dimensional Lattices." General
      theory for small-angle scattering cross sections for light, X-rays, and neutrons.
248   Halpern, O., and Gerjouy, E.   A
      Phys. Rev., *76*, 1117–1129 (1949). "Small-Angle Diffraction of Neutrons and
      Similar Wave Phenomena." Diffraction cross-section dependence on nature
      and orientation of scatterer, and on scattering angle.
249   Heller, R. B.   P
      Conf. Small-Angle X-Ray Scattering, No. 9, Columbia, Mo. (October 1949).
      "Small-Angle Scattering of Neutrons at Domain Boundaries in Magnetized
      Iron." Multiple magnetic refraction of neutrons in iron.
250   Hughes, D. J., Burgy, M. T., Heller, R. B., and Wallace, J. W.   A
      Phys. Rev., *75*, 565–569 (1949). "Magnetic Refraction of Neutrons at Domain
      Boundaries." Refraction of neutrons at magnetic domain boundaries.
251   Krueger, H. H. A., Meneghetti, D., Ringo, G. R., and Wensberg, L.   A
      Phys. Rev., *80*, 507–510 (1950). "Small-Angle Scattering of Thermal
      Neutrons." Experimental examination of (1) Halpern and Gerjouy's, (2) Van
      de Hulst's, and (3) von Nardroff's theories.
252   McReynolds, A. W., and Weiss, R. J.   Pa
      Am. Phys. Soc., No. V-6, Chicago (November 1950). *Phys. Rev.*, *81*, 326
      (1951). "Small-Angle Scattering of Thermal Neutrons (Experimental)."
253   Meneghetti, D.   Pa
      Am. Phys. Soc., No. X-7, Washington (April 1949). *Phys. Rev.*, *76*, 188–189
      (1949). "Small-Angle Scattering of Neutrons." Scattering in agreement with
      X-ray refraction theory.

254 Meneghetti, D.   P
     Pittsburgh Conf. X-Ray Electron Diffr., No. 5, Pittsburgh (November 1950).
     "Small-Angle Scattering of Thermal Neutrons." Multiple scattering of
     neutrons agrees in range of study with both refraction and diffraction theories.
     See Nos. 35, 168, 256, 355.

254' Shull, C. G., and Wilkinson, M. K.   P
     Am. Phys. Soc., No. Y-2, Detroit (March 1954). "Small-Angle Neutron
     Scattering by Iron at High Temperatures."

255 Weiss, R. J.   P
     ACA, No. H-2, New Hampton, N.H. (August 1950). "Neutron Small-Angle
     Scattering."

256 Weiss, R. J.   T
     N.Y.U., Ph.D. (1950). "Small-Angle Scattering of Neutrons." Verification
     of diffraction theory for small phase change in traversing particle, and of
     refraction theory for large phase change in traversing particle. See Nos. 35,
     168, 254, 355.

257 Weiss, R. J.   A
     Phys. Rev., *83*, 379–389 (1951). "Small-Angle Scattering of Neutrons."

258 Weiss, R. J., and Pasternack, S.   Pa
     Am. Phys. Soc., No. V-7, Chicago (November 1950). *Phys. Rev.*, *81*, 326
     (1951). "Small-Angle Scattering of Thermal Neutrons (Theoretical)." Phase
     change in neutron in traversing particle to determine validity of refraction or
     diffraction theory.

IV. BASIC THEORY

259 Born, M., and Green, H. S.   A
     Proc. Roy. Soc. (London), *A-188*, 10–18 (1946). "A General Kinetic Theory
     of Liquids. I. The Molecular Distribution Functions."

260 Born, M., and Green, H. S.   A
     Proc. Roy. Soc. (London), *A-190*, 455–473 (1947). "A General Kinetic Theory
     of Liquids. III. Dynamical Properties."

261 Born, M., and Green, H. S.   A
     Proc. Roy. Soc. (London), *A-191*, 168–181 (1947). "A General Kinetic Theory
     of Liquids. IV. Quantum Mechanics of Fluids."

262 Corner, J., and Lennard-Jones, J. E.   A
     Proc. Roy. Soc. (London), *A-178*, 401–414 (1941). "The Neighbor Distribution
     Function in Monatomic Liquids and Dense Gases."

263 Debye, P.   A
     Ann. Physik, *43*, 49–95 (1914). "Interferenz von Röntgenstrahlen und
     Warmbewegung."

264 Debye, P.   A
     Ann. Physik, *46*, 809–823 (1915). "Zerstreuung von Röntgenstrahlen."
     Scattering from non-crystalline substances.

265 Debye, P.   A
     Physik. Z., *28*, 135–141 (1927). "Über die Zerstreuung von Röntgenstrahlen
     an amorphen Körpern."

266 Debye, P.   A
     Physik. Z., *31*, 348–350 (1930). "Röntgenzerstreuung an Flüssigkeiten und
     Gasen." Diffraction by microscopic drop of liquid; large angles due to mole-
     cular arrangement, immeasurably small angles due to boundary of drop.

267   Debye, P.   A
Physik. Z., *31*, 419–428 (1930). "Röntgeninterferenzen und Atomgrösse."
Distribution of scattered X-ray intensity from polyatomic gases makes it
necessary to treat atoms as extended scattering domains.

268   Debye, P.   A
J. Math. and Phys., *4*, 133–147 (1925). "Note on the Scattering of X-Rays."
Liquid and gas scattering theory.

269   Debye, P., and Menke, H.   A
Physik. Z., *31*, 797–798 (1930). "Bestimmung der inneren Struktur von
Flüssigkeiten mit Röntgenstrahlen." Quasi-crystalline structure for mercury.

270   Debye, P., and Menke, H.   B
Akademische Verlagsgesellschaft, Leipzig (1931). *Ergebnis der technische
Röntgenkunde. II.* Method of Zernicke and Prins extended to liquid scattering.

271   Gingrich, N. S.   A
Revs. Mod. Phys., *15*, 90–110 (1943). "The Diffraction of X-Rays by Liquid
Elements." Inversion of liquid scattering data. Some patterns show
low-angle intensity.

272   Gingrich, N. S., and Warren, B. E.   A
Phys. Rev., *46*, 248–251 (1934). "The Interpretation of X-Ray Diffraction
Patterns of a Fluid at Various Densities." The method of Zernicke and Prins
applied to obtain scattering from a fluid at various densities for assumed radial
densities.

273   Green, H. S.   A
Proc. Roy. Soc. (London), *A-189*, 103–117 (1947). "A General Kinetic Theory
of Liquids. II. Equilibrium Properties." See Nos. 259, 260, 261.

274   Guinier, A.   A
Acta Cryst., *5*, 121–130 (1952). "Interprétation de la diffusion anormale des
rayons X par les alliages à durcissement structural."

275   Harvey, G. G.   A
Phys. Rev., *46*, 441–445 (1934). "The Effect of Pressure on the Intensity of
X-Rays Scattered by Nitrogen at Small Angles." Scattering curves at various
pressures resemble those of a liquid or solid. Concluded due to the closeness
of scattering centers rather than preferred orientation.

276   Hosemann, R.   A
Z. Physik, *127*, 16–39 (1950). "Röntgeninterferenzen an Strichgittern mit
Flüssigkeitsunordnung."

277   Hosemann, R.   A
Z. Physik, *128*, 1–35 (1950). "Röntgeninterferenzen an Stoffen mit flüssigkeits-
statistischen Gitterstörungen."

278   Hosemann, R.   A
Z. Elektrochem., *54*, 23–26 (1950). "Kristallitgrossenbestimmung in Hochmolekularen. Grenzen der Laueschen Methode."

279   Hosemann, R., and Bagchi, S. N.   A
Acta Cryst., *5*, 612–614 (1952). "The Interference Theory of Ideal Para-
crystals."

280   Kachkuruzov, G. A., and Todes, O. M.   A
Doklady Akad. Nauk, S.S.S.R., *66*, 77–79 (1949). "Principles of X-Ray
Diffraction Analysis of Polycrystalline Materials." (In Russian.) Review of
methods for particle sizes in polydisperse systems.

281   Kirkwood, J. G.   Pa
      Am. Chem. Soc., New York (April 1935).   *J. Chem. Phys.*, *3*, 300–313 (1935).
      "Statistical Mechanics of Fluid Mixtures."
282   Kirkwood, J. G.   A
      J. Chem. Phys., *7*, 919-927 (1939).   "Molecular Distribution in Liquids."
283   Kirkwood, J. G., and Boggs, E. M.   A
      J. Chem. Phys., *10*, 394–402 (1942).   "The Radial Distribution Function in
      Liquids."
284   Kirkwood, J. G., Maun, E. K., and Adler, B. J.   A
      J. Chem. Phys., *18*, 1040–1047 (1950).   "Radial Distribution Functions and the
      Equation of State of a Fluid Composed of Rigid Spherical Molecules."
285   Kirkwood, J. G., and Mazur, J.   PA
      Intern. Union Chem., Strasbourg (June 1952).   *J. Polymer Sci.*, *9*, 519-524
      (1952).   "The Radial Distribution Functions of Electrically Charged Macro-
      molecules in Solution."
286   Kottler, F.   A
      J. Franklin Inst., *250*, 339–356, 419–442 (1950).   "The Distribution of Particle
      Sizes I, II."   Distribution law from crystal growth law.   Use of weighted
      squares.
287   Krishnamurti, P.   A
      Indian J. Phys., *2*, 491–500 (1927-1928).   "X-Ray Diffraction and Its
      Bearing on the Molecular Complexity in the Liquid State."
288   Krishnamurti, P.   A
      Indian J. Phys., *2*, 501–507 (1927-1928).   "X-Ray Diffraction in Solutions and
      Liquid Mixtures, Part I."
289   Krishnamurti, P.   A
      Indian J. Phys., *3*, 209–223 (1928-1929).   "The Diffraction of X-Rays by
      Aqueous Solutions of Canesugar, Levulose, and Glucose."
290   Krishnamurti, P.   A
      Indian J. Phys., *3*, 225–240 (1928-1929).   "X-Ray Diffraction of Crystal
      Powders and Liquids in Relation to Their Constitution."
291   Krishnamurti, P.   A
      Indian J. Phys., *3*, 307-329 (1928-1929).   "On the Nature of Dextrin, Gelatin,
      and Sodium Oleate Solutions as Revealed by X-Ray Diffraction."
292   Krishnamurti, P.   A
      Indian J. Phys., *3*, 331-355 (1928-1929).   "X-Ray Diffraction in Liquid
      Mixtures."   Rings from binary mixtures.
293   Krishnamurti, P.   A
      Indian J. Phys., *3*, 507–522 (1928-1929).   "X-Ray Diffraction in Liquids and
      Solutions, and the Molecular Structure Factor."
294   Krishnamurti, P.   A
      Indian J. Phys., *4*, 99–108 (1929-1930).   "X-Ray Diffraction by Amorphous
      Solids."   Diffuse rings shift as amorphous resins change physical state.
295   Krishnamurti, P.   Á
      Indian J. Phys., *5*, 473–500 (1930).   "Studies in X-Ray Diffraction.   Part I:
      The Structure of Amorphous Scattering.   Part II: Colloidal Solutions and
      Liquid Mixtures."   Particle size and molecular weights related to extent of
      small-angle scattering.
296   LaMer, V. K., and Sinclair, D.   A
      O.S.R.D. Report 1857.   "Verification of Mie Theory."

297 Mathematical Tables Project (National Bureau of Standards). Columbia Univ. Press, New York (1947). *Tables of Spherical Bessel Functions.* (Vol. 1: pp. 25–47.) 3/2 order Bessels for argument 0 to 25.

298 Oster, G. A
Rec. trav. chim., *68*, 1123–1136 (1949). "Visible Light and X-Ray Scattering by Concentrated Solutions of Macromolecules." Interparticle interference for spheres and other shapes.

299 Patterson, A. L. A
Z. Krist., *90*, 517–542 (1935). "A Direct Method for the Determination of the Components of Interatomic Distances in Crystals."

300 Patterson, A. L. Pa
Am. Phys. Soc., No. 128, Washington (April 1936). *Phys. Rev.*, *49*, 884 (1936). "The Determination of the Size and Shape of Crystal Particles by X-Rays." Interference functions for several shapes.

301 Patterson, A. L. A
Phys. Rev., *56*, 972–977 (1939). "The Diffraction of X-rays by Small Crystalline Particles." Calculation of the shape functions for spheroids and various polyhedra.

301′ Prins, J. A. A
Physica, *6*, 315–325 (1926). "Diffractie van Röntgenstralen door Kwik."

302 Prins, J. A. A
Naturwissenschaften, *19*, 435–442 (1931). "Die Molekülanordnung in Flüssigkeiten und die damit zusammenhängenden Beugungserscheinungen." Radial distributions and scattering to fairly small angles.

303 Prins, J. A. A
Z. Naturforsch., *6a*, 276–277 (1951). "Der kolloidale Stand." Close-packed colloidal crystallites.

304 Raman, C. V., and Krishnamurti, P. A
Nature, *124*, 53–54 (1929). "A New X-Ray Effect." Central diffuse scattering observed on graphite. Interpreted as due to free electrons in crystal structure.

305 Raman, C. V., and Ramanathan, K. R. A
Proc. Indian Assoc. Cultivation Sci., *8*, 127–162 (1932). "Diffraction of X-Rays in Liquids, Fluid Crystals, and Amorphous Solids." A fluid cannot be treated as a continuum for X-ray scattering except at very small angles. An equation is derived which takes account only of the average structure of the fluid.

305′ Randall, J. T. B
Chapman and Hall, London (1934). *The Diffraction of X-Rays and Electrons by Amorphous Solids, Liquids, and Gases.*

306 Stewart, G. W. A
Revs. Mod. Phys., *2*, 116–122 (1930). "X-Ray Diffraction in Liquids." A review of experimental results.

307 Warren, B. E. A
J. Appl. Phys., *8*, 645–654 (1937). "X-Ray Determination of the Structure of Liquids and Glass." Effect of physical discontinuities in structure on small-angle scattering discussed. SiO_2 example qualitatively discussed.

308 Warren, B. E., and Biscoe, J. A
J. Am. Ceram. Soc., *21*, 49–54 (1938). "The Structure of Silica Glass by X-Ray Diffraction Studies."

309 Zernicke, F., and Prins, J. A. A
Z. Physik, *41*, 184–194 (1927). "Die Beugung von Röntgenstrahlen an Flüssigkeiten als Effekt der Molekülanordnung."

V. LIGHT

310 Bethe, H. A., and Rohrlich, F.   A
     Phys. Rev., *86*, 10–16 (1951). "Small-Angle Scattering of Light by a Coulomb
     Field."

311 Blumer, H.   A
     Z. Physik, *32*, 119–134 (1925). "Strahlungsdiagramme kleiner dielektrischer
     Kugeln. I."

312 Blumer, H.   A
     Z. Physik, *38*, 304–328 (1926). "Strahlungsdiagramme kleiner dielektrischer
     Kugeln. II."

313 Blumer, H.   A
     Z. Physik, *38*, 920–947 (1926). "Die Zerstreuung des Lichtes an kleinen
     Kugeln."

314 Blumer, H.   A
     Z. Physik, *39*, 195–214 (1926). "Die Farbenzerstreuung an kleinen Kugeln."

315 Bommel, H.   A
     Helv. Phys. Acta, *21*, 289–298 (1948). "Lichtstreuung von den durch Utraschall
     orientierten Kolloidalteilchen."

316 Brillouin, L.   A
     J. Appl. Phys., *20*, 1110–1125 (1949). "The Scattering Cross Section of
     Spheres for Electromagnetic Waves."

317 Bromwich, T. J.   A
     Philos. Trans., *A-220*, 175–206 (1920). "Scattering of Plane Electric Waves
     by Spheres."

318 Bueche, A. M.   A
     J. Am. Chem. Soc., *74*, 2373 (1952). "Size Distribution of Spheres by Light
     Scattering."

319 Bueche, A. M., and Debye, P.   Pa
     Am. Phys. Soc., No. N-5, New York (January 1949). *Phys. Rev.*, *75*, 1308
     (1949). "Scattering by Inhomogeneous Solids." See No. 322.

320 Bueche, A. M., and Debye, P.   Pa
     Am. Phys. Soc., No. G-4, Chicago (November 1950). *Phys. Rev.*, *81*, 3030
     (1951). "A Study of Crystalline Sizes in Polymers by a Light Scattering
     Method."

321 Debye, P.   A
     Ann. Physik, *335*, 57–136 (1909). "Der Lichtdruck auf Kugeln von behebigem
     Material." From dissertation at Munich.

322 Debye, P., and Bueche, A. M.   A
     J. Appl. Phys., *20*, 518–525 (1949). "Scattering by an Inhomogeneous
     Solid." Scattering measurements used to obtain the average square of the
     fluctuation in refractive index or electron density and a correlation function
     which measures the degree of correlation between two fluctuations as a function
     of this distance of separation. See No. 319.

323 Debye, P., and Bueche, A. M.   B
     Reinhold, New York (1950). *Colloid Chemistry, Theoretical and Applied*
     (J. Alexander). "Scattering by Inhomogeneous Materials." (Vol. 7, pp.
     33-46.)

324 DeVore, J. R., and Pfund, A. H.   A
     J. Opt. Soc. Amer., *37*, 826–832 (1947). "Optical Scattering by Dielectric
     Powders of Uniform Particle Size." Experimental verification of Mie minima
     in the scattering from uniform particles.

325 Engelhard, V. H., and Friess, H.   A
Kolloid-Z., *81*, 129–143 (1937). "Über die Brauchbarkeit des Mieeffectes zur Teilchengrossenbestimmung weisser Aerosole, insbesondere grossdisperser weisser Aerosole."

326 Forrester, A. T., and Mittenthal, L.   A
Phys. Rev., *81*, 268–271 (1951). "Small-Angle Diffraction of Light by a Glass Cube." Results incompatible with Halpern and Gerjouy theory. Born approximation apparently unjustified.

327 Gans, R.   A
Ann. Physik, *76*, 29–38 (1925). "Strahlungsdiagramme ultramikroskopischer Teilchen."

328 Hart, R. W., and Montroll, E. W.   A
J. Appl. Phys., *22*, 376–386 (1951). "On the Scattering of Plane Waves by Soft Obstacles." I. Spherical Obstacles."

329 Humphreys, W. J.   B
Lippincott, Philadelphia (1940). *Physics of the Air.* (Pp. 547-554.) Optical corona discussed; analogous to X-ray secondary maxima.

330 Jobst, V. G.   A
Ann. Physik, *76*, 863–888 (1925). "Zur Farbentheorie kolloidaler Metallsuspensionen."

331 Johnson, I., and LaMer, V. K.   A
J. Am. Chem. Soc., *69*, 1184–1193 (1947). "The Determination of the Particle Size of Monodispersed Systems by the Scattering of Light."

332 Kenyon, A. S., and LaMer, V. K.   Pa
Am. Chem. Soc., New York (September 1947). *J. Colloid Sci.*, *4*, 163–184 (1949). "Light Scattering Properties of Monodispersed Sulphur Sols. I. Monochromatic Ultraviolet Angular Scattering. II. Effect of the Complex Index of Refraction upon Transmittance." See No. 350.

333 LaMer, V. K., and Barnes, M. D.   A
J. Colloid Sci., *1*, 71–77 (1946). "Monodispersed Hydrophobic Colloidal Dispersions and Light Scattering Properties. I. Preparation and Light Scattering Properties of Monodispersed Colloidal Sulphur."

334 LaMer, V. K., and Barnes, M. D.   A
J. Colloid Sci., *1*, 79–91 (1946). "Monodispersed Hydrophobic Colloidal Dispersions and Light Scattering Properties. II. Total Scattering from Transmittance as a Basis for the Calculation of Particle Size and Concentration."

335 Ljunggren, T.   A
Arkiv Mat. Astron. Fysik, *A-36*, No. 14, 1–36 (1948). "Contributions to the Theory of Diffraction of Electromagnetic Waves by Spherical Particles."

336 Love, A. E. H.   A
Proc. London Math. Soc., *30*, 308-321 (1899). "The Scattering of Electric Waves by a Dielectric Sphere."

337 Mie, G.   A
Ann. Physik, *25*, 377–445 (1908). "Beitrage zur Optik trüber Medien, speziell kolloidaler Metallosungen."

338 Mitra, M. N.   A
Indian J. Phys., *3*, 175–180 (1928-1929). "Photographs of Coronas in Monochromatic Light." Water droplets—multiple rings.

339 *Natl. Bur. Standards, Appl. Math. Series*, No. 4 (1949). U.S. Govt. Printing Office, Washington, D.C. "Tables of Scattering Functions for Spherical Particles."

340 Pijper, A.   A
      Med. J. S. Africa, **14**, 211–218 (1918). "Diffraction Phenomena in Cultures of Microorganisms."

341 Preston, T.   B
      Macmillan, New York (1924). *Theory of Light.* (Pp. 228-236.) Theory of corona rings in light scattering, similar to X-ray secondary maxima.

342 Rayleigh, Lord.   B
      Cambridge Univ. Press, London (1899). *Scientific Papers.* (Vol. I, pp. 92-93, Vol. IV, p. 400.)

343 Rayleigh, Lord.   A
      Proc. Roy. Soc. (London), *A-84*, 25–46 (1911). "The Incidence of Light upon a Transparent Sphere of Dimensions Comparable with the Wavelength."

344 Ruedy, R.   A
      Can. J. Research, *A-19*, 117–125 (1941). "Absorption of Light and Heat Radiation by Small·Spherical Particles. I. Absorption of Light by Carbon Particles."

345 Ruedy, R.   A
      Can. J. Research, *A-21*, 79–88 (1943). "Absorption of Light by Small Drops of Water."

346 Ruedy, R.
      Can. J. Research, *A-21*, 99–109 (1943). "Scattering of Light by Small Drops of Water."

347 Ruedy, R.   A
      Can. J. Research, *A-22*, 53–66 (1944). " Transmission of Light by Water Drops 1 to 5 Microns in Diameter."

348 Ryde, J. N., and Cooper, B. S.   A
      Proc. Roy. Soc. (London), *A-131*, 451–475 (1931). "Scattering of Light by Turbid Media." Particle size determination in opal glasses by means of light diffusion.

349 Sinclair, D.   A
      J. Opt. Soc. Amer., **37**, 475–480 (1947). "Light Scattering by Spherical Particles." Test of Mie and Rayleigh equations.

350 Sinclair, D., and LaMer, V.   A
      Chem. Revs., **44**, 245–267 (1949). "Light Scattering as a Measure of Particle Size in Aerosols. The Production of Monodispersed Aerosols." Light scattering by aerosols and determinations of particle size by methods based on measurement of (1) transmission, (2) intensity, (3) color, (4) polarization. Technique for the production of monodispersed aerosols. See No. 332.

350′ Sivarajan, S. R.   A
      Proc. Indian Acad. Sci., *A-37*, 418–423 (1953). "Light Scattering in Gold Sols."

351 Storruste, A.   A
      K. Norske Videnskab. Selskabs Forh., **21**, 88–91 (1948). "Scattering of Waves by Circular Discs."

352 Stratton, J. A.   B
      McGraw-Hill, New York (1941). *Electromagnetic Theory.* (Pp. 563-573.)

353   Stratton, J. A., and Houghton, H. G.   A
      Phys. Rev., *38*, 159–165 (1931). "A Theoretical Investigation of the Trans-
      mission of Light through Fog."
354   Toraldo Di Francia, G.   A
      Atti accad. naz. Lincei, (Rend., Classe sci. fis. mat. e nat.), 4, 730–735 (1948).
      "Sulla luce diffusee da un vasto numero di aperture a saso su di uno schermo
      opaco."
355   Van de Hulst, H. C.   B
      Duwaer and Zonen, Amsterdam (1946). *Recherches Astronomiques de
      l'Observatoire d'Utrecht XI*, Part I. "Optics of Spherical Particles." Pains-
      taking analysis of scattering by spheres. Cases for different relative values of
      parameters discussed separately to derive range of validity of simplifying
      approximations.
356   van der Wyk, A. J. A.   A
      Arch. sci., (Geneva), 3 (No. 6), 419–444 (1950). "Diffusion de la lumière par les
      colloïdes."

VI. SOLUTIONS

357   Bergman, P. G.   Pa
      Am. Phys. Soc., No. C-6, Washington (April 1948). *Phys. Rev., 74*, 1209
      (1948). "Low-Angle Scattering of Colloidal Solutions." Distribution effect
      in concentrated monodispersed hydrosols.
358   Brady, G. W.   A
      J. Chem. Phys., 19, 1547–1550 (1951). "Fourier Analysis of the X-Ray
      Scattering from Soap Solutions." Spherical micelle model. Nearest neighbor
      distance.
359   Corrin, M. L.   A
      J. Chem. Phys., 16, 844–845 (1948). "Interpretation of X-Ray Scattering
      from Solutions of Long-Chain Electrolytes on the Basis of a Spherical Micelle."
      Small-angle patterns from long-chain molecules as readily explained by
      distribution of spheres as by periodic layers.
360   Davies, J. T., and Philippoff, W.   A
      Nature, 164, 1087 (1949). "A Test of the Interpretation of X-Ray Patterns
      of Micelles."
361   Harkins, W. D.   A
      J. Chem. Phys., 16, 156–157 (1948). "A Cylindrical Model for the Small Soap
      Micelle."
361' Harkins, W. D.   B
      Reinhold, New York (1952). *The Physical Chemistry of Surface Films.*
      Soap micelles.
362   Hughes, E. W.   A
      Nature, 165, 1017 (1950). "A Test of the Interpretation of X-Ray Patterns
      of Micelles." Soap solutions. Criticism of No. 360. Different models fit
      data—none unique.
363   Hughes, E. W.   P
      ACA, No. A-5, New Hampton, N.H. (August 1950). "The X-Ray Diffraction
      Patterns from Soap Solutions." It is concluded that it is not possible with
      best X-ray data to positively establish any particular micelle model.
364   Mattoon, R. W., and Mathews, M. B.   A
      J. Chem. Phys., 17, 496–497 (1949). "Micelles in Non-Aqueous Media."
      Small-angle scattering from aerosols.

365 Mattoon, R. W., Stearns, R. S., and Harkins, W. D.   A
     J. Chem. Phys., *15*, 209–211 (1947). "Structure of Soap Micelles as Indicated
     by a Previously Unrecognized X-Ray Diffraction Band."
366 Mattoon, R. W., Stearns, R. S., and Harkins, W. D.   A
     J. Chem. Phys., *16*, 644–658 (1948). "A New Long-Spacing X-Ray Diffraction
     Band, and the Relations of Other Bands." Band position independent of
     concentration; attributed to micelle thickness.
367 McBain, J. W., and Marsden, S. S., Jr.   A
     J. Chem. Phys., *15*, 211–212 (1947). "Non-Ionic Detergents as Association
     Colloids Giving Long X-Ray Spacings in Aqueous Solution."
368 Philippoff, W.   A
     J. Colloid Sci., *4*, 169–191 (1950). "Micelles and X-Rays."   53 references.
369 Philippoff, W.   PA
     Discussions Faraday Soc., *11*, 96–107 (1951). "The Micelle and Swollen
     Micelle on Soap Micelles."
369′ Porod, G.   PA
     Intern. Union Chem., Strasbourg (June 1952). *J. Polymer Sci.*, *10*, 157–166
     (1953). "X-Ray and Light Scattering by Chain Molecules in Solution."
     Debye formula to deduce low-angle scatter.
370 Riley, D. P.   A
     Brit. Sci. News, *3*, 7–10 (1949). "X-Ray Investigations of the Structure of
     Liquid Disperse Systems."   Protein solutions and oil-water emulsions.
371 Riley, D. P., and Oster, G.   PA
     Discussions Faraday Soc., *11*, 107–116 (1951). "Some Theoretical and Experi-
     mental Studies of X-Ray and Light Scattering by Colloidal and Macromolecular
     Systems."
372 Schulman, J. H., Matalon, R., and Cohen, M.   PA
     Discussions Faraday Soc., *11*, 117–121 (1951). "X-Ray and Optical Prop-
     erties of Spherical and Cylindrical Aggregates in Long Chain Hydrocarbon
     Polyethylene Oxide Systems."
372′ Schulman, J. H., McRoberts, T. S., and Riley, D. P.   A
     J. Physiol. (London), *107*, 49P–50P (1948). "X-Ray Investigation of Trans-
     parent Oil-Water Systems."
373 Schulman, J. H., and Riley, D. P.   A
     J. Colloid Sci., *3*, 383–405 (1948). "X-Ray Investigation of the Structure of
     Transparent Oil-Water Disperse Systems. I."   Structure suggested water
     spheres in oil and oil spheres in water.

VII. FIBERS AND PROTEINS

374 Adams, J.   A
     Nature, *167*, 78 (1951). "Low-Angle X-Ray Scattering from Ramie and Jute."
375 Anderegg, J. W.   T
     Univ. Wisc., Ph.D. (1952). "Small-Angle Scattering from Serum Albumin
     Solutions."   Slit corrections.   Concentration and pH effects.
376 Anderegg, J. W., Beeman, W. W., and Shulman, S.   Pa
     Am. Phys. Soc., No. C-7, Washington (May 1952). *Phys. Rev.*, *87*, 186 (1952).
     "Small-Angle X-Ray Scattering from Serum Albumin Solutions."
377 Anderegg, J. W., Beeman, W. W., Shulman, S., and Kaesberg, P.   P
     ACA, Tamiment, Pa. (June 1952). "Small-Angle X-Ray Scattering from
     Serum Albumin Solutions."

378   Arnett, L. M., Meibohm, E. P. H., and Smith, A. F.   A
      J. Polymer Sci., 5, 737–738 (1950). "New Observations on the Small-Angle
      X-Ray Diffraction of Synthetic Fibers."
379   Astbury, W. T.   Aa
      J. Intern. Soc. Leather Trades' Chemists, 24, 69–92 (1940). *Nature*, 145,
      421–422 (1940). "The Molecular Structure of the Fibers of the Collagen
      Group."
380   Astbury, W. T.   A
      Proc. Roy. Soc. (London), B-134, 303–328 (1947). "Structure of Biological
      Fibers and the Problem of Muscle." Resumé of X-ray studies on structure of
      proteins of the keratin and collagen groups. 66 references.
381   Astbury, W. T., and Weibull, C.   A
      Nature, 163, 280–282 (1949). "X-Ray Diffraction Study of the Structure of
      Bacterial Flagella." Flagella behave like long protein macromolecules,
      studied in dried films. Give patterns indicating relation to alpha-keratin in
      hair or muscle.
382   Bateman, J. B., Hsu, S. S., Knudsen, J. P., and Yudowitch, K. L.   A
      Arch. Biochem. and Biophys., 45, 411–422 (1953). "Hemoglobin Spacing in
      Erythrocytes." Intermolecular interference ring varied by swelling and
      shrinking blood cells. See Nos. 415, 486.
383   Bateman, J. B., Yudowitch, K. L., Hsu, S. S., and Knudsen, J. P.   P
      Soc. Exptl. Biol. Med. (Baltimore Section), Edgewood, Md. (October 1952).
      "Hemoglobin Spacing in Erythrocytes."
384   Baule, B., Kratky, O., and Treer, R.   A
      Z. physik. Chem., B-50, 255–297 (1941). "Die übermolekulare Aufbau der
      Hydratcellulose die Einführung der Blättchenmicelle in die Theorie der
      Deformationsvorgange."
385   Bawden, F. C., Pirie, N. W., Bernal, J. D., and Fankuchen, I.   A
      Nature, 138, 1051–1052 (1936). "Liquid Crystalline Substances from Virus-
      Infected Plants." Intramolecular spacings of infected sap from tomato and
      tobacco plants. Preparation of crystalline protein. Camera 40 cm. long.
      3' angular width beam gives spacings up to 1,200 A.
386   Bear, R. S.   A
      J. Am. Chem. Soc., 64, 727 (1942). "Long X-Ray Diffraction Spacings of
      Collagen." Fine slits, long collimating tubes. Ni filtered Cu; specimen-to-film
      distance: 26 cm. Twenty and more orders of spacing about 640 A observed
      in dried beef tendon.
387   Bear, R. S.   A
      J. Am. Chem. Soc., 65, 1784–1785 (1943). "Long X-Ray Diffraction Spacings
      of the Keratins." Chart of meridional and near meridional reflections. Low
      values are listed, since meridional and near meridional arcs had to be considered
      together, since large-spacing layer line components could not be resolved
      satisfactorily.
388   Bear, R. S.   A
      J. Am. Chem. Soc., 66, 1297–1305 (1944). "X-Ray Diffraction Studies on
      Protein Fibers. I. The Large Fiber-Axis Period of Collagen." Wet and
      dried samples differ. 640–680 A period. 30 orders from dried samples.
389   Bear, R. S.   A
      J. Am. Chem. Soc., 66, 2043–2050 (1944). "X-Ray Diffraction Studies on
      Protein Fibers. II. Feather Rachis, Porcupine Quill Tip, and Clam Muscle."
      Classification of protein fibers, relations between wide- and low-angle
      diffractions.

390 Bear, R. S. Pa
ASXRED and *AAAS*, No. A-1, Gibson Island, Md. (August 1944). *Phys. Rev., 67*, 196 (1945). "Small-Angle Diffraction Studies on Protein Fibers." Fiber axis periods from 20–40 layer lines.

391 Bear, R. S. A
J. Am. Chem. Soc., 67, 1625 (1945). "Small-Angle X-Ray Diffraction Studies on Muscle." Calculated spacings change with cosine of angle, indicating diffraction elements as two-dimensional.

392 Bear, R. S. P
Intern. Union Cryst., Harvard (1948). "The Large Unit Cells of Protein Fibers."

393 Bear, R. S. P
ACA, Tamiment, Pa. (June 1952). "The Structure of Collagen."

394 Bear, R. S., and Bolduan, O. E. A. P
CSA and *ASXRED*, New Haven (April 1948). "The Nature of the Order of Large Size Exhibited by Collagen Fibrils." Dry tendon model of cylindrical fibrils.

395 Bear, R. S., and Bolduan, O. E. A. A
Acta Cryst., 3, 230–235 (1950). "Deficiencies in Order of Large Size in Fibrous Systems."

396 Bear, R. S., and Bolduan, O. E. A. A
Acta Cryst., 3, 236–241 (1950). "Diffraction by Cylindrical Bodies with Periodic Axial Structure."

397 Bear, R. S., and Bolduan, O. E. A. A
J. Appl. Phys., 22, 191–198 (1951). "Periodic Statistical Distortion of Unidirectionally Ordered Diffractors, with Application to Collagen."

398 Beeman, W. W. P
Pittsburgh Conf. X-Ray Electron Diffr., No. 6, Pittsburgh (November 1950). "Some Problems of Interpretation in the Small-Angle Scattering from Proteins." Not delivered.

399 Beeman, W. W. P
Am. Chem. Soc., No. J-17, Boston (April 1951). "The Small-Angle Scattering of X-Rays by Protein Solutions."

400 Bergman, M. E., and Fankuchen, I. A
Science, 113, 415 (1951). "X-Ray Diffraction Studies of Inclusion Bodies Found in Plants Infected with Tobacco Mosaic Virus."

401 Bernal, J. D., and Fankuchen, I. A
Nature, 139, 923–924 (1937). "Structure Types of Protein Crystals from Virus Infected Plants." Oriented protein gels. None of the reflections in directions other than at right angles to the molecular length is due to the packing of the molecules, but rather to regularities within them, as shown by the fact that such reflections persist unchanged when the molecules are in dilute solution.

402 Bernal, J. D., and Fankuchen, I. A
J. Gen. Physiol., 25, 111–165 (1941). "X-Ray and Crystallographic Studies of Plant Virus Preparations. I. Introduction and Preparation of Specimen. II. Modes of Aggregation of the Virus Particles. III. Structure of the Particles. Biological Implications." See No. 385.

403 Bernal, J. D., Fankuchen, I., and Riley, D. P. A
Nature, 142, 1075 (1938). "Structure of Crystals of Tomato Bushy Stunt Virus Preparations." Two lines were observed of spacings 279 A and 160 A, respectively, corresponding to 340 A diameter spheres.

404 Bolduan, O. E. A. **P**
Electron Micr. Soc. Amer., Pittsburgh (1946). "A Long Spacing X-Ray Diffraction Camera." Camera design for resolution of multi-order reflections at small angles.

405 Bolduan, O. E. A., and Bear, R. S. **A**
J. Polymer Sci., *5*, 159–168 (1950). "Unidirectional Nature of the Large Periodic Structure of Collagen Fibrils."

406 Bolduan, O. E. A., and Bear, R. S. **A**
J. Polymer Sci., *6*, 271–284 (1951). "General Nature of the Extension of Structure Transverse to Collagen Fibril Axes."

407 Boyes-Watson, J., Davidson, E., and Perutz, M. F. **A**
Proc. Roy. Soc. (London), *A-191*, 83–129 (1947). "An X-Ray Study of Horse Methemoglobin." Cell contains variable liquid of crystallization. From data, horse hemoglobin molecules are concluded to be cylinders 57 A in diameter and 34 A high.

408 Cannan, C. M. M., and Bear, R. S. **P**
Am. Chem. Soc., No. C-72, Boston (April 1951). "Small-Angle X-Ray Diffraction Analysis of the Ultrastructure of the Myofilament."

409 Clark, G. L., and Corrigan, K. E. **A**
Phys. Rev., *40*, 639 (1932). "The Crystal Structure of Insulin." Large spacings (80–130 A) reported for insulin, using Mg and Al radiation.

410 Clark, G. L., and Parker, E. A. **A**
Science, *85*, 203–204 (1937). "Diffraction of X-Rays at Very Small Angles by Celluloses and Rayons."

411 Clark, G. L., Parker, E. A., Schaad, J. A., and Warren, W. J. **A**
J. Am. Chem. Soc., *57*, 1509 (1935). "New Measurements of Previously Unknown Large Interplanar Spacings in Natural Materials." Equatorial maxima in cellulose: Nerve, collagen, keratin, rubber, cellulose.

412 Corey, R. B., and Wyckoff, R. W. G. **A**
J. Biol. Chem., *114*, 407–414 (1936). "Long Spacings in Macromolecular Solids." X-ray diffraction photographs registering large spacings. General structures discussed.

413 Cowan, P., and Hodgkin, D. **A**
Acta Cryst., *4*, 160–161 (1951). "A Comparison of X-Ray Measurements on Air-Dried Tobacco Necrosis Protein Crystals with Electron Microscope Data."

414 Crowfoot, D., and Fankuchen, I. **A**
Nature, *141*, 522–523 (1938). "Molecular Weight of Tobacco Seed Globulin." Three lines recorded on X-ray photographs which correspond to the first three reflections from a cubic face centered lattice of dimension $a = 123$ A.

415 Dervichian, D. G., Fournet, G., and Guinier, A. **A**
Compt. rend., *224*, 1848–1850 (1947). "Mise en évidence d'une structure submicroscopique dans les globules rouges par la diffusion des rayons X aux petits angles." Shoulder in pattern attributed to spacing between hemoglobins. Cell order between crystalline and solution.

416 Dervichian, D. G., Fournet, G., and Guinier, A. **PB**
Barcroft Memorial Haemoglobin Conf., Cambridge, England (June 1948). Interscience, New York (1949). "An X-Ray Investigation of Haemoglobin and Haemocyanin in Aqueous Solution," *Haemoglobin*, pp. 131–134. Hemoglobin radius of gyration and hemocyanine spacing determined.

417 Dervichian, D. G., Fournet, G., and Guinier, A.   P
Sixth Intern. Congr. Exptl. Cytology, Stockholm. "Evidence for the Submicroscopic Structure of Red Cells by the Scattering of X-Rays at Small Angles." Shoulder in pattern attributed to spacing between hemoglobins. Cell order between crystalline and solution.

418 Dervichian, D. G., Fournet, G., and Guinier, A.   P
Pittsburgh Conf. X-Ray Electron Diffr., No. 3, Pittsburgh (November 1950). "Small-Angle Scattering Studies on Egg Yolk." Persistent ring at Bragg spacing of 260 A.

419 Dervichian, D. G., Fournet, G., and Guinier, A.   A
Biochem. et Biophys. Acta, 8, 145–149 (1952). "Étude par la diffusion des rayons X des modifications subiés par certaines protéines."

420 Dervichian, D. G., Fournet, G., Guinier, A., and Ponder, E.   A
Compt. rend., 235, 324–326 (1952). "Organisation submicroscopique des hématies contenantes des hémoglobines anormales."

421 Ehrenberg, W., and Franks, A.   A
Nature, 170, 1076–1077 (1952). "Small-Angle X-Ray Scattering." Total reflection focusing for resolution of large periods.

421' Engstrom, A., and Finean, J. B.   A
Nature, 171, 564 (1953). "Low-Angle X-Ray Diffraction of Bone."

422 Fankuchen, I.   A
Phys. Rev., 53, 909 (1938). "On the Structure of 'Built-Up' Films on Metals."

423 Fankuchen, I.   A
J. Gen. Physiol., 24, 315–316 (1941). "An X-Ray and Crystallographic Study of Ribonuclease."

424 Fankuchen, I.   A
Ann. N.Y. Acad. Sci., 41, 157–168 (1941). "Evidence from X-Rays regarding the Structure of Protein Molecules." Molecular weights determined by X-ray methods in good agreement with those obtained by other methods.

425 Fankuchen, I.   PA
Cold Spring Harbor Symposia Quant. Biol., 9, 198–203 (1941). "X-Ray Diffraction Studies of Protein Preparations." Continuous and discontinuous scattering.

426 Fankuchen, I.   A
J. Am. Chem. Soc., 64, 2504–2505 (1942). "X-Ray and Optic Measurements of β-Lactoglobin." Spacings of 60, 63, 110 A.

427 Fankuchen, I.   A
J. Biol. Chem., 150, 57–59 (1943). "X-Ray Diffraction Data on Ferritin and Apoferritin." Large spacings.

428 Fankuchen, I.   A
Ann. Rev. Biochem., 14, 207–224 (1945). "X-Ray Studies on Compounds of Biochemical Interest." 85 references.

429 Fankuchen, I.   A
Nature, 168, 684–685 (1951). "The Lotmar-Picken X-Ray Diffraction Diagram of Muscle."

430 Fankuchen, I.   B
Academic Press, New York (1945). *Advances in Protein Chemistry,* edited by M. L. Anson and J. T. Edsall, Vol. 2, pp. 387–405, "X-Ray Diffraction and Protein Structure."

431 Fankuchen, I., and Mark, H.   A
     Record Chem. Progr. (Kresge-Hooker Sci. Lib.), *4*, 54–57 (1943). "Improved
     X-Ray Technique for the Study of Natural and Synthetic Fibers."
432 Fankuchen, I., and Mark, H.   A
     J. Appl. Phys., *15*, 364–370 (1944). "X-Ray Studies of Chain Polymers."
     Small-angle scattering for larger polymer periods. Apparatus and technique
     described.
433 Fankuchen, I., and Mark, H.   B
     Interscience, New York (1946). *Currents in Biochemical Research*, edited by
     D. E. Green, pp. 439–452, "X-Ray Diffraction and the Study of Fibrous
     Proteins."
434 Fankuchen, I., and Schneider, M.   A
     J. Am. Chem. Soc., *66*, 500–501 (1944). "Low-Angle X-Ray Scattering from
     Chrysotiles." Dry gels of tobacco mosaic virus, 30 cm. specimen-to-film
     distance, spacings up to 500 A.
434' Fournet, G., and Antzenberger, P.   A
     Compt. rend., *236*, 394–396 (1953). Étude et interprétation de la diffusion des
     rayons X aux petits angles par la cellulose." Disordered regions swell when
     wet.
435 Frey-Wyssling, A.   B
     Elsevier, New York (1948). *Submicroscopic Morphology of Protoplasm and
     Its Derivatives*. (Pp. 67–81.)
436 Friedrich-Freska, H., Kratky, O., and Sekora, A.   A
     Naturwissenschaften, *33*, 78 (1944). "Auftreten von neuen Röntgeninter-
     ferenzen bei Einlagerung von Jod in Seidenfibrin von Bombyn-mori Typ."
     Meridian reflections indicating a 70 A period.
437 Furnas, T. C., Jr.   T
     Mass. Inst. Tech., Ph.D. (1952). "Point Focus X-Ray Monochromator for
     Diffraction Studies of Protein Fibers." See No. 229.
438 Furnas, T. C., Jr.   P
     ACA, Tamiment, Pa. (June 1952). "Diffraction Diagrams of Protein Fibers
     Taken with a New Point Focus Monochromator."
439 Heikens, D., Hermans, P. H., and Weidinger, A.   A
     Nature, *170*, 369–370 (1952). "Occurrence of Small-Angle X-Ray Diffraction
     Maxima in Some Artificial Cellulose Fibres."
440 Hermans, P. H.   B
     Elsevier, New York (1946). *Contribution to the Physics of Cellulose Fibres.*
     (Pp. 158–187.)
441 Hermans, P. H.   B
     Elsevier, New York (1949). *Physics and Chemistry of Cellulose Fibres.* (Pp.
     244–265.)
441' Hess, K., and Kiessig, H.   A
     Z. physik. Chem., *193*, 196–217 (1944). "Über Langperiodeninterferenzen und
     micellaren Faserfeinbau bei vollsynthetischen Fasern (Polyamide und
     Polyester)."
441" Hess, K., and Kiessig, H.   A
     Kolloid-Z., *130*, 10–19 (1953). Über Langperiodeninterferenzen bei syn-
     thetischen Fasern."
442 Heyn, A. N. J.   A
     J. Am. Chem. Soc., *70*, 3138–3139 (1948). "Small-Angle X-Ray Scattering of
     Various Cellulose Fibers." Measure of micellar orientation from small-angle
     patterns.

443 Heyn, A. N. J.   **PA**
Fiber Soc., Boston (1948). *Textile Research J.*, *19*, 163–172 (1949). "Small-Angle X-Ray Scattering in Various Cellulose Fibers and Its Relation to the Micellar Structure." Scattering related to micellar size, distance, and orientation.

444 Heyn, A. N. J.   **P**
Conf. Small-Angle X-Ray Scattering, No. 5, Columbia, Mo. (October 1949). "Small-Angle Scattering by Cellulose Fibers." Equatorial scattering modified by swelling fibers and by torsion.

445 Heyn, A. N. J.   **A**
J. Am. Chem. Soc., *71*, 1873–1875 (1949). "Small-Angle Scattering of X-Rays and the Micellar Structure in Cellulose Fibers." Distribution of the micelles, rather than their size, determines the scattering.

446 Heyn, A. N. J.   **A**
J. Am. Chem. Soc., *72*, 2284–2285 (1950). "Small-Angle X-Ray Scattering by Cellulose Fibers: Experimental Study of the Orientation Factor in Model Filaments and Rayons." Effects of controlled orientation changes.

447 Heyn, A. N. J.   **A**
J. Am. Chem. Soc., *72*, 5768–5769 (1950). "A Quantitative Evaluation of Small-Angle X-Ray Scattering by Various Cellulose Fibers for the Determination of Crystallite Size with Special Reference to the Problem of Interparticle Interference." Effect of dense-packing of micelles overcome by swelling fibers.

448 Heyn, A. N. J.   **A**
Rayon and Synthetic Textiles, *31*, No. 9: 29–43, No. 10: 42–43 (1950). "How to Identify Synthetic Fibers by Their X-Ray Diagram." Systematic examination of small-angle patterns from a number of fibers.

449 Heyn, A. N. J.   **B**
Textile Book, New York (1951). "Identification of Synthetic Fibers by X-Ray Diffraction," Chap. 19 of *American Handbook of Synthetic Fibers.*

450 Heyn, A. N. J.   **B**
Wiley, New York (1952). "X-Ray Diagrams of Natural and Synthetic Fibers," Chap. XXI of *Textile Fibers*, edited by Matthews. Sixth edition.

450' Heyn, A. N. J.   **P**
ACA, Cambridge, Mass. (April 1954). "Small-Angle X-Ray Scattering by Fibers."

451 Hosemann, R.   **A**
Z. physik. Chem., *A-179*, 356–360 (1937). "Quantitative Bestimmung der Orientierung der Kristallite in Faserstöffen."

452 Hosemann, R.   **A**
Z. Elektrochem., *46*, 535–555 (1940). "Röntgenographische Verteilungszustandes in einem Faserstoff. Diskussion des Cellulosemodells." Micelle size distribution in cellulose and paraffin.

453 Hosemann, R.   **A**
Acta Cryst., *4*, 520–530 (1951). "Die parakristalline Feinstruktur natürlicher und synthetischer Eiweisse. Visuelles Näherungsverfahren zur Bestimmung der Schwankungstensoren von Gitterzellen."

454 Hosemann, R.   **PA**
Kolloid Ges. (September 1951). *Kolloid-Z.*, *125*, 149–156 (1952). "Bestimmung der statistischen Strukturparameter der Mizellgitter hochmolekularer Faserstoffe."

455 Hsu, S. S.   T
Fla. State Univ., M.S. (1950). "An X-Ray Investigation of Red Blood
Corpuscles." Hemoglobin separation in swollen and shrunken red cells. See
No. 382.

456 Hsu, S. S., and Yudowitch, K. L.   P
Pittsburgh Conf. X-Ray Electron Diffr., No. 8, Pittsburgh (November 1950).
"Hemoglobin Spacing in Erythrocytes." Small-angle intensity shoulder due
to hemoglobin spacing varied by swelling erythrocytes. See No. 382.

456' Janeschitz-Kriegl, H., and Kratky, O.   A
Z. Elektrochem., *57*, 42–50 (1953). "Die Abhängigkeit der Röntgenklein-
winkelstreuung von Quellungsmittel bei regenerierter Cellulose."

457 Janeschitz-Kriegl, H., Kratky, O., and Porod, G.   A
Z. Elektrochem., *56*, 146–154 (1952). "Röntgenkleinwinkelmessungen an
porösen Hydratzellulosefaden."

458 Kaesberg, P.   P
ACA, Tamiment, Pa. (June 1952). "The Size, Shape, and Internal Hydration
of Several Viruses."

459 Kaesberg, P., Anderegg, J. W., Leonard, B. R., and Beeman, W. W. Pa
Am. Phys. Soc., No. C-6, Washington (May 1952). *Phys. Rev.*, *87*, 186 (1952).
"On the Size, Shape, and Hydration of Tomato Bushy Stunt Virus."

460 Kaesberg, P., Ritland, H. N., and Beeman, W. W.   A
Phys. Rev., *74*, 71–73 (1948). "The Use of the Double Crystal Spectrometer
in the Analysis of Bragg Reflections at Very Small Angles." Two-crystal
spectrometer used for nine orders of scattering from large periodicity in wet
collagen.

461 Kaesberg, P., Ritland, H. N., and Beeman, W. W.   Pa
Am. Phys. Soc., No. A-5, Madison, Wisc. (June 1948). *Phys. Rev.*, *74*, 1255-
1256 (1948). "Small-Angle Reflections from Collagen." Double-crystal
spectrometer for eight orders of Bragg reflections from collagen.

462 Knudsen, J. P.   T
Fla. State Univ., M.S. (1951). "X-Ray Investigations of Hemoglobin in
Human Erythrocytes and Particulate Inclusions in Bacteria and Fungi
Spores." Continuation of Nos. 455, 499. See No. 382.

Note: Item 463 is omitted.

464 Kratky, O.   A
Kolloid-Z., *64*, 213–222 (1933). "Zum Deformationsmechanismus der
Faserstoffe. I."

465 Kratky, O.   A
Kolloid-Z., *68*, 347–350 (1934). "Zum Deformationsmechanismus der
Faserstoffe. II. Die Ordnung der Mizellen von Filmen in kleinsten Berei-
chen."

466 Kratky, O.   A
Naturwissenschaften, *26*, 94 (1938). "Die Berechnung der Mizelldimensionen
von Faserstoffen aus den unter kleinsten Winkeln abgebeugten Interferenzen."
Micelle size of ramie. Closely packed colloids.

467 Kratky, O.   A
Monatsh. Chem., *77*, 224–250 (1947). "Neuere Ergebnisse aus der Röntgeno-
graphie der Eiweissstoffe." Review on kangaroo tail with regard to amino
acid connections. Egg whites.

468 Kratky, O. A
J. Polymer Sci., *3*, 195–215 (1948). "Low-Angle Scattering in Polymers."
Review including insulin solutions.

469 Kratky, O., and Porod, G. A
Rec. trav. chim., *68*, 1106–1122 (1949). "Röntgenuntersuchung geloster
Fadenmoleküle." Internal spacings in coiled chain molecules.

470 Kratky, O., Schauenstein, E., and Sekora, A. A
Nature, *165*, 527–528 (1950). "A New Type of Lattice with Large Periods in
Silk." New equatorial reflections indicating a network distance of 45 A.

471 Kratky, O., Schauenstein, E., and Sekora, A. A
Nature, *170*, 796–797 (1952). "Relations between Small-Angle Interferences
of Silk and the Wax Content."

472 Kratky, O., and Schossberger, F. A
Z. physik. Chem., *B-39*, 145–154 (1938). "Ein Beitrag zur micellar Struktur
der Cellulose." Scattered intensity is increased by introduction of finely
divided gold into ramie. Diffuse scattering is ascribed to an enlargement of
small-angle Bragg reflections due to some approximate orderliness of a large-
scale arrangement.

473 Kratky, O., and Sekora, A. A
J. Makromol. Chem., *1*, 113–121 (1943). "Die Auffindung von grossen Netze-
benenabständen bei Känguruh-Schwanzsehne. Ein Beitrag zur molekularen
Struktur der Faserproteine." Long period in kangaroo tail related to interferences with separate amino acids with assumed period structure.

474 Kratky, O., Sekora, A., and Friedrich-Freska, H. a
Anz. Akad. Wiss. Wien, Math. Naturw. Kl., *83*, 30–35 (1946). "Über Grösse
und Form von gelosten Hämocyaninmolekülen aus Messungen der Röntgen-
kleinwinkelstreuung." Aggregates of 260 A spheres. Compared with electron
microscopy and centrifugation. Maxima noted for neighboring spheres.

475 Kratky, O., Sekora, A., and Weber, H. H. A
Naturwissenschaften, *31*, 91 (1943). "Neue Kleinwinkelinterferenzen bei
Myosin." Myosin fibers showed 3 new weak reflections of 33, 42, and 66 A,
representing a lateral regularity, the 66 A dimension being the fiber thickness.

476 Kratky, O., and Wurster, A. A
Z. Elektrochem., *50*, 249–255 (1944). "Die Abhängigkeit der Kleinwinkelstreuung der Röntgenstrahlung von Quellungsmittel die Hydratcellulose."
Scattered intensity found dependent on third power of difference between
electron densities of cellulose and swelling centers.

477 Leonard, B. R., Jr. T
Univ. Wisc., Ph.D. (1951). "Small-Angle Scattering from Certain Spherical
Viruses (Southern Bean Mosaic, Tobacco Necrosis, and Tomato Bushy Stunt)."

478 Leonard, B. R., Jr., Anderegg, J. W., Kaesberg, P., Shulman, S., and
Beeman, W. W. A
J. Chem. Phys., *19*, 793-794 (1951). "On the Size, Shape, and Hydration of
Southern Bean Mosaic Virus and Tobacco Necrosis Virus in Solution."
Secondary maxima show viruses are spherical and internally hydrated.

478' MacArthur, I. A
Nature, *152*, 38–41 (1943). "Structure of Alpha-Keratin."

479 Mark, H. B
Springer, Berlin (1932). *Technologie der Textilfasern*. "I. Physik und
Chemie der Cellulose."

480 Meibohm, E. P. H., and Smith, A. F. PA
Pittsburgh Conf. X-Ray Electron Diffr., No. 7, Pittsburgh (November 1950).
J. Polymer Sci., *7*, 449–456 (1951). "Observations on Small-Angle Interference Maxima in Synthetic Organic Polymers." Non-meridional maxima observed in several orders.

481 Miller, E., Fankuchen, I., and Mark, H. Pa
Am. Phys. Soc., No. PC-2, New York (January 1949). *Phys. Rev.*, *75*, 1314 (1949). "Polymerization in the Solid State."

482 Miller, E., Fankuchen, I., and Mark, H. A
J. Appl. Phys., *20*, 531-533 (1949). "Polymerization in the Solid State." Spacings of 5 to 90 A.

483 Perron, R. A., and Wright, B. A. A
Nature, 166, 863–864 (1950). "Alteration of Collagen Structure by Irradiation with Electrons."

484 Perutz, M. F. A
Nature, 161, 204–205 (1948). "Submicroscopic Structure of the Red Cell." Mean distance between neighboring hemoglobin molecules in red cell.

485 Posner, A. P
ACA, No. 67, Ann Arbor, Mich. (June 1953). "Particle Size and Particle Size Distribution in Apatites."

486 Riley, D. P., and Herbert, D. A
Biochim. et Biophys. Acta, 4, 374–384 (1950). "Molecular Size, Shape, and Aggregation in Concentrated Protein Solutions as Revealed by X-Ray Scattering—Hemoglobin and Egg-Albumin." Diffuse rings related to sizes and shapes of packed molecules.

487 Riley, D. P., and Oster, G. A
Trans. Faraday Soc., 46, 791 (1950). "X-Ray Diffraction Studies of Solutions of Desoxyribonucleic Acid (Na Salt)."

488 Riley, D. P., and Oster, G. A
J. chim. phys., 47, 715 (1950). "Étude aux rayons X de solutions d'acide thymonucléique à diverses concentrations."

Note: Item 489 is omitted.

490 Ritland, H. N. T
Univ. Wisc., Ph.D. (1949). "Small-Angle X-Ray Scattering from Protein Solutions."

491 Ritland, H. N., Kaesberg, P., and Beeman, W. W. P
Conf. Small-Angle X-Ray Scattering, No. 10, Columbia, Mo. (October 1949). "Information on the Shapes and Hydrations of Protein Molecules in Solution from Small-Angle X-Ray Scattering." Gyration radii of six proteins measured. Axial ratio deduced and used to find extent of hydration.

492 Ritland, H. N., Kaesberg, P., and Beeman, W. W. A
J. Chem. Phys., 18, 1237–1242 (1950). Tech. Report, O.N.R. Contract N7 ONR–285, T–O III, NR 017–605 (1949). "An X-Ray Investigation of the Shapes and Hydrations of Several Protein Molecules in Solution." Gyration radii of five proteins from small-angle scattering used with molecular weights, densities, and fractional ratios to get axial ratios and hydrations.

493 Schmitt, F. O. A
J. Am. Leather Chemists' Assoc., 46, 538–547 (1951). "Structural and Chemical Studies on Collagen."

494 Sen, M. K., and Mukherjee, R. R.   A
J. Textile Inst. Proc. and Abstr., *43*, 114–121 (1952). "The Structure of Jute. I. The X-Ray Diffraction Pattern."

495 Shulman, S., Anderegg, J., Leonard, B. R., Jr., and Kaesberg, P.   P
Am. Chem. Soc., No. C-74, Boston (April 1951). "An X-Ray Examination of Tobacco Necrosis Virus in Solution."

496 Shurman, M. M., and Kaesberg, P.   P
Pittsburgh Conf. X-Ray Electron Diffr., No. 9, Pittsburgh (November 1950). "X-Ray Evidence concerning the Structure of Collagen." Fourier synthesis of pattern from beef tendon in agreement with electron micrographs.

497 Stone, L. L.   T
Fla. State Univ., M.S. (1950). "An X-Ray Examination of Selected Bacteria." Small-angle evidence for bacterial nuclei.

498 Vineyard, G. H.   A
Acta Cryst., *4*, 281 (1951). "Patterson Transforms and the Interpretation of X-Ray Scattering from Fibers."

499 Weibull, C.   A
Nature, *165*, 482–483 (1950). "X-Ray Diffraction Pattern Given by Bacterial Flagella." Periodicities detected in flagella.

500 Wright, B. A.   A
Nature, *162*, 23 (1948). "Low-Angle X-Ray Diffraction Pattern of Collagen." 27 orders. Found 630–672 A for 20–100 per cent humidity.

501 Wright, B. A.   P
CSA and *ASXRED*, New Haven (1948). "Information concerning the Water Uptake of Collagen as Evidenced by Its Low-Angle X-Ray Diffraction Pattern."

502 Wright, B. A., and Cole, P. A.   A
Rev. Sci. Instr., *20*, 355–356 (1949). "An Improved Low-Angle X-Ray Diffraction Camera." Collagen pattern with high resolution and facility.

503 Wright, B. A., and Wiederhorn, N. M.   P
ASXRED, Ithaca, N. Y. (June 1949). "An X-Ray Diffraction Study in Shrinkage of Collagen."

504 Wright, B. A., and Wiederhorn, N. M.   A
J. Polymer Sci., *7*, 105–120 (1951). "Studies Concerned with the Structure of Collagen. I. An X-Ray Investigation of the Denaturization of Collagen."

505 Wrinch, D.   A
J. Chem. Phys., *20*, 1332-1333 (1952). "Evidence for Globulite Molecules in Horse Hemoglobin."

505′ Wyckoff, R. W. G., and Corey, R. B.   A
Science, *81*, 365–366 (1935). "X-Ray Diffractions from Hemoglobin and Other Crystalline Proteins."

505″ Wyckoff, R. W. G., Corey, R. B., and Biscoe, J.   A
Science, *82*, 175–176 (1935). "X-Ray Reflections of Long Spacings from Tendon."

506 Zahn, H., and Winter, U.   A
Kolloid-Z., *128*, 142–153 (1952). "Über die Langperiodenreflexes im Röntgenogramm von Polyethanfaden."

AUTHOR INDEX TO BIBLIOGRAPHY

Note: Numbers refer to numbered items in the Bibliography, not to pages.

Note: Numbers refer to numbered items in the Bibliography, not to pages.

Note: Numbers refer to numbered items in the Bibliography, not to pages.

Note: Numbers refer to numbered items in the Bibliography, not to pages.

AUTHOR INDEX TO TEXT

SUBJECT INDEX

Absolute measurements, 121
Adsorption methods, 161
Age-hardening, 199
Albumin, 105, 169
Alloys, Al-Ag, 75, 165, 198, 203, 208
   Al-Cu, 211
Alumina, 193
Angular uncertainty, 87
Approximation for tail of low-angle scattering curve, 67, 80, 115
Argon, 48, 58, 59

Babinet's theorem, 38
Beam stops, 121, 124
   for absolute measurements, 121
Bragg's law, use of, 148

Carbon black, 105, 188
Catalysts, 192
Cellulose, 177, 179, 180, 181, 183
Characteristic function, isolated particle, 12
   system of particles, 77, 78
Charcoal, activated, 191
Chrysotile, 105, 184
Coiled chain molecules, 177
Cold-worked metals, 195
Collagen, 184
Collimators, 86
   optimum, 89
   with circular apertures, 91
   with rectangular apertures, 91
   with slits of infinite height, 86
Colloidal solutions, 194
Complementary objects, 38, 81
Compressibility, 47, 213
Compton scattering, 5
Correction, beam height, beam of finite height, 118
   beam of infinite height, 114, 116
   beam width, 112
Counter, Geiger-Müller, 85, 87, 89, 93, 121
   proportional, 96

Crystals, 52
Cylinder, homogeneous, 19, 27

Debye-Scherrer lines, 163, 196
Debye's model (*see* Spheres, hard)
Disc, homogeneous, 21, 23
Distance of heterogeneity, 81, 158

Egg yolk, 105, 176
Electron microscope, 161
Ellipsoid, homogeneous, 19, 26, 169
Ellipsoids, distribution of sizes, 154
Equation of state, 42, 46
Exponential approximation, 25, 27, 30, 114, 128

Fibers, 177, 185
Filters, balanced (Ross), 85, 95
Flocculation, 194
Fluids (*see* Particles)
Fluids, theories of, 41, 45
Form factor, 3
Fourier transformations, 4, 16, 18, 57, 206

Globulin, 169
Gold, colloidal, 162
Guinier's law (*see* Exponential approximation)

Helium, liquid, 214
Hemocyanine, 105, 174
Hemoglobin, 104, 105, 130, 137, 144, 170, 171, 173, 176
Heterogeneous matter, 70
High polymers, 176
Hypotheses H_1 and H_2, 30, 60

Inertial distance, 30
Inhomogeneity, range of, 158
Ionization chamber, 123

λ-point, 214
Latex, 131, 162